W9-DED-783

TO

PAT *and* JULIE
who helped me to look inward

Creative Ways with Children

by GERTRUDE LERNER KERMAN

foreword by JOHN L. MILLER
Superintendent of Schools, Great Neck, New York

pictures by Margaret Zimmerman

 HARVEY HOUSE, PUBLISHERS

Irvington-on-Hudson, New York

Copyright 1961 by Z. E. Harvey, Inc.,
Irvington-on-Hudson, N. Y.
The plays in this volume may be done without
payment of royalties by non-profit making,
non-professional groups. All other groups wishing to perform any of
these plays must seek written permission from
the publishers.
Printed in the United States of America
Library of Congress Catalogue Card Number: 58–13932

FOREWORD

The philosophy according to which Mrs. Kerman has developed her book is educationally sound in that she stresses the contribution which dramatics can make to the total development of the child. *Plays and Creative Ways with Children*, which reflects Mrs. Kerman's extensive knowledge both of dramatics and children, is creative and yet immensely practical. It should be equally effective with talented as with less-than-talented individuals. It will, I hope, inspire those working with children and youth to increasingly more satisfying and rewarding efforts.

JOHN L. MILLER,
Superintendent of Schools,
Great Neck, New York

CONTENTS

PART ONE

PART TWO

preface

INTRODUCING . . .

"And a short play will be presented by . . . ," the chairman breaks off to smile at you across the library table.

"You" may be an elementary school teacher at a staff meeting to discuss the approaching Christmas assembly program; or you may be a camp counselor, a scout leader, a settlement worker, a church club organizer. Whoever you are, you are now faced with two provocative challenges: finding a short play suitable for young performers, and preparing it creatively for presentation to an invited, non-paying audience.

"Suitable for young performers." This is your first big hurdle. You love dramatics, as distinguished from professional theater, and you believe wholeheartedly that dramatics and children belong together like candles and a birthday cake. But you are also aware of the danger of stumbling into the error committed by an earnest but inexperienced instructor. He presented his nine-year-olds in a play about a concentration camp, and they the offspring of a privileged background, sheltered from even the usual childhood vicissitudes! Or the plight of the sixth grade teacher who had fed her young players such pedantic speeches about the Australian jungle, that the observer was left with the unhappy sensation of tongue-twisted children mouthing meaningless sounds.

"And preparing it creatively." This is your next big hurdle. You recall the many times you were an uncomfortable spectator at performances in which the children spoke and moved like robots controlled by an unimaginative drillmaster.

To you, who face such problems, *Plays and Creative Ways with Children* is now presented. The book is a compilation of short, flexible, non-royalty scripts and a step-by-step guide for freeing a child's personality through drama. It evolved out of long association with children and creative dramatics.

For practical purposes, this book is divided into two sections. The first part offers leaders, who are interested in the philosophy of creative dramatics, a flexible plan to ready the children for dramatization and eventual participation in a play. This plan includes exercises designed to release and stimulate young imaginations, suggestions for creating an informal play with your group, ways to cast, rehearse, and stage a play. The second part of the book presents the plays.

Creative dramatics, a progressive concept in children's work, is improvised drama or "playmaking" as Dr. Winifred Ward calls it in her book, *Playmaking with Children*. It "is the activity in which informal drama is created by the players themselves. Such drama may be original as to idea, plot and characters, or it may be based on a story written by someone else. Indeed, it is often as simple as the reliving of a situation from past experiences or a fragment from a current event or a motion picture." [1]

Some educators confine the phrase to the specific activity of making up a play "planned by a group and played spontaneously with improvised dialogue which is never twice the same." [2]

In this book creative dramatics will denote the full process of creative doing through drama. Included here are rhythms, dramatic play, improvisations, freeing exercises, and the making of a play through discussion and acting improvisations. This last activity will be referred to as play-making.

At all times, however, creative dramatics differs from other forms of drama in that its purpose, to quote Dr. Ward again, is "not the training of actors, nor the production of plays for audiences . . . (but) to give each child an avenue for self-expression, guide his creative outlet, help him in the building of fine attitudes and appreciation, and give him opportunities to grow in social cooperation." [8]

As a member of the faculty of the Children's Centre for Creative Arts, Adelphi College, New York, I recognized that boys and girls meeting once a week can produce, at best, only brief, informal scenes suitable for presentation to friends of their own age. A long play, having involved structure and character development, demands time and concentration. Most children forget the details of a plot they discussed seven days ago. To review the details, meeting after meeting, taxes a child's interest.

When we had to present a short, structurally complete play, I followed a method which I shall later describe in detail. Embodying the principles of creative dramatics, this method enabled the children and me to collaborate in evolving a series of flexible scripts that allowed the young performers to move naturally and honestly within the framework of a tight, dramatic structure. The scripts we presented most often are found in this book.

The plays run from about ten to thirty minutes, and involve players up to fourteen years of age. They concern people, issues, and adventures, real or imaginary, to which a child can relate at his own level of experience. Odd as it may seem, the Income Tax Investigator in *It's a Wise Parent* was invented by a twelve-year-old whose father was the prosecutor in a tax-evasion case.

In addition, the plays were made with the collaboration of the children, and reflect their moods and reactions, their ideas of fun, and generally offer a simple truth. Many of the speaking lines are theirs, too. These were recorded at group sessions while scenes were discussed and improvised. Topics run the gamut from here-and-now problems to nonsense fantasies; fairy tales to "red-letter days"; adventures and legends; and a sprinkling of Shakespeare for the more experienced groups.

The new director may present many of the plays as they appear here, since they are structural entities in themselves. For those educators who want to apply the principles of creative dramatics during the performance as well as rehearsals, there are scripts which are sufficiently elastic to permit improvisation. The players may introduce their own stage business, a dance or a song, an original character in a crowd scene, and even original dialogue, all within the skeleton of the plot. And where a Narrator is included in the cast of a play, the director may use this character to tell the story while the children pantomime it.

A word about practical problems. You will find that many of the plays have expansible casts which will include as many children of different ages as you may wish. For the most part there are no starring roles, and responsibility for carrying the play is divided among several characters. This helps you to meet the problem of last minute replacements should illness strike. Few rehearsals are required for any of the plays and some can be performed after just one or two. (A Midsummer Night's Dream, which is difficult to do, took only ten one-hour rehearsals.) Sets and costumes are simple enough to encourage the young people to make their own. Finally, the plays can be done anywhere, indoors or out, in a classroom or the living-room, in an arena or on a proscenium stage.

Presenting plays before an invited, non-paying audience is an important consideration in creative work. An audience that pays for its seats expects a play to last about one and a half hours, to have subtle character delineation, an involved plot, talent in its performers, a polished production—in short, professional or formal theater. Such commercial pressure forces the director to put on the best performance he can. As a result, he will choose only the most gifted children and drill them in his interpretation of the play. He will also impose upon them the restrictions of professional production, "Face your audience. Speak up. Stand upstage right. Move on this line. Gesture after that word."

Unfortunately, emphasis on the finished product defeats the purpose for which you were called upon to present this play: to bring the joy of participation to every child in the group, and to offer him the opportunity for creative and social growth—true drama. Also, such emphasis can often result in a presentation lacking in the desired spontaneity which informal drama encourages.

The introduction to this book cannot be complete without an expression of gratitude to the people who helped direct my thinking and imagination into these channels: John Gassner, Sterling Professor of Playwriting, Yale University; Dr. John L. Miller, Superintendent of

Schools, Great Neck, New York; Grace M. Stanistreet, Director, Adelphi College Children's Centre for Creative Arts; Dr. Winifred Ward, author, retired educator, and dean of creative dramatics for children. And to the many boys and girls who have helped me in these adventures in creative collaboration, I am grateful. Their enthusiasm, their ability to create freely from within, are the stimuli that have renewed my own enthusiasm again and again.

Part One

chapter 1

DOING THROUGH DRAMA

"Now, Susie, stop talking this very minute!" Teacher's soft brown brows arched sternly at her pupil. There was a moment's quiet.

"Susie!" Dirt-roughened knuckles rapped the table sharply. "It's the third time I've had to tell you to let Bill alone. You've got to finish your arithmetic before you go home today. Did you hear, Susie? You're way behind the class. And tomorrow when . . ." Teacher's gentle voice turned to steel, "That does it! I'm going to 'phone your Mother and tell her how bad you are!" Her fingers poked at a telephone dial. "Stop crying! You're making my desk wet! Oh, Mrs. Lawrence, this is Susie's Teacher. Susie's been very bad today. She keeps yakating, yakating all the time the boys and girls are trying to study and . . ."

Susie, as you suspect, is no flesh and blood delinquent, nor is Teacher a member of the profession. Rather, Susie is the forlorn and wholly imagined victim in a game of make-believe through which a nine-year-old was releasing the tension she had experienced during her school day.

Nor is this dramatic play peculiar to our young Teacher. It is as much a part of every child's development as are eating and breathing. Make-believe permits the child to relive old adventures and to try out new ones. It is his "way of thinking, proving, relaxing, working, remembering, daring, testing, creating, and absorbing," as Peter Slade points out in *Child Drama*.[1] And because make-believe is an important part of the child's life, creative dramatics or *doing through drama* uses it to further his total growth.

The achievement of this goal is the aim of a doing-through-drama program for children. Out of the program's rhythmic exercises emerges the well-co-ordinated child. Group story discussions stretch his mind and imagination. Enacting characters of different backgrounds, the child broadens his outlook and judgment. Through the legitimate, emotional release which playmaking offers, even the mercurial-in-mood adolescent gains self-control and confidence. Acting out simple situations through improvisations, dramatizing a beloved tale, or helping to create an original script, the children develop inventiveness, initiative, and co-operation. The basic activity of performing with a partner, emphasizing as it does communication between two people—*listen, react, then reply* (see Chapter 6)—promotes respect for one's fellow. In addition, sensitivity to the beauty of language and visual design is developed.

An ambitious goal for a creative program? Not at all. Just walk into an after-school session in dramatic doing for ten- and eleven-year-olds. Walk quietly, please, for adult visitors should be "invisible," and your presence may block the flow of thought and action. Sit inconspicuously in a corner. Listen to some of the eager voices discussing the familiar and well-loved fairy tale, *The Emperor's New Clothes*. Since these boys and girls have had some fourteen meetings in preparatory creative techniques, their ideas come freely, with little urging from the leader.

The children are sitting on the floor in a relaxed circle, their eyes intent on the leader. She has just retold the Hans Christian Andersen story of the ruler who doted on clothes so much that he spent all his time and money acquiring them. Having stressed the humor of the tale, she is now probing for ethical and dramatic values inherent in the character of the Emperor himself.

At her opening questions about that clothes-loving gentleman, a ten-year-old boy springs up, tense and eager.

GARY: He's an old show-off! (*Pushing his shoulders back,* GARY *parades arrogantly as an emperor might.*) Out of my way, everyone! You'll step on my train. Out of my way or I'll chop off your head!

JULIE (*objecting delicately*): The story didn't mean that kind of show-off. The Emperor just liked showing people his clothes. He's not cruel.

GARY: Sure he is! He makes his chauffeur drive him around in his "Caddy" . . .

LYNN (*a boy-conscious tease*): Uh-uh, they didn't have Cadillacs then.

GARY: Well . . . well, anyway, he likes to go around showing people he's more important than them. That makes him a show-off. (*Momentarily unsure of his point,* GARY *flops down on the floor.*)

HELEN (*speaking rapidly from the loftiness of a high I. Q.*): That only makes him stupid. An Emperor *is* the most important man in the kingdom. He doesn't have to prove it.

LYNN: I agree with Gary though. Except the Emperor shows off because he thinks he's good-looking—like Marlon Brando.

GARY: Marlon Brando don't care for clothes. He wears jeans.

HELEN: "Doesn't"—not "don't."

LEADER (*interrupting quickly*): Lynn, why don't you try being the Emperor and show us what you think he's like. Let's pretend you're in your dressing-room, and you just got out of bed.

LYNN (*jumping up to improvise*): Okay! (*Pointing to a table*) This will be my mirror—it's full length—and (*selecting several boys and girls*) you are my servants. (*Clapping her hands imperiously*) Now you! Bring my Imperial Majesty some things to wear. Be quick!

Some children, impersonating Servants, scatter to bring imaginary garments to the Emperor. Four other children, acting as Guards, assume positions of attention at invisible archways. The whole forms, without direction, a pleasing and appropriate picture.

LYNN (*as Emperor, striking a pose of boredom*): What have you got here?

CHILD 1 (*as Servant*): Your royal coat, Your Majesty.

LYNN (as Emperor):   I don't want this one, stupid! I wore it yesterday. Bring me another.

CHILD 2 (as Servant):   Will Your Majesty graciously look at this one? It's got mink on it.

LYNN (as Emperor):   Too common. Everyone has mink. Where's the one with the diamond cinch belt? I look handsome in it.

CHILD 3 (as Servant):   It went to the cleaners, Sire. It'll be ready the day after tomorrow.

But the end of Lynn's improvisation finds Julie still disturbed by the Emperor's personality.

JULIE: But can't the Emperor like clothes without being mean? *I* like to dress up.

TONY (*breaking out of his habitual shyness and speaking hesitantly*):   Or he . . . he may like to look at them and . . . and touch them . . . like you touch a caterpillar. You know . . . feel it. (*A few children extend their hands experimentally, stroking invisible caterpillars.*)

HELEN: Tony's right. The Emperor's artistic. Our neighbor next door is artistic. Or it may be like psychology.

LYNN: What's that?

HELEN: I was reading a book on psychology once, and I think the Emperor liked to dress up because he was ugly. For instance, my mother told me when people have scars on their faces, they put on big hats so you won't pay attention to their scars, only their hats.

TONY (*persisting earnestly*):   Or he may love clothes because once he was poor when he was small. I mean if he never had a good suit, or whatever he was supposed to wear then, he may want to make up for it now that he is rich.

An analysis of this bit of dramatic doing demonstrates how playmaking can benefit the children even at an early stage of dramatization. Through creative dramatics such as this, they begin their "move toward life," to quote Harry A. Overstreet, author of many fine books on psychology and sociology.

Doing through drama is not new. It is a very old process that has been rediscovered. Our Stone Age ancestor probably dramatized his joys and fears through spontaneous dance in much the same way our children dramatize theirs. Later, primitive man's improvisations gave way to formal rituals. Dance steps became fixed, and he performed them over and over again to urge his brothers on to war, or perhaps to placate angry gods who held back the rain.

The trend toward formal rituals grew through the years and into the Victorian Age, which all but forgot the original need for release and education through doing. Instead, histrionic ability and spectacular production, or "theater," as we know it, became the paramount objective. Dramatics were for the professional actors. Everyone else turned audience.

It is interesting to note, however, that improvisation and spontaneity, both of which creative dramatics stress, were prominent in the work of the famous *commedia dell' arte* of the sixteenth century. Though he portrayed the same character many times, the Italian actor did improvise dialogue and stage business within the framework of his scene. If he felt the urge to talk, he talked. If he felt the urge to sing, he sang.

When colleges first introduced dramatics into their curricula, they followed the formal pattern for classes in speech improvement, acting, scenic and costume design. The pendulum started to swing back when high schools and, later, community theaters began to emphasize the fun in the doing. Here again, talent and production requirements were still placed before inner, creative expression.

With the gradual change in educational methods—from teaching by mechanical drill to learning through project work—came imaginative teachers who used dramatic techniques to make academic subjects more attractive. When a child acts out facts, he vitalizes a topic that might otherwise seem dull. This helps the child to absorb the information.

In time, dedicated educators, such as Alice Minnie Hertz in 1911, and later, Corinne Brown, Hughes Mearns, Winifred Ward, and S. R. Slavson, recognized the value of using creative dramatics in work with young people.

Creative dramatics is education through the medium of *drama*. There are leaders who tend to shy away from the use of dramatic techniques because they lack "know-how." Playing a record for mood music (Chapter 2), such a leader asks her young people to "get up on the floor and act." She hesitates to make a suggestion, however simple, for fear it will interfere with the children's creative impulses.

She may as well leave the young people to their make-believe games of

"Call the Doctor for Baby" or "Cowboys and Indians." She fails to recognize that the inhibited boy needs help to break through his emotional shell, or that the eager girl enjoys the orderly process of creating under guidance. She does not understand that children welcome the security of form and balance. Certainly this leader shudders at the thought of children performing in any play, even one of the group's own making.

Such an approach can be as damaging as the professional director's emphasis on theater. Children's drama is neither polished performance, with its concern for an audience reaction, nor is it aimless doing. It is true that the young child does not require an audience reaction in order to enjoy himself, but this does not hold for the older boy and girl. They will be content to "do" for many sessions, then a certain restlessness sets in, the effect perhaps of seeing many motion pictures and television programs. These children want to put on a play.

Children who have been introduced to creative techniques will enjoy and benefit by presenting a play with a beginning, a middle, and an end. Where the script is of their own making and is played with lines created during the performance, so much the better. Where a prepared script is used, the young people will benefit if the play is one to which they can relate, where they have some creative latitude, and which is cast, rehearsed, and staged in accordance with the philosophy of creative dramatics.

Take, for example, the adaptation of A Midsummer Night's Dream which appears in Part Two of this book. Using Shakespeare's own lines, the script challenges the imagination of the young player. Rehearsed creatively, our production was sparkling. Could many adults be as original as the eleven-year-old Oberon who awoke his Fairy Queen from her slumbers in the arms of Bottom with a peremptory snap of his fingers?

The best endorsement for doing through drama comes not from the psychologist or the dramatist or the educator, but from the child, himself. In the blunt but truthful words of one young man, "I'm almost glad my troop leader sprained his ankle. I can come to dramatics instead."

chapter 2

"YOU ASK . . ."

The time has come, and you are eager to organize your first group in dramatic doing. The two objectives that will govern your program have been determined: to inspire even the most repressed of your boys and girls to dynamic growth, and to prepare them for artistic participation in a play.

Let us first define the terms that will come up most frequently in the course of this work.

Creative Definitions

DOING THROUGH DRAMA, already discussed, is the phrase I use to cover the over-all creative procedure with children, from freeing rhythms and limbering-up acting exercises to play dramatization and informal presentation.

DRAMATIC PLAY is that improvised doing in which the child examines situations gleaned from the here-and-now happenings in his daily life. Dramatic play has no special beginning, middle or end. In fact, it is often terminated by the child's saying, "That's all there is."

PLOT is the design that distinguishes dramatic play from the play that is performed. Plot is the structure, or skeleton, of the play. It involves *complications* or incidents which generally lead to a *major crisis*, popularly called the climax, and a final *resolution* (Chapter 8).

An eleven-year-old student defined plot development this way: "The story starts interesting then suddenly something very bad happens that makes you very worried. It gets very exciting and goes up a hill sort of, builds up and up, and you don't know what's going to happen. That is where the climax is. Then, suddenly, you go right down the hill, you know what happens, the excitement ends and," she let out a long sigh, "you're relaxed at what happened."

IMPROVISATION and PANTOMIME are both well known. In this book, the first is the process of extemporizing freely, through acting, on any theme or situation. The second is the process of expressing a thought or action through facial and bodily movement only.

PLAYMAKING will refer specifically to the activity of creating informal plays through acting out improvisations on a story that has incidents which lend themselves to dramatization.

DRAMATIZATION has several meanings. Professional playwrights apply it only to the work of adapting into play structure a story that has already been written. Leaders in creative dramatics, however, use the term "dramatization" interchangeably with *story dramatization*, or *playmaking*, to signify the action in which players make up an informal drama through acting improvisations on a story.

Here, dramatization will refer to the activity of "writing" a play in which both leader and children participate co-operatively. Taking an original idea or familiar story as their springboard, they first evolve a plot through group discussions, then develop it through the acting improvisations of playmaking. If necessary, the leader will follow this up with work at home (Chapters 8, 10).

Dramatization is more than playmaking. Dramatization is concerned with the whole process of building a plot, from the germ of an idea to the finished script.

The play itself, whether it is improvised at the time of performance or presented with lines that have been written down and memorized, will be known henceforth as an *informal play*. This differs from the *formal play*. The emphasis during rehearsals of the informal script is on giving creative range to the players in the areas of interpretation, dialogue, and staging. Guidance, not drill, is the aim of the director, even at the cost of a polished, audience-acceptable result. The informal play is presented to non-paying children, parents and friends.

CONFLICT is the key to plotting. Material is said to be dramatic when it revolves around a *conflict*, or struggle, between opposing forces. It can be a struggle of ideas or desires within oneself, or oneself pitted against another person, persons, environment, nature. Conflict changes ordinary activities into dramatic situations.

Let us take, as an example, walking across the street: Johnny leaves the school building and crosses the boulevard to go home for supper. Johnny's crossing is simple physical activity. The activity becomes dramatically alive, however, when Johnny, about to cross, spies the school bully waiting for him on the opposite sidewalk. This situation sets Johnny against another person and creates an inner struggle for him. Should he cross the street, or should he run back into the school?

The building of plot will be considered at length in the chapters devoted to dramatization (Chapters 8, 10).

Physical Requirements

Number of Sessions

The boys and girls should meet at least once a week during the school year, with as many meetings as possible devoted to creative techniques. It is desirable that minds and bodies be limbered up before the group attempts to dramatize and act in a play.

Length of Session

This depends on the number of children in your group, their concentration span, and how often they can meet. Where school systems introduce playmaking into their daily curricula, each period can be as short as forty-five minutes and still have telling effect.

Groups that meet only on a once-a-week basis require from one hour to one hour and a half for each session in order to obtain results. The shorter span is adequate for children from five to seven years of age. The older children, especially when the group is large, can enjoy as much as two hours of doing, provided they are not burdened with many extracurricular activities.

Size of Group

This varies. An ideal unit consists of eight to fifteen boys and girls of similar maturity level. Working with only a few children, you will find, reduces the benefits to be derived from one child's reaction to another. On the other hand, working with too many, as the school teacher often must today, poses for you the problem of sustaining the group's interest while you give each child opportunity to participate actively.

The difficulties may be lessened by planning to use the entire group at the same time. So that all may participate, consider the following:

(a) The Integrated Project. A large space, such as a school gymnasium, all-purpose room, or several smaller rooms, is necessary for this program which utilizes the simultaneous services of instructors in music, dance, art, and drama.

You start by telling a story to the entire group (Chapter 10). After discussion and improvisations relating to the dramatization of the story, the children decide whether they want to act or dance in the proposed informal play, accompany it with music, or paint sets. They then go off to private corners or rooms where they develop their part of the presentation with the help of the various instructors. Toward the end of the period, they reassemble to co-ordinate their materials and present the play informally for themselves.

Adelphi Children's Centre has an integrated program. About one hundred and fifty children are assigned to groups of about fifteen which meet every Saturday morning during the school year. As a rule, each group instructor works out his own theme for the morning. Groups are co-ordinated several times a year. The co-ordination may be loose, when the same theme dominates the efforts of all the groups which are otherwise independent of one another,[1] or tight, as in the performance of *The Pied Piper of Hamelin*. This production involved all the boys and girls, as actors, dancers, singers, set and costume designers. Another tightly-integrated project, *The Emperor's New Clothes*, included a puppet show (put on by the Puppet Unit) for the Emperor's amusement.

(b) Assistant Leaders.   Where there is a shortage of instructors, older children with creative dramatic training may act as aids to the adult instructor.

(c) Audience Involvement.   Most young people will watch with in-terest while their colleagues perform as long as they know that they will be called upon to analyze what they have seen, and to do their own improvisations on the same situation. Use the device sparingly, since children tend to imitate what they see.

You can overcome the tendency to copy by suggesting that the boys and girls who are observing join in the improvisation. They may become dancers at Cinderella's Ball or a crowd of people watching the royal carriage roll by. Then again, they may be any stage properties or furniture required by the actors in a scene, such as the forest trees in *Hänsel and Gretel*, or a standing lamp in a here-and-now story.

(d) Careful Selection of Material.   Choose dramatic situations which can involve a number of players. For example, a group of children waits for a tardy school bus in the rain; or many witches mutter incantations in an improvisation of the Witches' scene in Shakespeare's *Macbeth*.

(e) Rhythms, Choral Poems, etc.   These media also allow the par-ticipation of the entire class at one time (Chapters 3, 6).

Playacting and dramatization figure prominently in the approaches just described, at the expense of individual work on creative acting tech-niques.

Place of Operation

Any space, sufficiently large to allow young people to move freely, even to run, is suitable for your program. Best is the floor of a gymnasium, a lawn, a large room, with some furniture or levels that may be used as props and pushed around. The child enjoys the possibilities offered by an informal area. Through the magic of his imagination, he transforms the space into any set he desires, often making it serve as two or three sets at the same time. In the "Johnny-crosses-the-street" incident, a part of the space becomes the school which Johnny leaves; another part becomes the street where he sees the bully; and still another part, the kitchen of his home where his mother waits anxiously. This use of area resembles the simultaneous sets seen in modern theater.

Unnecessary to a creative program, especially in its early period, is the proscenium or picture stage of an auditorium. The conventions of "speak up" and "face front," imposed by a high platform, disturb the child's concentration. The very emptiness of the large auditorium shocks him out of his world of make-believe. As a result, his inventiveness freezes and artificiality creeps in. The tendency to show off is also promoted by the raised stage.

If such a stage is the only area available to your class, forget the purpose for which it was built and use it as you would any other flat area. Closing the proscenium curtain will make it cozy though hot. Or you may work on the auditorium floor, and use the stage itself as though it were a level, letting it serve as a throne for a king, a railroad train, the balcony of a house.

If you are a teacher in a congested school, you may have to use a classroom for dramatic activity. In that case, you can make the desks a part of dramatic doing by moving them and permitting the boys and girls to sit or stand on them. Avoid thinking of Teacher's end of the room as a stage, or considering the desks as fixed seats in an auditorium. Fluidity in movement is one of the essentials.

Equipment

A young child can create for himself a castle out of matchsticks. His remarkable ability to invent requires little in the way of realistic props. A half-mask or two, some battered hats, colored scarves, old curtains, wisps of material—anything can start his fertile imagination on designing costumes for Neptune, Robin Hood, or the policeman on the beat. Aluminum-foil pie pans make crowns that are more fascinating to him than Queen Elizabeth's coronation headdress. Discarded necklaces, wooden sticks for wands or swords, cups and saucers, toy telephones become the starting points of many a joyful improvisation.

If the child has a table, a chair, a couch, a lamp, levels to work with, good! If he does not have these things, he will create his furniture out of old boxes and bridge chairs. Or he may invite other children to act as his props. The main thing to remember here is that too many props will confuse your player, while a few props will stimulate him. The child under ten years of age should not have costumes which hinder his physical movement, or many hand props to distract him. With the older performer, the picture changes. Curious about real people and real relationships, he will want to recreate the life around him through costume and prop.

Material Sources

The sources from which a group will draw most of its material for dramatic exercises fall mainly into two broad categories: (1) here-and-now experiences, and (2) stories and poems.

Here-and-Now Experiences

These are current situations and problems derived from daily living as experienced by the child or discovered through newspapers, books, television, radio, motion pictures, and comics. Here-and-now figures prominently in the pantomime exercises with which your boys and girls will begin their approach to doing through drama (Chapter 4).

Stories and Poems

These may be animal stories, ballads, fairy tales, folklore, history, or mythology, gleaned from literature and legend. Such material has inspired many excellent, informal plays and will be consulted by the young people, particularly when they are ready to try their first dramatization (Chapter 9).

Music

Music in any form, instrumental or vocal, should be introduced at all meetings of your group. Not only will music accompany the rhythmic exercises that start the session (Chapter 3), but it will also serve as a most valuable tool for overcoming self-consciousness, for establishing mood during improvisations, and for stimulating personal expression and ideas.

Music has a special worth for a child between the ages of four and seven. Because its continuous flow of varying rhythms resembles our language flow, music leads him into expression through sustained dialogue (Chapters 3, 6). The changes in musical moods and tempi, too, serve to introduce him gradually to the dramatic rise and fall of a play's structure (Chapter 8).

If possible, obtain the services of a pianist. She should be sensitive enough to follow the child's ever-shifting dramatic moods with responsive, musical improvisations. Or, when dramatic doing falters, she may suggest through music a fresh idea for development to the player. While the boys and girls improvise an imaginary visit to the circus, her music may evoke images of tumbling clowns, trunk-swinging elephants, graceful trapeze artists. Or it may picture the movements of the bus that is taking the children to a picnic at the seashore—the jerking of the vehicle, the unexpected turns, the braking for a red light. In the first situation, the children enact the characters suggested by the music. In the second, they are performing as themselves, and react dramatically to the ever-changing rhythms.

If the services of an imaginative pianist are not available, a phonograph and records may be used to good effect. Play parts of several recordings consecutively to produce background mood or to help stimulate ideas. Instruments, such as triangles, gongs, drums, whistles, cymbals, tambourines, bells, hooters, may be used in conjunction with the phonograph. Avoid sentimental, popular tunes and recordings of the slow movements of symphonies. Folk songs are a must, especially for the younger children who enjoy dramatizing them. In his *Child Drama*, Peter Slade describes the interesting results he obtained with jazz. He found its primitive beat and unrestrained feeling excellent in working with children.

Music may be used simply as exercises to stretch the imagination or to help in characterization (Chapter 7). Liszt's *Rhapsodie No. 2*, Part 1, stimulated a group of teen-agers into creating quick character impressions that ranged from a conventional one from *Peter Pan*, Captain Hook striding along his deck, to a highly original caricature of a fanatic musician sawing away at his cello!

Your Attitude

More important than place, hours, and equipment is your own attitude with the children. That you wish to share with them the joys of creative adventure is evident, or you would not be planning a program that makes unlimited demands on your time and resourcefulness. But you and the group are both new to dramatic experience, which could prove frustrating unless you consider certain factors.

First among these factors are the friendliness and informality with which you conduct each session. Chat with the boys and girls as you all relax in a circle on the floor. No rigid seats, please. Refrain from laughing at an effect or calling it "cute." Make a humorous remark instead of a sarcastic one. Touch the shoulder of the child to whom you are speaking. Give everyone ample opportunity to release his tensions in physical interludes.

Important, too, is your recognition of the fact that each child's mental potential as well as environmental conditioning are uniquely his own. Study the several facets of his personality carefully, then plan a variety of exercises and projects around them.

Empathy and encouragement, rather than adverse criticism, are as valuable in your program as a knowledge of dramatic techniques. You do not eliminate correction, however. Try to achieve it indirectly without hurting anyone's feelings. Let the young player do his scene without interruption, then ask for comments from the observers. Supervise the criticism carefully so that it does not become unpleasant or unfair. The group may offer suggestions to improve an interpretation or change a stage movement, but if the performer has definite ideas of his own, let him try them out and discover for himself which way is best.

At no time impose your own interpretation of a part or a scene. Instead, through discussion and skillful questioning before the scene starts, lead him to form his own fresh approach. Help him and his colleagues to believe in themselves and you will break through the wall that dams up the creative flow.

As for your own participation in an improvisation, it is best to watch quietly from the sidelines unless the players ask you to take part. Again, avoid enacting a role to illustrate a point. This will only serve to encourage imitation.

You can aid the self-conscious child who hesitates to perform by beginning your sessions with projects that involve many children simultaneously. Rhythms, pantomimic exercises, and situations which call for crowds are useful. Once he finds others participating, he will join in readily, and before long will surprise you by his eagerness to work alone.

A word about behavior problems. Preaching is unpleasant and unnecessary. The conduct of a spoiled child, for instance, may be improved by having her enact a role with character elements resembling her own, like Janie, perhaps, in A Christmas Story in this book. Experiencing, as Janie does, the disapproval of her fellows in the script, the young player will begin to recognize her own shortcomings. Or give the young bully a chance to play Robin Hood. It will lead him to an appreciation of the high-minded sense of values a hero possesses.

One final point. It takes time, and then more time, to produce a fresh, colorful bit of work that is as original as it is true. Do not let your adult consciousness of time harry you. Pressing for results will only bring about the very artificiality and mannerisms that these steps in creative techniques are designed to eliminate.

chapter 3

TEACHING PROCEDURE

Freeing the young imagination is a gradual process. Actually, it is two processes that go on simultaneously: (1) artistic development which involves rhythmic exercises, creative acting, and dramatization techniques; and (2) educational development which co-ordinates physical, mental, and emotional reactions. In any piece of dramatic doing, both processes are related and dependent on each other.

Take for example an improvisation on a visit to the dentist. This can serve as the basis for exercises in acting technique and in emotional release. The "dentist's" pantomimic activities of examining, drilling, and filling a tooth help bring about the sense of authenticity a dramatic instructor seeks. To impersonate a patient in the chair affords release for the fears which many young people associate with the dentist or other persons in authority.

Even the concentration required in the correct playing of the improvisation produces both artistic and educational benefits. *Concentration*, to the extent of being completely absorbed in what one is doing, tends to exclude other thoughts, especially an awareness of the audience. Concentration brings *relaxation*, which in turn encourages sincerity in acting, self-confidence, and poise in the player.

The creative techniques necessary to produce these developments are divided into two general age categories: (1) for the child under eight, and (2) for the older child. Common to both categories are the use of rhythms, exercises on concentration and relaxation (Chapter 4), and the manner in which these and other exercises are introduced. The introduction need not be planned in advance of the session but should result from the imaginative way in which the teacher greets the young people each time they come to class.

Introducing an Exercise

Some nine-year-olds are assembling on a clear, brisk, autumn day when the smell of burning leaves hovers everywhere.

"I can smell the leaves all the way into this room. Can you?" you ask the class.

"The windows are open, that's why," says Mike the realist.

This may start off an animated talk about fall and no more swimming and being cooped up in a schoolroom on a vibrating day when boys and girls would prefer sloshing through the yellow leaves or swinging at a baseball or . . .

"Well, what about playing ball here?" you suggest, adding excitedly, "Look out! Here comes the ball! Dicky, catch it! Now, who wants to bat and pitch?" Right away, three or four youngsters are up on their toes, pitching and swinging at the ball.

"Oh—oh!" a fifth cries out, "Larry hit a high one!"

"I missed!" shouts a sixth who jumped to catch the imaginary object.

"I saw the ball fall way over there, there among the leaves. Can you find it?" you interject quickly, and in a flash the entire group is off searching for the missing ball.

This is a preliminary exercise in the creative teaching of concentration.

Teaching the Child Under Eight

For this age group, more emphasis is placed on self-expression than on technique. The teaching process is described briefly.

Rhythms, Riddles, Dramatic Play

Rhythmic material is used extensively in working with little children. It helps to develop muscular flexibility and also contributes to their play-acting. Because they have a limited vocabulary, they are happiest when communicating through facial and body movements, many of which they performed in infancy.

You will concentrate on rhythms which engage the entire group as a unit, in order to promote physical co-ordination and quick response to changing beats. Piano improvisations, recordings, or percussion instruments will prompt the very young child to react immediately and happily. Or replace the instruments with hand and foot clapping (reminiscent of our square dancing and the Spanish dance of today), or with vocal noises. The long and short sounds will suggest the long vowels and the short consonants of speech. Let each child have a chance to clap, chant, or beat out a rhythm even if he produces but a single sound. Change rhythms and contrast the sounds. This will not only interest him but will also give him a feeling for the rise and fall of drama.

Do not look for rhythmic patterns at once. There will be many unexpected, disjointed bursts of hopping and running, and several meetings will go by before all the children will "feel" the rhythmic beat and respond correctly.

When a little one is reluctant to join in the physical activity, let him abstain. Before long, you will see him chanting and clapping in accompaniment. Chanting is an aid to the development of language flow and diction.

The Milkman's Horse [1] is typical of the poems used at this time:

> *On summer mornings when it's hot,*
> *The milkman's horse can't even trot;*
> *But pokes along like this—*
> *Klip-klop, klip-klop, klip-klop.*

> *But in the winter brisk,*
> *He perks right up and wants to frisk!*
> *And then he goes like this—*
> *Klippity-klip, klippity-klip, klippity-klip. . . .*

Dramatic play with simple characterization follows quickly on the heels of such a poem. The "horses" are sure to count among their numbers a hungry one, a lazy one, a frisky one or, perhaps, a lame one.

You will be charmed with the original versifying at this level. It is so fresh and wonderfully rhythmic. One pert miss of six composed a chant of her own while she gravely jiggled a puppet up and down:

> *Walk on step, walk on step,*
> *Walk on step, step,*
> *Walk on step.*
> *Walk on hooji, booji, jooja,*
> *Walk on step, step,*
> *Walk on step.*

The other members of her group just as gravely performed to her chanting.

For the child under eight, riddles are fun. They offer opportunities for working on speech, body movement, and playacting. Here is a riddle about the falling leaves of autumn:

> *Happy dancers, fast and slow,*
> *Bowing farewell, off they go;*
> *Now by ones, and now by threes,*
> *Soaring, dipping, with the breeze.*

Have a child recite these simple lines, and suggest to several other children that they move their bodies to illustrate the action. Then ask the rest of the group to guess the answer to the riddle.

Older players, too, will enjoy such exercises. A riddle about laundry on a clothesline was the inspiration for *A Line in a Storm* that a group of ten- and eleven-year-olds created under guidance (see Part Two of this book). This was the same group that, later, performed *A Midsummer Night's Dream!*

Elementary Dramatization

Dramatic songs, folk ballads, simple tales which take only a few minutes to play are excellent pieces for the very young child's introduction to dramatization. Select material that is elastic enough to allow everyone to play at the same time—the clothes hanging on the line, for instance. When the situation permits, let the child act as many roles as he likes within the same dramatization. In the poem, *Jonathan Bing* [2] by Beatrice Curtis Brown, he may be, at one moment, poor old Jonathan who tries to call on the King; at the next, the Soldier who prevents him; and at the third, he may be the carriage itself!

There are many lovely poems which are suited for work with this age unit in *When We Were Very Young* by A. A. Milne.

Later in the program, you may experiment by assigning different parts to individuals. Or you may tell the boys and girls a story without completing it, and suggest that they make up their own ending. Or you may even start with a rhythmic exercise and use it to lead them through dramatic play into dramatization as in the following incident.

A group of seven- and eight-year-olds was asked, one day, to invent clapping rhythms to which the boys and girls could move. Using both hands and feet, each child beat out sounds which his colleagues guessed as belonging to galloping horses, a clock tick-tocking, a giant walking, school children playing ball. After acting out these sounds through body movements, the young players created, under guidance, a brief, dramatic tale.

The scene is a school. It is eleven o'clock in the morning. You can hear the tick-tock of the school clock.

"Recess time!" cries Teacher, and the boys and girls run out to play. In the schoolyard, some play "Pease Porridge Hot," some skip rope, some play ball. Listen. Everyone is busy except for one unhappy boy who is called silly because he wants to play the piano. No one pays attention to him. He wanders back into the schoolroom and starts to play the piano. Listen.

Suddenly the tick-tock stops. The boys and girls are surprised and look at the clock. It reads "Five minutes to eleven!" When they first ran out to play, it was eleven o'clock. How strange! Who moved the time back?

Did it go back by itself? Why? Some of the children start to cry. The unhappy little boy continues to play the piano.

All of a sudden, they hear a galloping horse. A big, big giant rides into the playground. "Ha!" he shouts. "Here is my supper at last!" and leaping down from his horse, he grabs several children, then gallops away with them.

The others cry more than ever—all of them, that is, except the boy who is playing the piano. Suddenly they hear the galloping horse again. The horse is coming back to the schoolyard. It has heard the music of the unhappy boy. The horse likes the music so much that it dumps the kidnaped children and starts to dance. It keeps time to the music, too. The giant, mad as a hornet, chases the horse away.

Now everyone laughs and runs about. "Listen!" says a girl. "Tick-tock, tick-tock, tick-tock . . ." It is the clock. It is running again! They look at it. The time is now five minutes after eleven!

"Recess is over!" calls Teacher, and the boys and girls run back to their lessons.

Having created the story, the group selected a narrator and, to her telling, enacted the incidents in pantomime.

Play Performance

Children of this age level are content with dramatic play, the doing itself. If you need to put them on stage, the crowd scenes in scripts, such as *Where the Sea Breaks* and *How the Snowman Got His Broom*, will give the players several opportunities to appear without self-consciousness.

At no time expect polished results or try to push children into activity. In fact, during those moments of silence when the children seem to be at a standstill, they are really absorbing what they need. A moment later, they will contribute actively again. Your concern, now and always, is to encourage free movement and expression, to develop the children's interest in language, and to expose the boys and girls to an art form.

Teaching the Child Over Eight

Rhythmic exercises are given to the older child in order to relax and release him emotionally. They should begin each session and continue for ten or fifteen minutes.

Rhythms

Begin simple exercises to musical improvisation on the piano or drum. Start with arm movements, and follow with leg movements. Now have the children use arms and legs at various tempi—slow, fast, mixed—and in walking, skipping, running. Chanting and hand-and-foot clapping, mentioned for the younger children, may also be introduced here, depending of course upon the age and interest level of the group.

From such exercises, you now progress to more complicated rhythmic forms in which the whole body is involved and which may show the first signs of characterization. Use animal rhythms, such as hopping like a frog, falling like an elephant, jumping like a monkey, curling up like a cat.

The following poem suggests many physical movements:

The Squirrel [8] (Anonymous)

> *Whisky, frisky,*
> *Hippity hop,*
> *Up he goes*
> *To the tree top!*
>
> *Whirly, twirly,*
> *Round and round,*
> *Down he scampers*
> *To the ground.*
>
> *Furly, curly,*
> *What a tail!*
> *Tall as a feather,*
> *Broad as a sail!*
>
> *Where's his supper?*
> *In the shell,*
> *Snappity, crackity,*
> *Out it fell.*

Other poems, such as *Wind Is a Cat,* by Ethel Romig Fuller, and *Fog,* by Carl Sandburg, have been used with great enjoyment.

At later meetings, extend the variety of movements to include *inanimate objects*, such as moving like a rocking chair, rolling like a ball, swinging like the pendulum of a clock, spinning like a top. And still later, when the group is on characterization (Chapter 7), suggest running like grandmother, father, baby sister, the minister, a sailor, a wrestler, a dancer, a sales person.

Several mature groups have benefited from the psycho-physical exercises originated by Michael Chekhov (nephew of Anton Chekhov, the great Russian writer). The exercises are described in his book, *To the Actor.* By means of these exercises, the player "can increase his inner strength, develop his abilities to radiate and receive, acquire a fine sense of form, enhance his feelings of freedom, ease, calm and beauty." [4]

To achieve these qualities, to relax emotionally, to build from within, spontaneously, honestly, are also the objectives of creative acting techniques for children.

Creative Acting Techniques

The method of teaching such techniques is arranged in simple steps related to acting fundamentals, executed in this order: (1) in pantomime, (2) with mood, (3) with dialogue, and (4) with characterization. An analysis of dramatization, recommendations for casting, rehearsing, and staging the play follow. The players will enjoy a planned approach, which can be used successfully with groups over eight years of age. Subject matter and manner of presentation, however, will vary with each age level. Romance as an exercise theme, for instance, fascinates teen-agers but bores nine-year-olds.

The reason for using this teaching procedure is sound. Working on several points in a scene simultaneously—mood and dialogue and characterization—produces too many burdens for the inexperienced player. He has so much to do in performing an assignment that he "thinks" rather than plays the scene *from moment to moment,* letting mood, dialogue and characterization happen of themselves. He is approaching his work artificially, or from without, instead of dynamically, or from within. The result is loss of authenticity, naturalness, technically known as *truthfulness.*

As one point is mastered dynamically—and the length of time needed to accomplish it depends on age, maturity, and ability of group—a second point is added, then a third, a fourth, and so on, until the child is handling all the elements in a scene, truthfully and also simultaneously.

The techniques themselves, as set forth here, are based to a degree on the theories and practices of Constantin Stanislavski, co-founder of the Moscow Art Theatre. Actor and director, Stanislavski gained universal recognition for his Theatre when he taught his actors to enter into the lives of their characters. This, each accomplished by exploring himself as he played a role, using his own inner feelings instead of relying merely on physical expression.

Stanislavski's stress on an actor's reference to his inner life contrasted sharply with the teaching of his contemporaries who advised the actor to build a role through physical devices alone. To them, a drooping head meant shame, a raised fist anger, a scream fear.

Best known among the American followers of the "Method," a name often applied to Stanislavski's approach, is The Actor's Studio in New York City.

These inner techniques, as adapted for children, will now be explained, step by step, in succeeding chapters.

chapter 4

CREATIVE ACTING—FIRST STEPS IN TRUTHFULNESS

Acting is doing things truthfully. And to achieve this sense of reality, you must first find a purpose, an *objective* for the doing.

To illustrate, let us examine an elementary activity, "I open the telephone book." If you ask an inexperienced player to execute such a bit of doing, he will open the book and put it down quickly. His eyes will be on his audience and not on the pages. He will move artificially. He will be tense.

Now give the same player an objective, "I open the telephone book to look up the address of Charley Smith." The change in performance will be striking. Knowing the *why* of the activity, he will proceed with confidence. He will open the book and hunt for Charley Smith's name. He will be absorbed in his search and forget the audience. He will believe in what he is doing. He will move naturally. He will be relaxed.

Having an objective justifies or motivates the activity. It encourages concentration and, therefore, relaxation. It imbues the movement with truthfulness.

This bit of doing, incidentally, is a non-dramatic, purely physical task performed in pantomime. It does not concern itself with mood, dialogue, characterization, conflict, or plot structure. It is the most minute unit in the play scenes your group will eventually present.

Preliminary Exercises in Truthfulness

Your teaching begins with momentary, one-dimensional activities, like the one described. Your goal will be to encourage concentration and relaxation and, as a result, truthfulness. The child works alone, without a partner, performing each assignment in pantomime, and playing himself. That is, Rod looks up the telephone number, as he really would any day of his life, and not as he imagines a crusty, near-sighted shopkeeper might. The themes for the first exercises are drawn from a child's here-and-now experiences. At this time, physical states—being tired, hungry, sleepy, sick, hot, or cold—are avoided to keep the exercise elementary.

Wherever possible, let all the players do these exercises simultaneously. Ask everyone to get up at one time and gather leaves, pick apples, or tidy up the room. And remind each actor to invent an objective before he performs the activity: "I gather leaves to paste in my scrap book."

Concentration

Some exercises, which strengthen concentration and are fun at the same time, can be given now and anytime that you feel your group needs them.

(a) "I am writing a letter while my friends try their hardest to distract me." At the end of the exercise the player should present a completed letter to the leader.

(b) "I am studying a poem in the face of the same distractions."

(c) "I am singing a song before a boisterous, jeering audience."

Playing games like "Simon says" will make even the youngest children participate gleefully in concentration exercises.

Teaching Procedure

If any player breaks into dialogue or introduces more elements than you want in these first exercises, do not dampen his enthusiasm by insisting on the one-dimensional. Guide him, instead, into working on the technical points within the structure of his more complicated playmaking.

Let us say that you want to stress concentration at the second meeting of a group of eight to ten-year-olds. You ask the girls to perform in a series of simple, pantomimic activities, such as sweeping the floor. As it happens, they have seen *Cinderella* presented by the local Junior League only yesterday and their enthusiasm prompts them into spontaneous improvisations on the theme.

Do not cut their happy playmaking short. Use it, instead, as the starting point for your exercises. In the discussions that precede and follow this improvisation, emphasize the tasks Cinderella must carry out—sewing a hem on Esmeralda's dress, fetching her Stepmother's tiara, removing the cinders from the fireplace, washing the dishes. When they return to their playing of Cinderella, the girls will concentrate on these physical activities.

Where? What? Why?

In the general discussion following your first pantomimic exercises, try to clarify the players' thinking by asking concrete questions that will contribute to the truthfulness of their work.

"Where were you?" (Place)

"What were you doing?" (Activity)

"Why were you doing it?" (Objective)

Older players with experience will be able to ask themselves, without prompting, "Where am I? What am I doing? Why am I doing it?"

Prompt the young people to visualize the scene of their activity. If they are pretending to be outdoors playing ball, the place may be a field dotted with three maple trees, two large boulders and a clump of daisies. Encourage them to see the trees, smell the daisies, feel the hot sun on their faces. Now, mark off a portion of the room to represent the field. Arrange chairs around the area, or include the non-performing children by asking them to serve as props—the trees, the boulders, and the clump of daisies. When the players repeat their ball-playing exercise, their improvisation will have greater reality.

Charades

The children will be eager to invent their own simple activities, especially after you discuss the general situation with them. Try picnicking at the seashore for the eights and nines, cleaning house before the Thanksgiving dinner for the ten-to-twelves, waiting in the railroad station for a delayed train for the teens. Each player chooses an activity with an objective to suit the situation. He acts it out in pantomime while you try to identify what he is doing. You are playing charades! For the station episode, the various activities may include studying a time table, making a telephone call, eating a candy bar, knitting a sweater, and reading a magazine. In a short time, you will find the shyest of children volunteering to work alone without the support of the others.

In another exercise, the performer's activity may be suggested in a whisper to him by another child, in order to have several children participate. Tell the actor to consider beforehand the *where? what? why?* of his assignment. Ask the others to guess what it is, after he pantomimes it.

Objects

During the introductory steps to creative acting, real objects should be used to help concentration and truthfulness—a book to read, a vase to dust, cups and saucers to place on the table. Later, imaginary objects can replace the real, although you will continue to watch for authenticity in the handling of any invisible prop.

Before working from memory, however, devote time to a *handling-of-objects* exercise. Present it to the younger people in the usual "let's play a game" manner. Seat them on the floor in a circle. Ask each child to choose an object that starts with the letter of the alphabet which had been previously assigned to him—apple for A, banana for B, cat for C. He then pantomimes the handling of the object, using as many of his five senses as the article suggests. The others attempt to identify it.

Variations of this game can include a make-believe visit to the toy shop or the corner grocery store.

More Exercises in Truthfulness

When?

Very soon in the course of their pantomimic acting, your players will be confronted with the problem of *when? When?* not only implies time, it often involves a sense of urgency. For instance, in an activity such as "I enter the kitchen to get some cookies Mother has just baked," *when?* asks not merely "What time of day do I enter?" but, more important, "Why must I enter this minute and not a minute before or later?"

The answer may be, "Mother does not like me to eat any cookies before dinner. But the smell of fresh baking is so tempting that when she leaves the kitchen for a moment, I run in and snatch a handful. It is now or never!" There is a note of urgency in the time element.

What will happen to me if . . . ?

The urgency in a situation increases when the player asks of himself, "What will happen to me if Mother finds me at the cookie jar? Will she punish me?" Or to phrase it technically, "What are the consequences for me? What's at stake?"

Urgency often embraces matters of life and death. "My dog has just swallowed a chicken bone. If I don't reach a doctor at once, he'll choke!"

With the appearance of urgency, the plotless activity you have been occupied with until now acquires suspense and dramatic impact. There is an underlying struggle. The group has taken its first important step toward dramatization.

Elementary Dramatization

Now is the time to ask the older player to invent, without help, a story situation for an assignment such as "I enter a room."

He is to decide for himself where the room is—a doctor's office, the minister's study, a police station—why and when he is entering it, and what is urgent about his entering. He still improvises as himself and in pantomime, although this last restriction is never enforced. Teen-agers have enjoyed working with "I run into the police station to report that my money has been stolen."

Incidentally, during the here-and-now period, gory stories involving gangsters, spies, and murderers are conceived regularly, especially by the male contingent. Do not be alarmed. Once there has been a little blood-letting, the boys will welcome dramatizing on a less sanguinary level. "Cops and Robbers" pave the way to *Robin Hood!*

Teaching Procedure

A reminder. A point that the children have absorbed should not be dropped in favor of a new one. Let them add a second point to it, and then a third, until they are using all their tools in dramatic doing.

Professional terminology is best omitted in your work with young people. Use the key words, *where? what? why? when? what will happen to me if* . . . *?* to lead them into imaginative doing. The teen-ager, however, enjoys learning technical language and he may be encouraged to do so.

The length of time it takes to absorb the first steps in creative acting techniques depends upon the ability and readiness of the group to grow. You can maintain interest and enthusiasm for any number of meetings, if you keep varying the situations and methods of presentation. A leader's own flexibility and imagination make up the formula for a successful project.

When the group has mastered these simple exercises in truthfulness, it is ready to experiment with mood.

chapter 5

MOOD AND OBSTACLE

Mood—or feeling or emotion—helps to transform a simple activity into a complex one that resembles a unit in a well-constructed play.

How would I feel if . . . ? are the words that a performer asks himself now. "How would I feel if I were confronted by a bully?" Or, in acting a character in a story or play, "How would I feel if I were Hänsel lost in the woods at nightfall?" The performer is trying to arrive at the specific mood the situation demands.

Yet asking *how?* is not enough. To decide quickly that "I would feel frightened," and then to act frightened in playing the situation would only result in a superficial, affected performance. And the player's approach would be described as "playing the emotion."

To feel the *how?* dynamically and to let the emotion come through from within, in the moment-to-moment playing, are the prime objectives of the next, big step in creative technique.

Particularization

One of the tools that adults sometimes use to attain mood is personal association, or particularization. Stanislavski called it "emotion memory." Through this device, emotion is generated by a player's recalling his personal experiences.

In a play situation involving a car accident, for instance, the mature player may think back to an actual episode in his own life when he was in an accident, or he may recall another experience which similarly terrified him. The incident in his past has particular meaning to him. He reacted to it in a highly personal way. His response was unlike that of any other person's, even that of someone who was also present at the event. The very thought of his own accident may be enough to induce the terror he felt then, and needs now, for his performance. Or, if the thought of his accident does not evoke the terror, he may have to recreate the old scene in vivid detail in order to generate the mood.

He recalls how the place looked, what time of day it was, whether it was hot or cold, who was in the car with him, what he wore, what brought on the accident, what he did immediately after it. He relives the experience to the extent of repeating, now, some act he performed at that time —crawling on his knees, perhaps. The emotion he then felt is reawakened dynamically in the present. "What did I do then?" helps to bring on "How do I feel now?"

But self-exploration is most productive only when the individual is old enough to have an accumulation of experiences—usually at about eighteen years of age. The younger the performer, the fewer episodes has he undergone to which he can relate.

Young people, however, have used particularization with worth-while results. A tense, thirteen-year-old girl was improvising the scene in *The Blue Bush* (see Part Two of this book) where the picnickers feel an invisible barrier closing in on them. No matter how hard she tried, she was unable to convey the terror truthfully, which the situation required. She had never been frightened, she claimed, absolutely never! It did not take long for the leader to dig up an experience which had terrified the girl— one that had occurred on the previous day! It was her injection against polio. The sight of the doctor's hypodermic needle had been enough to drive the nervous girl into a fit of trembling. The next time she played her scene, our adolescent used the needle incident to help her create the necessary emotion.

When particularization cannot serve for lack of experience, the player resorts to other means of producing the desired emotion truthfully.

Devices to Produce Mood

What would I do if . . . ?

At your prompting, the child asks himself what action, big or small, he would do in a certain situation—perhaps, the one where Johnny wants to cross the street and finds a bully waiting for him on the other side (Chapter 2). "What would I do if I were confronted by a bully? Would I start to cry? Would I shout at the bully to go away? Would I run away?" The child is exploring himself in terms of doing something. He is not thinking solely of how he would feel in the situation.

Once the child decides on the action, tell him to get up and play the scene, using this action. Concentration on the circumstances and the doing of the action will release the emotion.

What will happen to me if . . . ?

Getting the child to visualize the consequences of an action will also help to bring about the true feeling. "What will happen to me if the bully catches me?" the player asks himself.

Imagination

Tell the child to imagine a situation, a picture, which will give him the emotion he is seeking. By visualizing ink all over her new formal dress the teen-ager may induce the feeling of horror she requires in order to portray Lady Macbeth in the play's sleepwalking scene. Choose episodes or mental pictures with which the child can associate easily, and present them in a dramatic way. Stimulate him into "living" these episodes; help by playing appropriate background music.

Present the Situation Vividly

In giving the younger boys and girls a situation to perform, do not say "You come home to find mother gone." Elaborate on the situation, presenting it in a manner designed to arouse mood.

"You are in school. The final period of the day is slowly dragging by. Suddenly the bell rings, the last bell! 'Whee,' you sigh in relief. Time for fun now. And what fun! Rosalind has promised to meet you after school, and the two of you are going to plan the games for your birthday party.

"You are slipping into your winter coat when Teacher gives you a message. It's from Mother. 'Come right home,' she says, 'We'll go out to buy your birthday present.'

"Your heart jumps up! A birthday present! What can it be? No, it can't—but then it may be—that portable radio you've been dreaming of for more than a year. Daddy had promised to give it to you last Christmas, but then he got sick, and the doctor's bills were high and . . . But Daddy is okay now. Everything is okay, and—oh, it must be the radio, it's just got to be the radio. Mommy wouldn't dream of anything else.

"You run all the way home, not even stopping for your daily candy treat at the stationery store. Your breath comes out in little round balls of smoke. You run up the walk to your house. You push the door open. 'Hi, Mom,' you call out, 'I'm home!' No answer. You call again. 'Mom, I'm home!' Silence.

"You hurry into the kitchen. No one. A lump forms in your throat. 'Mom, Mom, where are you?' You hunt in the pantry, the bedroom, the bathroom. Empty, all empty. You stop suddenly. You stand still, very still. You listen. Your ears hurt from listening hard. Listen. No one. Nothing. The house is one big, empty nothing. Mommy has forgotten your present, has forgotten you, has gone away. . . .

"The lump in your throat slips down into your chest. You are alone. Alone . . ."

An unexpected and amusing block occurred at the session where this situation originated. "But my Mother is always home," one literal young man objected.

"Well, perhaps she was called away unexpectedly to help a sick neighbor," the leader suggested confidently.

"Then my grandmother would be home."

"Well, let's pretend Mother had to help a sick neighbor, and Grandma went to the supermarket."

"Then I wouldn't be coming home in the first place!" he scored triumphantly.

The situation was abandoned.

Incidentally, all such mood-producing devices are used by the player, not only when he performs as himself in a scene, but also when he portrays another character. During the second phase of acting fundamentals, the child still performs in pantomime, as himself, without a partner. He also avoids the portrayal of physical states, such as being tired, hot, or sick (Chapter 4).

Preliminary Exercises in Mood

Exercises begin with the projection of a single emotion, which has started before the opening of the scene and is continued throughout the improvisation.

(a) "I have to practice my hated violin when my pals want me to play ball." (rebellion)
(b) "I hand Father my bad report card." (fear)
(c) "I restring the beads of my necklace which my bratty brother has broken." (anger)
(d) "I dash into the house to tell Mother our cocker spaniel has just been run over." (anguish)
(e) "I put on lipstick for my first date." (happy excitement)

When suggesting these situations to your group, do not mention the conventional emotions given in the parentheses. Urge each member, instead, to respond to the situation as he, himself, would. Welcome originality if logically motivated. Her first date may pleasantly excite one girl. It may make another sick to her stomach. Either reaction may be used in acting exercises, where the real goal is to awaken the unique creativity that lies within everyone. In the performance of a play, however, the actor gives the specific feeling demanded by the scene.

A particularly amusing bit of dramatic doing evolved on one occasion, when some older players were asked to do mood exercises in reverse.

Given the mood, "gaiety," they had to invent the circumstances which would produce the feeling. Several conventional situations were presented: a boy acting noise-happy at a party after the big football game; a girl giggling as she watched a cartoon on television. Finally, one young lady played out a situation in which she went into a millinery shop to buy a hat. The business of trying on hats always buoyed up her spirits, she claimed later. But what the group saw was a girl pulling hat after hat over her ears with a deadpan concentration that was as hilarious as it was remarkably original. Professional comics, beware!

Other moods may involve anxiety, caution, distress, curiosity, recklessness, gloom, loneliness. Give the children a situation and have them arrive at the mood truthfully. Or give them the mood, and let them find the circumstances which would justify it. Always help them to analyze the assignment through the described *where? what? why? when? what will happen to me if . . . ? what did I do? what would I do if . . . ?* method.

More Exercises in Mood

Five Senses

In your work on mood, the five senses—sight, smell, hearing, taste and touch—often come into play. Your boys and girls will find specific work on them valuable.

    (a) "I see a beautiful rainbow in the sky." (sight)
    (b) "I walk into the kitchen and smell apple pie baking in the oven." (smell)
    (c) "It is nighttime. I am alone in our big house. Suddenly there is a soft scratching at the door." (hearing)
    (d) "I try to swallow an aspirin and the bitter pill dissolves on my tongue." (taste)
    (e) "I pick up a pot on the stove. It's hot!" (touch)

Music Response

At one session, ask the young people to listen to music you have selected beforehand. Suggest that they let themselves react to it physically and emotionally.

"Let's pretend we are spending the day in the cool woods," you say to start off a group of eight-year-old boys. "Our bus has just come to a stop, and here we go, piling out of our sticky seats as quickly as—oh, oh! We can't leave yet! I forgot to open the door. Wait! Before I open it, let the music tell each one of us how he feels about getting out of the bus."

Now, as prearranged, the pianist breaks into a ripple of music that has a carefree motif. Eyes sparkle, smiles appear, and before you can say "Jack and the Beanstalk," agile bodies are hopping up and about the room, in time to the music.

At the music's conclusion, question the boys on their reactions and their individual reasons for feeling the way they did. "I was happy," one may say, "because it was my very first hike." "It was my first day out of the house in two years," may be the response of another who had fallen from a tree and been confined to his bed for a week.

Older groups with playmaking experience will be able to make up their own stories in response to the music.

Vary Circumstances

After the children have acted out single-mood exercises, as themselves, let them try acting as characters of their own sex and age, and in various circumstances. For instance, a situation such as "I find a baseball mitt on the sidewalk" may be performed by the player as a boy who has never owned a mitt, or as one who has more mitts in his drawer than he can count.

Many Moods

When the group is adept at projecting a single mood truthfully, follow up with situations that involve a change in feeling. First use one change, then several changes. Each child continues to work in pantomime, as himself, without a partner, and with discussion preceding and succeeding the improvisation:

(a) "Mother and I are buyng Christmas presents in the town's largest toy department. The counters are jammed with shoppers. I turn my head to look at a walking doll. When I look back, Mother is gone. Did she go home without me? My stomach hurts. I search the witches' faces about me. Mother must have forgotten me. My fingers creep to my mouth, my eyes screw up, I begin to . . . Why, there she is at the end of the counter speaking to a sales person! Mommy!" (anxiety to relief)

(b) "I've been itching to play in the hockey match this afternoon, but Coach put Brad on the team instead of me. I am moping around the house when Coach calls me to say, 'Brad is sick. Will you be his substitute?' Will I? Oh boy! Oh boy! I run to my room for my hockey duds. I get into my uniform, I reach into the closet for my hockey stick. It isn't there! My brother must have taken it again! That pest!" (depression to excitement to anger)

(c) "I am at our Girl Scout dance. The music has been playing for ages, but no boy has asked me to dance. I wish the floor would open up and swallow me. Suddenly I see Jeff crossing the dance floor toward me. I can hardly breathe. Surely, surely he is going to ask me to be his partner. My palms are sticky. He's coming nearer and nearer and . . . Oh! He's walked right past me to speak to that pretty girl at the door." (humiliation to hope to despair)

Several changes of mood will frequently involve two people in a scene. This brings your program to the next step in the teaching of creative acting—the *obstacle*.

Creative Acting: The Obstacle

Take the scene in which Hänsel and Gretel, deserted by their Father, are lost in the woods. The two children are hunting anxiously for the way home. When both want the same thing, their relationship is harmonious. They are not opposed to each other. However, should Hänsel insist on going to the left against Gretel's wish to go right, their contrary desires may lead to a quarrel, from which complications and crises can develop (Chapters 2, 8). They are in conflict with each other, and Gretel is called Hänsel's obstacle, or opposing force.

An obstacle may be a person or a thing that stands in the way of a character's achieving his objective. It may be an obstacle outside the character. The bully is Johnny's obstacle in the Johnny-faces-the-bully situation (Chapter 2). Then again, it may be a need or emotion within the character. Crossing the street, Johnny wants to appear brave; but his inner fear betrays him, and he runs back to the schoolyard.

Having an obstacle in a scene will also help the player to awaken the mood the action demands.

Exercises with Obstacles

Introduce variety into your program, (1) by placing the obstacle (here, a person) in the room (the *where?* of the situation) before the scene starts, (2) by placing the obstacle outside the room, although he may enter at any time, (3) by having the obstacle asleep in the room, and (4) by making the obstacle blind.

> (a) "Patty tries to sneak out to the movies without being seen by Sister who wants to go along." (Sister, who is Patty's obstacle, is out of the room but may enter.)
> (b) "Cliff walks into his father's bedroom to take his father's new tie without permission, only to find Dad asleep on the bed." (Dad, who is Cliff's obstacle, is asleep in the room but may wake up.)

Because it produces conflict, an obstacle is necessary for successful dramatization (Chapters 2, 8).

Playacting Procedure

As you have noticed, the method of performing an assignment is now undergoing several changes. The young player takes his situations from any source he chooses, here-and-now as well as literature. Since he is working with a partner, he uses dialogue where he needs it. And he is often called upon to act as a character other than himself.

Elementary Characterization

To illustrate, Allan, fearless as they come, is playing the role of Hänsel in the scene where the Witch first accosts him. Allan may act it as himself, that is, a brave Hänsel not in the least bit afraid of the Witch. Or, having decided in discussion that Hänsel is a timid soul, Allan may invent a character who runs at the slightest sound. His partner, Liz, who is impersonating the Witch, will be projecting a character unlike her own sweet self.

When the group uses scenes involving two or more characters, be sure to analyze beforehand how each character affects and is affected by the others.

Do not anticipate much from characterization now. Learning to work with an obstacle is your group's current objective. Characterization will be examined at length in Chapter 7.

Elementary Dramatization

This is also a good moment to try extending the child's knowledge of dramatization. In the acting out of a situation with two characters, ask each character to improvise activities which will make the scene progress, and possibly bring it to a dramatic conclusion.

Let us look again at the incident in which Johnny and the bully face each other across the street. The boy acting Johnny may determine in advance what course of action Johnny must take to cross the street safely. Johnny may decide to plead with the bully to let him pass; then, if the latter remains adamant, to shout "Fire!" in order to divert the bully's attention, and thus escape. In short, Johnny has created two activities to accomplish his objective.

Of course, the boy impersonating the bully may improvise his own activities in response to Johnny's first plea. Or he may or may not be fooled by Johnny's "Fire!" device. If he holds his ground, Johnny will have to improvise a third activity on the spur of the moment. Perhaps he will call upon Butch, the policeman, to escort him home.

Exercises will become even more creative and dramatic when both the main character and the obstacle want to do things which are conflicting and urgent:

"I want Daddy to take me to the movies. Daddy wants me to go with him to the symphony, instead. The movies and the concert start at the same time, and we barely have time to make either!"

From here on, you will find that the improvisations have many of the characteristics of a scene in a well-constructed play—mood, characterization, conflict between opposing forces, urgency, complications leading to a major crisis, and resolution (Chapters 8, 10). These more complex situations give you many chances to further not only the artistic objective of your project but its educational goal as well—the creation of fine, social attitudes in the growing personality.

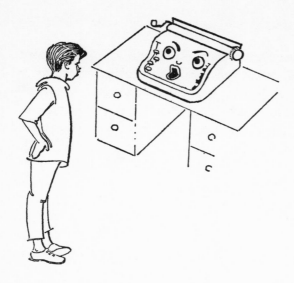

chapter 6

DIALOGUE FLOW

Once the players have learned to relax creatively, you will find that their transition from pantomime to acting in dialogue evolves without difficulty. *Say* is added to the list of key words. "What do you think Johnny would say to the bully?" *Communication* between the partners in a scene is the element you will try to work for now.

Communication

Not knowing in advance how his opponent is going to act, Johnny is forced to listen carefully to what the bully says. Johnny digests his obstacle's words, both intellectually and emotionally; and then, and only then, makes his own response.

This *listen, react, then reply* brings about communication on stage, and is a valuable factor in achieving truthfulness. Although the players will generally communicate in improvisations, they often fail to do so when the development of a scene is already familiar to them. This may happen during the rehearsals and the performance of a written play. Here the children may jump their cues or recite their lines in a sort of dead, parrot-like whine, telegraphing their advance knowledge to the audience.

There are ways to correct such "indicating": (1) by giving exercises in creative improvisations on the scene, itself, and on invented scenes that involve the same characters, and (2) by reminding the players of the inner values of the scene.

Paramount among these values are the separate objectives of the characters. Ask each character to concentrate on what he wants to do to his obstacle. Johnny may think, "I want to force the bully to run away; I'll shout 'Fire.'" The bully thinks, "I want to get hold of Johnny and punch him in the nose." With their aims constantly in mind, Johnny and the bully play their scene from moment to moment, and what they say will always sound spontaneous and real.

Caution the actors against saying more than is absolutely necessary during improvisations.

Dialogue Flow of the Child Under Eight

Of children under eight years of age whose vocabulary is limited, little should be expected in the way of line continuity. Here, your goal lies in satisfying their urgent need to communicate—a need which drives baby to kick and cry, his three-year-old brother to shout and scream, and his really grown-up brother, who is old at five or six, to experiment gleefully with words.

"The cow slopped away," announced one six-year-old solemnly during improvisation.

"I have a sister. She pins everything on me as though I was a porcupine!" a seven-and-a-half-year-old exploded on another occasion.

"Dugan's Bakery," chirps a third child, answering an imaginary telephone. "What crumb do you want to talk to?"

The use of rhythm exercises, suggested in Chapter 3 for this age group, makes an excellent foundation for the language flow that will soon begin.

Dialogue Flow of the Child Over Eight

If you need to do specific work on dialogue with the older children, here are several exercises that encourage fluidity of speech.

Monologues

The child, acting as himself, speaks to an invisible partner. The exercise may be:

(a) "I complain to my doll about my parents who pack me off to bed right in the middle of my favorite television program."
(b) "I 'phone a friend to tell him about the basketball game I saw yesterday."
(c) "I 'phone a friend to persuade him to spend the night with me in a haunted house."
(d) "I carry on a conversation with an imaginary object, non-human, but capable of answering me: an ant who gave up working; a fly who comes to dinner; a tree that grows money; a typewriter that complains about my compositions."

Music

Background music, "telling" a player how he feels, will help him to speak with greater ease.

General Notes and Suggestions

When the children are working with characterization, remind them to speak "in character." A bully may talk like a "tough," and use slang; an emperor will be commanding in his speech, and use good grammar.

When a player "goes dry" during a scene, "But I don't know what to say next," review the scene thoroughly—its characterization, objectives, urgencies, and so forth. Then ask him to try it again in pantomime.

Crowd Scenes

When improvising words in a scene that involves many characters, the children may find themselves enmeshed in confusing dialogue—unless you plot the course of its development beforehand. Having discussed what happens in detail, you assign to certain players cue lines that will introduce a change in mood or a new complication. The other performing members are guided by these cues.

Let us say that the group that analyzed *The Emperor's New Clothes* in Chapter I is now improvising the procession scene in the story. The scene can involve everyone as Paraders and People lining the streets. To avoid chaos in doing, decide in advance that Gary, enacting the Emperor, will issue the order, "Let the procession begin!" Helen, impersonating an Old Woman, will shout, "Aren't his clothes beautiful?" Julie, as the Child, will insist, "But he's in his underwear!" Instruct the other children to use these lines as cues to indicate the changing themes of their dialogue. Following Gary's order, the Guards and Courtiers fuss about organizing the parade. Following Helen's exclamation, the People "ad lib" their praises and hosannahs.

More Exercises in Dialogue

When dialogue is flowing easily, vary the assignment.

Poem or Song

Ask each member to recite a dramatic poem or to sing a song. As he performs, he must remember to think of his audience as his obstacle. In the poem, *Missing* by A. A. Milne, for instance, the player wants "to make his listeners tell him" where his mouse has gone.

Line of Dialogue

At this stage, experiment by giving your group a line of dialogue and asking the boys and girls to use it as the opening words of an improvised scene.

(a) "You can't come to my birthday party."
(b) "Come in here, I want to see you."

The group invents characters and a general situation of conflict that starts with either line. A school principal, perhaps, calls the class truant into his office with, "Come in here, I want to see you." After the children discuss the situation from various angles—*where? what? why?*—they play the scene, improvising dialogue and complications as they go along.

At another session, give both an opening line and a closing line to a situation:

OPENING: "Come in here, I want to see you."
CLOSING: "If you don't leave, I'll 'phone the police!"

The plot may concern a business tycoon who calls into his office the gangster who has been sending him disturbing letters. The tycoon wants the gangster to stop annoying him. The gangster becomes menacing. Angry words lead to angry threats from the gangster, and the tycoon can get rid of him only by shouting "If you don't leave, I'll 'phone the police!"

This scene was actually created by a group of eleven-year-old boys who analyzed the general situation beforehand—the characters of the two opponents; their involvement with one another; the nature of the threatening letters; how the tycoon hoped to rid himself of the gangster; the gangster's reaction. The improvisation was electrically alive!

Similar "opening and closing lines" improvisations can also be used as introductory exercises in dramatization.

Diction

Good diction is important in acting and in every-day life, but since its achievement depends mainly on habit-forming drills, it does not lie within the province of dramatic doing. When children are absorbed in creating spontaneously, they should not be forced to attend to speech problems as well.

However, some correction of grammar and diction may be introduced pleasantly in the discussions following a performance. Or a bit of drill may be given in a palatable way through choral speech, poem chanting, and a variety of games that children enjoy. These devices include "tongue twisters"; dramatic poems; whistling the rhythm and cadence of the words in a story, instead of enunciating them; games in which the child counts as long as he can on one breath; performing in plays in which he rehearses the same words many times.

There are other useful suggestions to be found in books devoted to speech improvement. Now it is enough to say that creative dramatics can further good diction by helping the boys and girls to relax emotionally, and by making them conscious of vocal clarity and quality. Although the child's first reaction to correction may be, "But nobody talks like that," he will accept tactful criticism, especially when you impress upon him an audience's need to understand what the actors say in a play. One of the reasons for presenting the adaptation of A Midsummer Night's Dream was to encourage good speaking habits.

If drill is used at all, give it during the few minutes which precede the playacting and dramatization. At no time allow it to interfere with or replace the creative act itself.

chapter 7

CHARACTERIZATION

Until now, the child has worked on creative acting, a single step at a time. He improvised simple exercises in truthfulness; situations with objectives; situations with time and consequence urgencies; situations with obstacles, either animate or inanimate; situations with mood. These, he performed for the most part as himself; but occasionally he played the personality of another character when he began to work with a partner.

Even for adults the study of *characterization* is difficult, dealing as it does with the interplay of the physical, mental, social, and psychological traits of a character. Personality is the sum total of many elements. For example, the girl with a disfigured face is likely to be withdrawn. Her withdrawal, in turn, may affect her manner of walking. She sidles into a room, head averted, eyes down. The beautiful Miss America, on the other hand, radiates inner confidence, and her movements reflect her security.

With children the approach to characterization must of necessity begin on an elementary level, one related to their understanding and ability. The older and more observant the player, the greater is the depth of his character portrayal. The younger the player, the more superficial and one-dimensional is his work. But before we start on exercises for young people, it may be well to examine the different elements that make up any character portrayal.

Composition of a Character

Physical Characteristics

These cover the external attributes of a character—sex, age, height, weight, hair, eyes, skin, posture, gestures, movements, clothes—in brief, his general appearance.

This category also includes *physical handicaps* and *occupational disabilities*. Polio-shriveled muscles cause the boy's limp. The mailman's left shoulder sags permanently because he has used it to carry his heavy mail bag.

Background Characteristics

These pertain to a character's social life, occupation, education, home life, nationality, interests, and place in the community.

Inner Characteristics

These are concerned with a character's psychological traits—the attitudes that the character has before the play opens, his temperament, complexes, drives, attitudes toward life. A character may be innately shy, sensitive, highly imaginative, hard to please, domineering, excitable. The *inner attitude*, as it will be called from now on, differs from that controlled by a scene's development. To illustrate, the character, a boy who is customarily brave (inner attitude), finds himself spending the night in a haunted house. The weird noises he hears make him cower during that scene (scene's emotional state of being).

Inner attitudes influence not only a character's reaction to situations and to other characters, but also influence the way a character talks, walks, and gestures. A suspicious cowboy may frown all the time, be abrupt in his speech, and walk with a stealthy step, peering over his shoulder to see who is behind him.

Observation and Imagination

Your first move in guiding young players through the study of characterization is to make them aware of the importance of observation. Suggest that they spend some time watching people who walk down Main Street or shop at the supermarket. Ask them to select a specific individual and report on his physical characteristics at your next meeting. At that session, tell the children to describe as exactly as they can the individual's general appearance in terms of sex, height, clothing, walk, and gestures.

But do not let the children's training in observation remain at the discussion level. Urge each one, instead, to get up and enact a single, physical action that is typical of the individual he has studied and which he can understand. By acting out a character's mannerisms the player is helped to become that character.

After the boys and girls have studied the physical characteristics of a person, guide them to an understanding of the person's background and his inner attitudes which produced the external traits.

"The girl was biting her thumbnail as she stared into the store window," you sum up a teen-ager's observations of a real person he saw on Main Street. "Now, why do you suppose a ten-year-old would do this? Is it because she broke it? Is it because she is unhappy that she cannot buy the skates in the window?" (her mood of the moment) "Or is it because she is a tense person, who always bites her nails?" (inner attitude)

As with a real person, in working with a fictional character, you proceed from physical characteristics to inner attitudes. For instance, your discussions during the first attempts at portraying Hänsel's Witch may contain leading questions such as:

"What do you think the Witch looks like?"

"She's skinny." "She has big teeth." "She has long hair," most of the children will volunteer.

"What color hair?"

"Red!" "Black!" "Gray!" "And it flies in the wind when she's on her broomstick!"

"How old would you say she is? As old as Cindy?" The "No!" is firm.

"As old as I am?" The "No" is more dubious.

"Older?"

"She is as old as my Grandma," one young lady graciously decides.

"As Grandma?" You jump at the chance to use the image of a person familiar to the girl. You know that associating an imaginative picture with a real person will make the fictional person come alive.

"How does an old Grandma walk when she strolls in the park?" you ask. "Is her back straight? Does she move as quickly as you do? Why is she so much slower? Show us." Here, the older groups will be receptive to a brief talk about the body's skeletal and muscular equipment and how advancing age will affect both.

"Does the Witch walk like Grandma?" you continue. "Show us." Stooping in a manner typical of the Witch, the player begins to assume her personality.

Additional probing and doing may create for your Witch a hobble—"She fell off her broomstick one Halloween,"—and a crooked grin!

"A crooked grin?" Now you feel the moment is right to start digging for those inner attitudes. "Why do you think the Witch smiles that way? Has she a toothache? Or is it because of something special she feels deep down inside of her? Perhaps she's happy, or kind to children or . . ."

"Kind, ha!" Excited answers shout out. "She's wicked!" "She loves children like my great Dane loves meat; gobble, gobble!"

Eventually, the boys and girls arrive at their own picture of the Witch. "She's old and has a lined face like Grandma. She has long, gray hair that snaps behind her like a kite. She has a humped back and limps when she walks. She grins through all her crooked teeth because she is wicked. And she's wicked because she hates the whole world."

More discussion brings out the fact that the Witch's attitude of hatred influences not only her grin but her every action. In the scene where she first greets Hänsel and Gretel, her attempt at a kindly manner may result in a sneering voice and a claw-like grasp for a handshake.

Again, terminate the intellectual analysis by asking each player to get up and perform the Witch-greets-Hänsel-and-Gretel situation. Help each one to do it truthfully through the devices where? what? why?

when? what will happen to me if . . . ? what do I want to do to my obstacle? As the player becomes absorbed in this bit of doing, he will slowly be transformed into a character other than himself—the Witch.

Preliminary Exercises in Observation and Imagination

Physical Characteristics

Tell the members of the group to enact a series of simple, physical activities in pantomime: (1) as themselves; (2) as persons older or younger than they are; (3) as persons of the same or opposite sex. Suggest large movements to the young children: walking, running, dancing, sitting down, lying down, making a bed, mowing the lawn, painting a fence.

When the group has mastered the exercise, introduce pantomimic work on physical handicaps. They may include a sprained ankle, a broken arm, a stomach ache, short-sightedness, poor hearing. Help each player determine just where and how badly he is hurt, then tell him to keep his handicap in mind throughout the improvisation. For example, slipping on the handball court, Bob is afraid he broke his leg. Being alone, he must drag himself to the nearest telephone booth to call for help.

At later sessions, ask the group to do simple activities, still in pantomime, in the manner of a cowboy (bowlegged from riding), a model (sinuous in movement), a charwoman (with drooping shoulders). The children will enjoy inventing a variety of such occupational differences and the "game" will sharpen their sense of observation.

Background music will help the younger players achieve the physical movements they want in the above exercises.

Inner Attitudes

Give the group a general situation, such as relaxing in the park. Ask each child to choose a simple, physical activity and to perform it as a character with a particular inner trait. Acting in pantomime, the child may walk, run, or dance, as would a serious person, a shy person, a domineering person, a boisterous person. Invent, or help him to invent, the background and circumstances which would make his performance truthful. A tale such as *The Pied Piper of Hamelin* offers many situations for this exercise.

Follow up with a specific activity, "I look through the library catalogues for science material." Ask each player to do it in the manner of a person who is serious, shy, domineering, or boisterous.

At this point, the older, experienced performer may combine an inner attitude with a physical characteristic. He does the catalogue activity as a character who has an inner attitude and who also suffers from a physical handicap or occupational disability. A shy porter, his joints aching from years of heavy cleaning, hunts through the catalogues.

Elementary Dramatization

Have two or more players enact the above situation as characters of contrasting inner attitudes, and let them resolve the conflict that ensues. A serious girl and a boisterous boy are looking through the catalogues at the same time. The girl is working toward a scholarship, the boy would much rather be outdoors playing ball. His noisy movements interfere with the girl's application, and an argument follows.

During this improvisation or, for that matter, any improvisation dealing with inner attitudes, caution the actor against "playing the adjective, playing the result." That is, the performer who is portraying the serious girl, should not say to herself, "I am a serious person. Therefore, I'll put a frown on my face to look serious." If she acted "serious," she would be merely copying a picture she remembers of a serious individual.

Instead, the performer concentrates on the *where? what? why? what will happen to me if . . . ? what do I want to do to my obstacle?* of the serious character in the situation, and the personality of the character will slowly envelop the actor.

More Exercises in Observation and Imagination

Rhythm exercises that portray animals, plants, and inanimate objects may be used as a springboard to the creation of human characterizations.

Animals

If possible, take the boys and girls to the zoo to observe the characteristics of animals. Encourage the young people to use as many of their physical senses as possible. Question them about the impressions they receive. To one child, the lion's slow, measured walk may suggest dignity; to a second, arrogance; to a third, laziness.

At the following session, ask the children to portray the animals they liked most. Vickie may become the lion; Bob will be the sinuous panther; Barry, the clumsy gorilla; and Penny, the agile monkey. Guide them to project not only the external characteristics of the animal but also the inner quality they find in it. Vickie's delineation may reveal dignity; Bob's, cunning; Barry's, force.

Now tell the players to enact the real or imaginary people their animals suggest. Vickie's dignified lion reminds her of her minister at church, and she portrays the clergyman walking toward his pulpit. Bob, with the panther in mind, creates a cowboy-thief sneaking up to the gold-laden train. Barry invents a brutish wrestler stalking his opponent in the ring.

Children as young as eight years of age have done similar animal exercises with enchanting results. One nine-year-old based her image on the squirrel. She captured its staccato movements and nervousness, and used them in the character of a female athlete limbering up on the day of the big race. The athlete did setting up exercises, ran back and forth on an invisible track, and skipped rope vigorously. Nine years old!

In a group of adolescents, two members used the image of the squirrel to originate a scene, violent and startling in its honesty. A timid girl walked over to a newspaper stand to pick up her father's evening paper. The stand was deserted except for an older boy, a hoodlum, who eyed her approach malevolently. Each time she neared the stand, he would flick his right hand into his coat pocket and stare at her. The girl kept darting to and from the stand until the atmosphere grew tense. "I got goose pimples," one know-it-all confessed later.

In the tycoon-gangster situation of Chapter 6, the players used the typical movements of various animals to help them vitalize their characterizations. The tycoon incorporated the sharp, quick movements of the chipmunk in his role, and the gangster had the slow walk of a massive bull, chewing grass. The gangster's deliberate gestures and his rhythmic, gum-chewing jaws added menace and authenticity to the role.

You may not always agree with, or approve of, the children's interpretations. But children need to express their emotions, expurgate their fears. Creative dramatics offers a socially acceptable outlet for discharging such tensions. While the boys and girls draw on their own vision, experience, and imagination, the understanding teacher is their guide.

Plants and Inanimate Objects

You can also work with plants or inanimate objects, which can often result in characterizations that are sparkling and fresh. One child visualizes a leaf tumbling in the wind, suggesting a light-footed dancer. Another sees it wet and crumpled in the autumn mud, conjuring up a picture of Cinderella weeping beside the cold fireplace. The showy orchid reminds a teen-ager of a preening movie star, while the intermittent blinking of a lighthouse beacon prompts into being a country cousin blinking at the sight of the Empire State building.

A rocking chair, a rolling ball, the swinging pendulum of a grandfather clock, a hissing radiator, a twirling top—all can stimulate the imagination. A rusty key creaking in a keyhole becomes a muscle-bound adolescent trying to roll out of bed one school morning. A candle flame, flickering in the wind, turns into a teen-ager trying to be the life of the party, and sputtering from exhaustion.

Painting and Music

To the mature player, a painting or a piece of music will also suggest images. An image is then enlarged into a character. During discussion, the leader asks about the character's outer and inner traits.

Gesture

A forward thrust of the body, or a strong, well-shaped movement of the arm may suggest an original image to the onlooker. Again, such an approach is for the experienced groups. And again, to use Michael Chekhov's word, "investigate" the characters by asking questions.

Costume

Take any long piece of soft material—a scarf, a kitchen curtain, a torn sheet—and drape it on a child. Wind it around his head as a turban. Hang it from his shoulders as a train. Tie it around his waist as an apron. Each time it is fastened, ask him to portray any character that the drapery may suggest. The turban may evoke Aladdin's Genie. The train reminds him of Hans Christian Andersen's Emperor and his new clothes; and the apron, the Shoemaker of Tolstoi's well-known story, *What Men Live By.*

On another occasion, wear a costume typical, perhaps, of an elegant lady of Sleeping Beauty's court. Greet the members of the group in the dialogue and movement of the character. The device is sure to start the young people on the invention of other characters of the court, whom they will later discuss and portray.

Scramble Characters

Everyone enjoys this trick. Bring together in a situation two or more well-known characters, who are real or fictional and of contrasting backgrounds. Ask the children to portray these people and to develop the situation logically. Jack Benny was never funnier than the day he discovered Sleeping Beauty and woke her up. Sherlock Holmes was never more astute than the time he tracked down Julius Caesar's assassins. Peter Pan was never in greater danger than when he met Red Riding Hood's Wolf. Eventually, Peter calmed Mr. Wolf by getting old King Cole to play a violin!

Play Selections

Use monologues or short scenes from written plays, and guide the experienced players into becoming the fictional characters involved in the scenes. You can accomplish this through (1) discussion, (2) specific work on the character itself, and (3) work on the character within the play.

Discussion

For the purpose of illustration, take the dramatization of *The Emperor's New Clothes.* On reading the version in the second part of this book, you will notice that a number of new facts have been added to the famous story, among them a brief reference to the Emperor's background. Kidnaped when an infant, the ruler was found and raised by a fisherman who was too poor to give him anything but rags to wear. This will turn up in the group's discussion of the play which now follows.

"What is the main idea of the play?" you ask the group. "What is its theme?"

"Vanity," the members murmur vaguely, then more specifically, "He loves fine clothes so much that he has no interest in important things. That makes him unfit for his post."

"How does the playwright make this point, through whose story?"

"The Emperor's story," the boys and girls agree. "His love of finery brings him to parading in his underwear at the end."

"What does the play tell us of the Emperor? What does he do? What does he say? What do the other characters—the Minister, the Empress, his People—say about him? How does the playwright describe him in the stage directions?"

These and many other questions bring the group to several conclusions. Although the Emperor is vain, he is not wicked. He is childish but good at heart. He loves fine clothes because he was deprived of them as a boy. In fact, he loves them so much that his motivating desire, his main objective, is to display his wardrobe. "I want to dazzle my People with my clothes," is the way the Emperor (and the child portraying him) would put it. This goal so absorbs His Majesty that he neglects his imperial responsibilities.

So ends the preliminary discussion of the written play. As you have observed, the Emperor's inner attitudes and background emerge first. It now becomes the aim of the group to discover his general appearance, walk, and gestures. Nothing is said about these in the script.

It is more than likely that, at some time during the analysis, someone will mention a physical mannerism pertaining to the ruler's motivating desire. "He always throws his shoulders back to show off his clothes," perhaps. Here is your cue to cease the talk and get the boys and girls to act out what they know, so far, of the Emperor's physical characteristics.

Work on the Character Itself

To acquire the physical characteristics of the Emperor, have the children do the "shoulders" gesture in another situation, which they invent, rather than a situation taken from the play. The use of the play situation will only burden the children with additional problems and take their concentration off doing the "shoulders" bit. Encourage each player to work on a similar, small, uncomplicated action (the Emperor strokes his chin when he is thinking). Remind him to think of himself as the Emperor while he is performing. It will enable him to become the character.

If, during the first discussion, the children cannot think of any physical characteristics to do, you can lead them to discover any number of such traits through the *what did I do? what would I do if . . . ?* process of self-exploration.

To facilitate getting further into the character, the player may wear a "royal" costume, associate the figure of the Emperor with a real person he knows, and act out his improvisations against a background of appropriate music. The mature player may also extract a quality he sees in an animal or a plant or an inanimate object to help him build his character.

The Character Within the Play

Now, turn the player's attention to the role of the character in a situation from the play itself, such as the opening scene of *The Emperor's New Clothes* where the Emperor is trying to select materials for the processional garments. Encourage the player to determine the *where? what? why? when? what will happen to me if . . . ? what do I want to do to my obstacle?* of the scene, from moment to moment. When these points are clear to him—how much he will retain depends upon his age and experience—have him act the scene as written, concentrating on the monarch's objectives and what His Highness does to gain them.

And, bit by bit, the player will emerge—the Emperor!

chapter 8

"LET'S MAKE A PLAY!"

"Let's make up our own play! Oh, let's, let's, let's!"

The plea, voiced occasionally during the weeks spent on creative acting, is insistent now. Pat yourself on the back. It means you have succeeded in achieving what you had hoped for, what perhaps you alone had believed could be achieved. You have helped the children to reach out, and to grow.

And you have brought them to the threshold of creating a play, the building of which will be limited only by their enthusiasm and experience and by your own knowledge of dramatization techniques (Chapter 2).

Generally speaking, the child under eight is more interested in formless, dramatic play than he is in plot development. He has few experiences in life to draw upon, and does not possess the power of concentration needed for developing a plot. His dramatic play, however, will reveal signs of structure, especially when he improvises on a poem or tale that possesses plot elements.

The nine-to-eleven-year-olds are fascinated with playmaking. Working with a dramatic outline, they will add to it, discard, and enlarge it, as their understanding of dramatic unities and conflicts progresses.

Young people of eleven and older find dramatization most rewarding and when given time they will be able to bring the adventure to a satisfying conclusion. For through their previous improvisations, they have learned that in a suspenseful scene a character has an objective (*why?*), that he will attempt to achieve it through various activities (*what?*) that urgency is a factor in his attempt (*when?* and *what will happen to me if . . . ?*), that there will be a person or object opposing it (*obstacle*), that a fight will ensue (*conflict*), that this fight will pass through a series of incidents (*complications*) to reach a crucial point (*major crisis*), after which it will come to an end, one way or another (*resolution*). In brief, the children have absorbed many of the component elements of plot structure in a complete play, whether it be designed for either informal or formal presentation.

What Is a Play?

Webster's Universal Unabridged Dictionary describes a drama as "a composition . . . representing a picture of human life, arranged for action, and having a plot developed by the words and actions of its characters which culminates in a final situation or climax of human interest." A good definition but in need of elaboration, particularly for the leader who is about to start his first group dramatization.

To begin with, a play tells a *story*. That is, a play is an account of certain events related to a person or persons. There are contemporary adult plays that have had a "succès d'estime" in spite of the barest of stories, but our first requisite holds true, especially for children's plays. Boys and girls want a story, one that has plenty of fast-moving action. Any interest they may have in character study or social problems can be sustained only if both are revealed through an action story.

But a play is not a mere collection of events, however interesting. These events must be selected and organized in order of increasing tension to form a *plot* (Chapter 2). To quote Kenneth Thorpe Rowe, "A plot is a series of events of a kind and so arranged as to arrest our attention and hold our interest by creating and maintaining suspense. What is necessary to creation of suspense is a *conflict*, an opposition between two forces, with the outcome uncertain . . . like a good tug-of-war, in which two sides strain against each other." [1]

Conflict

Your boys and girls have encountered conflict in their creative improvisations. Now they are to discover that it is also essential to the evolution of the whole play.

Conflict may originate in several ways (Chapter 2): (1) by two opposing drives existing within the same person, (2) by the will of one person opposing the will of another or several persons, (3) by the will of one person opposing the will of society or of nature, and (4) by the clash of opposing ethical ideas.

In the main, young children are fascinated by simple, action conflicts in which one individual is pitted against another—the sheriff against the bad cowboy, Robin Hood against the Squire, Shakespeare's Petruchio against Kate. As the children mature in understanding and in dramatization skills, they will be attracted to thematic conflicts, such as Judy against society in *A Real Birthday Present* in Part Two of this book.

Still, to present and solve a conflict in a single episode is not enough. The result will be only a brief dramatic scene, not a complete play. It is like bringing two boxers together in the ring and then seeing one knock out the other with the first punch! *Complications* are needed to develop the scene into a suspenseful, involved drama (Chapter 2).

Complication

A new fact or character added to the situation before it is resolved creates a new situation, another crisis, and presses the plot into mounting suspense. Complications affect the way a conflict moves.

In the Johnny-faces-the-bully episode of Chapter 2, Johnny may find himself retreating before the bully who confronts him. Then a teacher emerges from the school building. The teacher's mere presence halts the menace and encourages Johnny to try to cross the street again. Just as Johnny begins to relax, however, the teacher unexpectedly turns to go back into the building, leaving the poor boy at the mercy of his watchful enemy. The entrance and exit of the teacher, a new character, are complications that change the progress of the conflict and intensify its suspense. Or as Kenneth MacGowan, author of many books on the theater, puts it, they "make an audience worry."

The younger child is seldom able to invent more than one complication, and his "play" will be little more than a scene moving in a direct line from beginning to end. The older child, with direction, will delight in thinking up complications that can turn the struggle to favor one side and then the other, building up excitement in the plot by rendering the hero more and more desperate.

Dramatic Unity

Now, no matter where the conflict for the short play stems from—an idea, a character, or a physical situation—it requires confinement to one time and to one important focal incident. Such focusing will produce taut drama. Two sisters, let us say, may feel jealous antagonism toward each other throughout their lives. But the playwright shows their lifelong conflict at a time when it is most intense—an hour, a day, a week. He chooses one critical incident in this period when the struggle will logically come to a head.

All the other events in the play are then selected to act as complications leading up to and away from the climactic moment, the scene of major crisis.

To illustrate, let us refer to *A Real Birthday Present*. Briefly, the story concerns Judy Hicks, a neglected, lonely girl, who wants to be friendly with Cathy Fields and her group. The plot revolves around Cathy's birthday party. Judy, who has not been invited, pretends that she has an invitation. Lynn, Judy's implacable enemy, uses Judy's "lying" to turn the group against her. After several complications, Cathy befriends Judy and invites her to the party.

The world is a wonderful place for Judy until Cathy misses her wrist watch, the birthday present from her parents. Lynn accuses Judy of stealing the watch, and for a few tense moments it seems as though Judy has done so. Cathy's mother rescues Judy, and now at last Cathy welcomes Judy as a friend.

Since *A Real Birthday Present* will be used to explain dramatic unity and plot-building techniques, a reading of the entire script in Part Two of this book is suggested at this point.

The original source of the play was a "real-life" situation, a girl in conflict with a hostile society. In dramatization, the general struggle began to acquire a pointed clarity when Judy was opposed by a specific group of hostile girls of whom Cathy was the least antagonistic, Lynn the most. Judy was opposed in her objective to become friendly with Cathy and the whole group. The struggle gained dramatic unity when it was confined to a special time, the day of Cathy's birthday party, and it reached its crucial peak in the missing wrist watch episode.

The clash between Judy and society existed at many other times, in many other places, and concerned many other incidents. But, for the purpose of our short play, a single time and a single incident were chosen. All other incidents—Judy's lie about her invitation to the party; the ice-cream pop episode; Mrs. Fields' attempt to make Cathy understand Judy—are not only related to the problem of conflict but are complications which lead up to the focal scene where Judy is accused of stealing the watch.

The problem of conflict as set forth in the play itself is also known as the *dramatic problem.*

In the short play, the same principle of confinement, as of time, may be applied to the *number of backgrounds* you create to tell the story. The risk of losing dramatic impact increases with the number of settings you use. The experienced dramatist may invent as many places as he feels are necessary to his plot, and still compensate for the loss of suspense that "background jumping" incurs. The novice is safer using one set or, at most, two.

To choose only what is essential in a story and to organize it into scenes of continuous, rising tension are two processes that differentiate a dramatic play from a narrative play (or, in the children's words, a dramatic play is "exciting," the other kind is "boring.") Both kinds of plays contain theme, objective, obstacle, etc. The narrative play, however, is spread over a long period of time in which many events, loosely related to the general conflict, occur. These events are not tied tightly or inevitably to the major crisis. Actually, a narrative play is a sequence of incidents held together by dialogue, a defect apparent in too many scripts for children.

Resolution

The term, resolution, is commonly applied to the ending of the play, the conclusion (Chapter 2). The important thing to remember here is that the resolution must not result from accident or chance. It must develop naturally and logically from the dramatic problem of the play.

In the short play for children, the resolution is generally a happy one. It follows immediately after the major crisis and brings the play to an end. Judy, exonerated of the wrist watch theft, is quickly and genuinely welcomed by Cathy and her circle of friends.

A play, then, is a story of conflict, a special kind of story that has resulted from a selection of events. Further, these selected events or complications have been arranged in a certain order designed to develop and intensify the initial problem of conflict. The development reaches its highest point in the crucial scene of the play, the major crisis, after which the dramatic problem is brought to a resolution, and the play to an end.

The Structure of a Play

Now you ask, "How do I go about creating a play? How do I build its skeletal structure or plot?"

A simplified picture of structure in the play for children looks like this:

(a) *Introduction.* The scene or scenes leading up to the attack.
(b) *Attack.* The point at which the play's dramatic problem embodying the conflict is posed.
(c) *Complications.* A series of scenes that lead up to the major crisis, developing the conflict with increasing suspense.
(d) *Major Crisis.* The crucial point of the play when the problem must be resolved one way or another.
(e) *Resolution.* A happy one for children.

Major Crisis

The major crisis is your first concern. When the area of conflict is known, you choose the incident that will produce it, and then decide how this crisis, and the play itself, will be resolved (resolution). After these structural problems have been solved, you direct your attention to the attack, introduction, and complications. (Of course, such a rule of procedure cannot be rigidly adhered to. It is merely a guide.)

Assume that you and your group have agreed to dramatize a situation of a girl surrounded by a hostile society (see Judy in *A Real Birthday*

Present). Your initial discussion reduced this general situation to a more specific area of conflict: Judy against a group of girls, of whom Cathy was the least antagonistic, Lynn the most. Pinpointing the plot further, you created Judy's main objective in the proposed play: her desire to make friends with Cathy and her group. Next, recognizing the need to confine the struggle to a special time, you chose the day of Cathy's birthday party. You decided that some incident during that time should bring the dramatic problem to a head—the major crisis of the play. The dramatic problem revolves around Judy's desire to become Cathy's friend, and Lynn's opposition.

Suggesting that the incident be tied in with the birthday party for the sake of unity, you ask the children, "What could this incident be?" Out of the many possibilities they propose, you choose the loss of a present and Lynn's accusation of theft which will turn Cathy against Judy. The present is soon defined as a wrist watch given to Cathy by her parents.

Resolution

The discussion swings next to the resolution of the incident. The ending, everyone decides, should be a happy one. Judy will be exonerated and will become Cathy's friend. Just how the exoneration will be brought about remains to be determined.

Attack

Now you have a general picture of the major crisis and its resolution. What you still need is to find the story line and the complications that will bring the play to the determined turning point and the end.

Therefore, you will select, discard, and select again incidents relating to the critical event. Finally, you may produce the following story line, subject to change and improvement.

Judy has not been invited to the party. Judy lies about being invited. Cathy, influenced in turn by Lynn and Mrs. Fields, eventually befriends Judy and invites her. At this point, Lynn prophesies darkly that Judy will ruin the party. The dramatic question is now posed, "Will Judy really spoil the party and thus lose Cathy's friendship? What happens now? How will the struggle end?"

This moment, the one in which the conflict is presented to the audience in the form of a dramatic question, is known as the *point of attack*.

As a general rule, the attack comes as close to the major crisis as possible and, in plays for children, the earlier it is presented to the audience the more exciting is the script.

The attack, incidentally, makes the subsequent action of the play inescapable.

With the attack, major crisis, and resolution defined—"the three points of the play to which and from which the writer must build" [2]—your next step is to select the introduction.

Introduction

In the preliminary scenes of the play, the possibility of a dramatic problem is indicated to the audience in order to gain its attention. Such scenes set the stage, introduce characters and give enough exposition about them and their potential struggle to arouse the concern of the audience.

In the first part of *A Real Birthday Present*, the audience learns about Cathy's forthcoming party, Judy's lie about being invited, and the attitudes of the other characters toward Judy. The audience also learns a little about the circumstances which occurred before the play opened. All this *exposition* is designed to interest the spectator in Judy, to arouse his dislike for Lynn, and to awaken his hope that Cathy will befriend Judy.

The introduction may be one scene or, as in this play, several scenes, each with a minor crisis and complications which aid or discourage Judy in achieving her objective.

Exposition, incidentally, is given not only during the introduction but is also constantly being revealed throughout the dramatic action of the play. This is particularly true of the longer script in which character illumination and growth are predominant features.

Again, exposition is not communicated through talk alone, where one character tells another the details an audience must know. Instead, the information is supplied through minor scenes of conflict. When Lynn yanks Judy into Cathy's garden, the audience learns dramatically of Judy's lies, and how Cathy and the group feel about her.

Complications

Once the attack has been presented, complications keep the conflict going with increasing tension until the major crisis is reached. The number of complications will naturally depend on the dramatic problem and the length of the play.

Introduction, attack, complications, major crisis, resolution, these are the main branches of a plot's spine, and a working knowledge of them is sufficient to create the short play for children. However, a few suggestions on *preparation*, *dialogue* and *suspense* are in order.

Preparation

Any fact or character needed to resolve a dramatic problem should be "planted," or prepared for, early in the script. This will eliminate a disturbing sense of contrivance and will make the conclusion seem natural and logical. For instance, Cathy's wrist watch, which is needed for the crucial scene, was planted in the first Mrs. Fields–Cathy scene, then referred to by Mrs. Fields in her second speech to the audience and mentioned again by Esther, the maid, in the gift-receiving scene.

Dialogue

The purposes of dialogue in a play are several. It gives information, both past and immediate; it delineates character; it reveals an author's attitude toward an idea or toward life; and it furthers the development of the plot. Where the children are improvising during presentation, the dialogue may not always fulfill its objectives, but the loss of dramatic conciseness will be more than compensated for by the spontaneous sparkle of the playing and the dialogue.

Suspense

This is the most desirable quality in a play and one which all instructors of playwriting advise you to strive for. But they do not always explain just how suspense is achieved.

The moment you present on stage the possibility of a conflict between two well-but-not-equally-matched opponents, such as Judy versus Lynn, you introduce suspense. Each time you create a complication that reverses the dramatic direction, you sustain and promote that suspense. If the protagonist is a sympathetic one, if he has a deadline to meet and will lose something vitally important to him should he fail to meet it (*what will happen to me if . . . ?*), the suspense will continue to mount.

General Notes and Suggestions

The short play usually consists of one or two *acts* which present and develop the main conflict and bring it to a major crisis and resolution. Each act contributes to that major crisis and that resolution. At the same time, each act has its own conflict, introduction, attack, crisis and resolution, with a complication introduced to project the conflict into the next act.

In turn, each act is divided into big and small *scenes*, and each scene into *units*. Both scene and unit have the same dramatic development as the act.

In plays for children, the characters should be individualized, sharply defined, and interesting to young people; but these characters must not be complex. The protagonist is good, the antagonist bad. Rapid character growth, that is, radical change of a character's inner attitudes in a very short time, is acceptable here though it is frowned upon in the realistic adult play.

The script for children should possess significance, a worth-while idea, a bit of truth. Ethical values, such as integrity, courage, responsibility, or kindness, touch boys and girls as long as there is no obvious or lengthy moralizing. However, it is best to avoid making up plays for the sole purpose of "teaching a lesson." They often turn out to be very dull.

Mystery and nonsense sequences (see the scenes with the Three Doctors in *A Christmas Story*, herein) are always attractive to the child.

The scripts in this book frequently incorporate a Narrator. This character was deliberately introduced to make the plays easy to rehearse and present. Some plays, for example *How the Snowman Got His Broom*, can be performed after one session of telling, discussing, and improvising.

Other devices—crowd scenes, dance sequences—make a script flexible for casting purposes. They permit a leader to use many children or few, depending upon the size of the group. *The Emperor's New Clothes* has been presented with as few as nine children and also with as many as seventy-five! In the first instance, the roles of the Second Jester, the Second Guard and the Old Blind Man were eliminated, and the audience participated as spectators of the procession. In the latter instance, the Jesters introduced to the Emperor artisans who displayed their designs for the ceremonial garments. Dancers, singers, and musicians entertained His Imperial Majesty (this is another example of the integration of the arts in creative drama) and the ranks of the beggars and spectators were expanded.

A word of caution. There is a danger in stretching a script this way. It tends to weaken the plot structure and to lower the suspense. Such devices, therefore, must be used carefully and only when they merge with the plot development.

The bibliography in this book contains a list of several excellent sources of information on plot development. These books should be consulted by group leaders who wish to work on the long or formal play.

chapter 9

IDEAS AND STORIES

"Which ideas and stories interest a child, and where shall I find them?"

Everywhere. In the here-and-now incidents of a child's life. In the daily newspaper. In the vast library of folklore, fairy tales, ballads, myths, nonsense tales, nature and animal stories. In history. In literature. The kind of material you choose will determine whether your group's first dramatization effort will result in an original script or an adaptation.

Here-and-Now Material

Ideas from the here-and-now category present the greatest technical responsibility. Because it is derived from a situation of conflict, a particularly striking character, or an ethical theme encountered in daily living, an idea must have a dramatic action story to carry it.

A *conflict situation* requires characters and complications. A *character* requires a conflict story that evolves logically out of his personality. A *theme* requires conflict, story, characters, and complications to project it. And all three—conflict situation, character, and theme—call for a knowledge of plot construction to make the story dramatic.

Another objection to using here-and-now material is that the child, with his limited knowledge of the world, is not likely to find any real character, situation, or theme that will spark his imagination. More likely than not, he will suggest characters and situations out of the last movie or television program he has enjoyed.

Familiar Material

The choice of a well-loved tale from literature eliminates many hazards. Recognizable characters and conflict situations are ready-made; the theme is usually worthwhile; and the many, or few, incidents of the plot often occur in an order of mounting intensity. Look at *Cinderella*, a heroine in constant struggle with her family. Look at the many fast-moving episodes that build in suspense. Look at the quick "they lived happily ever after" ending. No wonder the abused cinder maid has stayed with us so long!

Such a tale, handed down from generation to generation, is your safest choice for the first dramatization. This is particularly important if the result is to be shown publicly. Later, when the group feels secure in creating, their work on original materials will be rewarding. Adolescents enjoy this type of dramatization, and will make up plays in school, commemorating the various holidays or "red-letter days."

Winifred Ward's book, *Stories to Dramatize*,[1] is a fine collection of beloved legends and tales suitable for dramatization. Shakespeare is a never-ending source of exciting action drama for the older players. Other stories may be gleaned from the many anthologies of children's literature.

The time at the group's disposal will also determine your choice of the original or the familiar material for creating plays.

A Real Birthday Present, which has held performer and audience interest wherever presented, is a short, original script that was prepared by a group of ten-year-old girls who met once a week. It was modeled after a real person, a foster child who, since the age of four, had been shuttled from home to home. Friendless and unhappy, Judy, the name used in the play, resorted to "stealing" in order to attract attention. Actually, whatever she "stole" she also eventually "found" and returned to its owner who then gave her the praise she sought.

My own eagerness to promote, among her hostile schoolmates, an understanding of Judy's need for acceptance prompted the dramatization of her situation. Incidents and characters were changed, invented, and enlarged until there was an entirely new plot and the whole group—the foster child too—performed in *A Real Birthday Present* without being aware of the script's origin.

The problem is finding the tale most suitable to the tastes of your specific group. The choice is of first importance, and in making it, you will consider again the pertinent factors of the age, ability, experience, and interests of your boys and girls. Their interests will be influenced not only by their national background, social environment, and temperament, but also by the public's mood at the time of choice. There was no point in talking about Milne to a group of players on the day that the newspapers broke out with the story of the Mad Bomber who was terrorizing New York City!

Do not impose your own preferences. Literature cannot be shoved down anyone's throat. Instead, be flexible in your attitude. Give the children every chance to dramatize their current excitements, even when you do not find these wholly desirable. Once their excitements have been released legitimately, introduce quality material through short, active improvisations. The same individuals who threw themselves into the melodramatic action of *Bank Notes and Music*, later jumped, with even greater enthusiasm, into playing *The Taming of the Shrew*.

Likes and Dislikes

A brief review of some known likes and dislikes of each age group reveals helpful points.

The child under seven is concerned with himself and only gradually is he drawn into an awareness of the life outside of himself. As has been noted, his creativity is confined mostly to plotless, dramatic play (Chapter 8) that deals with the familiar figures of his world—the doctor, the postman, the policeman—in imaginary adventures. Any real experience at the circus, the beach, or in kindergarten absorbs him. Animal characters delight him, and he endows them with human characteristics, such as speech. As he matures, a few magic figures—elves, fairy queens, giants, and witches from the stories read to him—will catch his fancy.

He likes to act out several roles in the same scene. One moment, he will be the father who examines his feverish child. Next, he will be the ailing child, and finally, the know-it-all doctor who pops a thermometer into the little patient's mouth.

Noises and detached words make up the language flow for the younger child. This is the age when it is easier to express feelings in actions than in words. His creative work is enriched with nonsense sounds, amusing names, and simple rhymes. "Hello, Miss Poopledinger," one five-year-old Wolf greeted Red Riding Hood during playmaking sessions.

At about seven years of age, the child becomes less interested in his here-and-now life and more involved in the world of enchantment.

Love for the magical "once upon a time" is at its height with the sevens and eights. To these children, fairy godmothers, sleeping princesses, beanstalks that grow and grow and grow, jealous queens immersed in witchcraft are more alive than their own families. Dramatic play runs longer and begins to assume the plotted development of a very brief play. Characters are still either good or bad.

Around the age of ten, the magical trend is still evident. Now, the child's attention is gradually turning to hero stories, real or fictional. The plays he likes are packed with the adventures of personalities such as Robin Hood, Davey Crockett, Joseph and his Brethren, King Arthur of the Round Table, and Dick Tracy. Even the girls want to impersonate male heroes.

Tales of heroism and idealism continue to dominate the tastes of the elevens to thirteens. Interest in the first stirrings of romantic love appears among the older, movie-wise girls, although kissing and sentimental love-making scenes are awkward and usually taboo. The boys, maturing more slowly, will scoff self-consciously at such stuff for many months to come.

From fourteen up, the problems of growing up and away from the family overshadow all others. The teen-ager's creative work will reflect his concern with boy-girl relationships, marriage, career, and religion. While an idealistic, hopeful attitude generally prevails throughout these preoccupations, a pseudo-sophistication may creep into his playmaking. Love is treated lightly, humorously, rather than emotionally—the reason which prompted the omission of the tender love passages in this book's adaptation of A Midsummer Night's Dream.

chapter 10

DRAMATIZING THE TALE

For the purpose of instruction, let us now construct a short, flexible play of ten to thirty minutes. The play is to be enacted before a non-paying audience, with dialogue and stage business improvised on the spot or, more formally, with memorized, rehearsed dialogue. An established tale will be used as the basis of our demonstration.

Selecting the Story

Your first step is to select several tales which you feel have possibilities for group dramatization. Read or tell the stories to the boys and girls as they sit facing you, and ask them to choose the one they enjoyed the most. Do not confuse this read-or-tell procedure with *story-telling* which will be described shortly.

Suppose the children decide on *The Emperor's New Clothes*. A delightful satire, it tells of the clothes-loving monarch who devoted all his time and attention to the display of his many and gorgeous costumes.

"Life was very gay in the great town where he lived," [1] reports the Andersen tale. And to this town, one day, came two Swindlers who passed themselves off as accomplished weavers. So skilled was their weaving, so they said, that the clothes made of their fabric had the magic quality of becoming invisible to any person who was not fit for the position he held.

This unique quality impressed the Emperor. Not only did he pay the Swindlers a huge amount of money to weave him some cloth, but he gave them the finest silk and the purest gold thread with which to weave it. All these valuables the rogues pocketed, of course, while pretending to weave long and hard at the empty looms.

The curiosity of the town knew no bounds. Everyone, including the Emperor, "was anxious to see how stupid his neighbor was." [2]

After some time, the Emperor sent his faithful old Minister to see the cloth. "Heaven preserve us!" thought the old Minister, "I can't see a thing! Is it possible that I am not fit for my post? It will never do to say that I cannot see the stuff." [3]

So back he went to the Emperor to report on the charm and exquisite coloring of the cloth. And the Swindlers went on merrily as before, demanding more silk and more gold while pretending to work at the empty looms.

And whoever went to see the stuff at the Emperor's request, reacted in much the same way as did the Minister, lavishly praising the cloth he did not see for fear of losing his post.

His Imperial Majesty himself fell into the same trap when he visited the weavers' workshop. "This is terrible! Am I not fit to be Emperor?" [4] thought he, but aloud he exclaimed, "It has my highest approval!" [5] And at his courtiers' urging, he decided to wear a coat and trousers made of the stuff at the great procession which was about to take place. He then bestowed upon the crafty Swindlers the high title of "Gentlemen Weavers."

After much make-believe weaving and cutting and stitching, the rogues finally announced "Now the Emperor's new clothes are ready." [6] The monarch took off his regular garments, and the Swindlers pretended to dress him, putting on one piece of clothing after another and turning the Emperor 'round and 'round in front of a great mirror.

The master of ceremonies announced that the procession was awaiting His Majesty. His chamberlains bent to raise the long train from the ground and all of them walked along in the parade, their heads high in the air.

"How beautiful the Emperor's new clothes are! And they fit to perfection!" [7] exclaimed the people in the streets, too fearful to tell the truth. Everybody exclaimed, that is everybody but one little Child. "But he has got nothing on," [8] the Child cried, over and over again, until his father and the father's neighbor and the neighbor's neighbor were all shouting "But he has nothing on! He has nothing on! He has nothing on!"

The Emperor cringed, for he knew that the people spoke the truth. But he thought, "The procession must continue."

And so it did. His Imperial Majesty held himself more erect than before, and the chamberlains lifted the invisible train again, and the procession went on and on . . .

So the fairy tale ends, and the group discussion begins.

Preliminary Discussion

You begin the discussion with simple questions such as "What did you like about the story?" "Did you find it funny? Why?" Thinking out loud not only starts the conversational ball rolling but also reveals everyone's first and most distinct impressions.

During the period of broad probing, you may introduce factual information about the background of the story. Study the names, customs, occupations, and dress of the people. Display several pictures that set the atmosphere. The formal play requires more preparation of this kind than does the informal.

For most children, the satire will be lost. But all will be enchanted with the humor-provoking episodes—the Swindlers weaving at the empty looms; the Emperor and his retinue praising the non-existent cloth; His Graciousness putting on the imaginary robes and then proceeding with the foolish, humiliating procession.

General questioning is followed by probing the personality of the

Emperor, the pivot of the tale. And since satire has little meaning for the children, replace it with a *bit of truth* they will understand.

You start the exploration with questions about the ruler's *physical traits.* "How do you see the Emperor? How old do you imagine he is? Is he short, is he tall? Is he thin, is he fat?" Where the Andersen tale does not supply the answers, the children's imaginations will.

Lead the discussion carefully to an analysis of His Majesty's *inner attitudes.* "Do you like the Emperor? What do you think of him?" "Is he vain? Is he selfish? Is he just thoughtless?" "Why is he like that? What do you suppose made him that way? Take a few moments to think."

Let us pretend that an analysis, like the one recorded in Chapter 1, ensues: the Emperor likes fine clothes because he did not have them when he was a poor little boy; he is not mean, selfish, cruel; his objective is to impress everyone with his fine clothes.

Beware of too much discussion. "Show us" is a reminder that should be given frequently throughout the entire procedure. And so, time permitting, everyone is urged to play out his mental concept of the Imperial Majesty—physical characteristics, as well as inner attitudes—in much the same way that Lynn did in Chapter 1. Get each child to begin his play-making with a small, physical action related to the Emperor's inner drive.

Incidentally, it is interesting to see how character discussion fascinates children. Far from being bored by it, they will talk endlessly about it if you do not call a halt.

Now, you start searching for that *bit of truth.* "What happens when a person is so occupied with clothes?" you ask. "How does it affect the people around him?" And before you know it, the group is enthusiastically analyzing the ethical implications of His Majesty's failing. "He spends so much time on himself, he doesn't do the things a king should." "He neglects his responsibilities." Even the greatest laggard among the young players agrees that such an attitude is wrong. "He doesn't have time to see that the roads are built." "He doesn't meet with his Ministers to talk over the needs of his kingdom. His People begin to hate him."

What is evolving here, you soon recognize, is a *general* situation of conflict between two forces: *the Emperor* against *his People.* Now you try to reduce the general struggle to a *specific* conflict between two individuals.

Finding the Specific Conflict

The preliminary exploration may have given you a clue. Sometime during that talking stage, one young voice must have piped up to ask indignantly, "If the Emperor means well, why doesn't someone tell him what he's doing? Why doesn't someone show him he's unfit for his job?" Suddenly you see what you need—a conflict between His Majesty and a person who champions the People's cause. You feel a dramatic line developing, the line which is pursued in the dramatization used in this book.

You ask, "Who could make the Emperor realize he is harming his subjects? Who will be his opponent? The Swindlers? A beggar? The faithful old Minister, the Emperor's wife, if he has one?"

The Swindlers, the children feel, would support rather than oppose the Emperor's interest in clothes. A beggar would be too fearful of losing his head to pit himself against His Magnificence. But his Minister or the Empress would be in a good position to do so.

"Let us say then," you summarize, "that the old Minister, worried about the state of the kingdom, will be the person to try to open His Majesty's eyes." You plan to keep the invented character of the Empress on tap, in case the plot needs her. Besides, you know that the girls in the group will enjoy acting the Empress, a role they like to identify with in playmaking.

A brief talk on the physical and inner characteristics of the Minister follows. "He is old." "He worked for the first Emperor, our ruler's father." "He is kind." "He is understanding." "He loves his king so much, he will do anything to cure his Majesty of vanity even if it costs the Minister his head." Now you have two opposing characters, the Emperor against the Minister—around this struggle a plot may be developed.

Your next requirement is to find an angle in the original story which will dramatize the struggle. "How can the Minister make the king realize that he is an unfit ruler?" you ask the group. "What do you see in the story that will help the Minister to do that?"

The chorus of voices is deafening. "The robes, of course!" At this point, you can easily lead the children to select the scene of the *major crisis*—the procession.

It is not clear to you, as yet, how the Minister will utilize the business of the processional robes to gain his objective. You will need to work on this plot problem. But these talks have brought the tale and the players to the threshold of a first, crude, structural draft. The draft will be kept flexible during the many hours of playmaking to come, because you will want to add, change, or discard characters, scenes, and speeches, until you obtain a version that satisfies you.

Building the Structure

You summarize again the characters and the episodes that the children have agreed upon, so far. These are:

(a) The clothes-loving Emperor.
(b) The old Minister, his opponent.
(c) The situation of the invisible robes that projects the Emperor-Minister struggle dramatically.
(d) The major crisis of the situation—its highest point is the Child's cry, "But he has nothing on!"
(e) Other characters—Swindlers, Court Officials, People, Empress, etc.

All these usable elements are not tightly or dramatically interwoven as yet. The Minister and the Swindlers, for instance, are operating independently of each other. You now concentrate on the problem of tying the elements together to make for *dramatic unity*.

The thought may occur to a player that, since the Minister in the dramatization is going "to do something about the Emperor," why can't *he* arrange the whole deception? Why can't he engage two tailors to weave the magic cloth as part of his plan to open the Emperor's eyes?

The business of the robes begins to take on a new dimension. The Swindlers cease to be crafty thieves, which you feel is just as well in a play for children. Instead, they are transformed into two honest Tailors whom the Minister enlists to help him. And because the children, in their discussion, made a big point of a famine in the kingdom, this state of affairs is used to motivate the Tailors' falling in with the scheme. They need food desperately for their families, and food is the Minister's payment for their co-operation.

"What happens after the turning point?" you ask next. "How does the conflict end? What is the *resolution?*"

The tale itself concludes on a bit of situation humor. Writhing inwardly, the Emperor forces himself to uphold the mockery of a parade and the procession goes on. In the dramatization that is now expanding, the original ending is not enough. Everyone will want to know how the Minister's plan fared. Because the Andersen story does not resolve the dramatically-conceived problem, you proceed to invent a new and logical ending.

Through discussion and acting improvisations, one player may discover that the Child's accusation makes the monarch "so mad, he wants to kick!" More appropriately, he orders sundry heads chopped off. You point out quickly that the Emperor is a good man at heart. He overcomes his mood of violence, which soon changes to one of shame at his foolish vanity, and he acknowledges the Minister's wisdom. In short, the ruler experiences a change of inner attitude, and the growing plot has its happy ending.

You will recall that earlier in the plot building, you wondered how the Minister would use the invisible robes to advance his plan. You return to that dramatic difficulty now.

The boys and girls offer their ideas. Best among them is, "The Minister wants to teach the Emperor a lesson. The monarch will make a fool of himself at the procession. Then he will understand how his vanity makes him unfit."

Under your guidance, the group considers this suggestion carefully. On the surface it seems like an intelligent bit of thinking. And it is certainly related to the Minister's plot objective "to make the Emperor realize he is unfit." But, unfortunately, it has a drawback. Would the Minister, loving his monarch as he does, expose him to the jeers of the People?

"Maybe," a player contributes hesitantly. "Maybe, if the Minister was pushed into doing it."

With this you agree. Pressed hard enough, and given sufficient motivation, anyone may react in an unaccustomed way.

Thus, after much deliberation, you arrive at a *tentative story line.* The Minister begins by gently reprimanding the Emperor on his irresponsibility. Because the scolding has no effect, the old man decides to play a trick which will push the ruler into a realization of the truth. He hopes that His Majesty will learn the lesson when he fails to see the garments that everyone else will swear they see. Therefore the Minister will have real robes ready for the Emperor to wear at the procession.

The plan starts to work when the Emperor goes to inspect the invisible clothes. Since he cannot see the garments, he is stunned by the revelation of his unfitness. The Minister is happy in the belief that the Emperor will now try to mend his ways. But suddenly, the Emperor decides to wear the "magic" garments in the procession! His wish to dazzle the People is stronger than his good sense or his conscience. Now the wise old man is ready to confess the trick to spare his king a humiliating experience. He is persuaded, however, that a drastic measure is needed to cure the Emperor. Therefore, the Minister lets His Magnificence parade in the robes that are not there.

With this and other facts temporarily decided upon (the main opponents, the focal situation, the major crisis, and the resolution), your next problem is to determine the point of attack—when the audience asks itself, "What happens now? How will the struggle end?"

Because the focal situation concerns the processional robes, the scene of attack may well be one where the Minister introduces the Tailors to the Emperor. When the ruler orders the robes, he unwittingly falls in with the Minister's plan. There is no turning back now, the dramatic problem must go forward to its crisis and its conclusion.

All through your first steps in plot-building, something else has been taking place. Through selection, alteration and compression, you have been discovering what distinguishes dramatic from narrative writing. Two episodes of the original story—(1) where the Emperor orders the Swindlers to weave some cloth, and (2) where the Emperor commands that the cloth be tailored into the processional robes—have been telescoped into the single attack scene. From this point on, the process of selection, alteration, and compression is continuously pursued. In fact, this process helps you to determine which incident, or incidents, must go into the introduction of the play.

The introduction presents the main characters and also reveals the possibility of a conflict. The introduction lies as close as possible, in time and in plot development, to the crucial point in the play. Bearing this in mind during the discussion, you and the children decide that the opening scene of the play is supposed to take place the week before the climactic parade, and you invent a scene to show the Emperor fretting over what he will wear for the procession. As he examines silks and jewels, the Minister presses him to see the famine delegation. Exposition, relating to the Emperor's objective and the state of his kingdom, is given during this preliminary episode.

Complications intensify the Emperor-Minister conflict, and push the plot forward.

In Act 1 of the finished dramatization, two scenes—the Beggars' scene and the scene where the Empress pleads with the Minister to try to cure her husband of his vanity—serve to propel the hesitant Councilor into going through with his plan. Now, further complications keep us worrying about the plan and its chances of successs.

(a) The first Minister-Tailors scene. We wonder whether the frightened Tailors will co-operate.
(b) The presentation of the Tailors to the Emperor. We wonder if he will receive the Tailors and order the robes.

In Act 2 the threat to the plan increases through still other complications.

(a) The Tailors are unwilling to proceed with the deception.
(b) The Emperor puts off inspecting the robes.
(c) The nervous Jesters and Guards almost "spill the beans."
(d) Just as the plan seems about to succeed, the Emperor's need to "dazzle" his subjects interferes.
(e) The Minister wants to reveal the trick in order to spare his ruler the humiliation of parading without clothes.
(f) During the parade, the People's fear of the Emperor's wrath makes them praise the invisible robes and thus contribute to His Majesty's self-esteem.

Of course, this is not the only plot that can be derived from the Andersen material. You must be prepared to weave back and forth, altering and adjusting the plot, as you work alone or with your group, before you find the characters and the structure you like best. This weaving is good, since you are always interested in the "doing." The dramatization process, remember, is not confined to just the "writing" of a plot. It involves playacting, and not merely the character improvisations by the young people in the preliminary discussions, but also the improvisations on scenes that the group may or may not include in the play.

Playmaking

Improvisation starts long before you arrive at the final structure of the script. It starts, in fact, the moment you prepare the first tenuous outline which will serve as a guide in building a plot.

A simple outline for *The Emperor's New Clothes* may include in its first act the following scenes.

(a) The Emperor tries to choose a costume, while the Minister urges him to see the famine delegation.

(b) The Minister, deciding to do something about his neglectful ruler, speaks to the Tailors.

(c) The Minister presents the Tailors to the Emperor, who then orders the robes.

What is missing, in this early draft, is information which improvisations will gradually provide. For instance, you need information about:

(a) The lesser characters with their urgencies and their objectives— the Empress; the Beggars; the Jesters; the Guards.

(b) The small, connecting scenes that explain, motivate, and tie one big scene to another—the scenes between the Beggars and the Guards; the Beggars and the Minister; the Minister and the Empress.

(c) How, where, when, and with whom each scene begins, develops, and ends.

(d) Many little details related to characterization, exposition, and preparation.

By playing out characters and incidents—in the light of what we learned of character and plot building (Chapters 7, 8)—by evaluating what has been tried out, by adding, discarding, altering, and then playing out again, the children expand and polish the temporary structure.

The procedure of "playing out and evaluating" may be broken down into the steps which follow.

Story-telling

This precedes playmaking. *Story-telling* denotes the dramatic manner in which you present to the children the rough outline of the plot you have evolved during discussions and have jotted down. Such telling revitalizes the material by establishing the main characters as living persons, thereby heightening the drama. Your face and body, as you speak, can emphasize the critical events and point out the potentialities for playmaking.

To acquire this skill, you study the outline. You need not memorize it word for word, for if you do, the children will find it lifeless—a test of your ability to remember, rather than your talent to stimulate. Instead, read and reread the outline until the backgrounds, characters, atmosphere, plot, picturesque phrases, and moods become a part of you; until it suddenly ceases to be written words, but like Cinderella's pumpkin, it is transformed into a magical bit of the living moment, with you as an active participant.

Visualize each incident and person against the setting. Try to see pictures of the dramatic action, scene by scene, in the theater of your mind. If the sequence of events is too difficult to remember, use notes on an index card to help you in the telling. And always, always, when you speak use action verbs and improvised dialogue.

Next, practice telling the story-outline aloud to yourself or to a patient listener, other than the players. Practice until the telling runs on like a sparkling improvisation. When this happens, you know that you are ready to present it to your boys and girls.

Naturally, there are times when you need to read from the written outline. The story line may be too complicated to remember without the draft before you, or as with *Alice in Wonderland* you may wish to retain the flavorsome speeches of the original. But the best reading can rarely replace skillful story-telling.

First Playmaking

If the young people have participated sufficiently in the building of the temporary plot, nothing more need be said after the telling than "Who would like to get up and act out the play?" What you are aiming for now is a free, uninterrupted improvisation on the whole outline. This will give the players a satisfying sense of the dramatic whole, and will start them off on the detailed development which is to follow.

The advisability of running through the entire outline will naturally depend on its length as well as on the acting freedom of the children. If they have not had much limbering up, let them begin with improvisations on units—small scenes within a scene. For instance: the Emperor tries to decide which robes to wear; the Minister tells his worries about the starving People; the Tailors express their fears about the plan.

Encourage everyone to try out as many of the characters and bits of scenes as there is time for. Team up an imaginative child with one who is inhibited—it will help the latter to carry his share of the scene. Urge the players to use the entire room as their sets, determining in advance only the general areas, such as the Guards stand at the classroom door; the Throne Room is next to the blackboard with Teacher's desk as throne; the procession winds up and down the streets indicated by aisles. Later on, boundaries, entrances, and props will be fixed.

During this flexible period—how often the outline is enacted must be left to the leader's judgment—jot down any original ideas or speeches that the actors make. At this point, the chances are that you will hear little that is fresh. The young people will act out the plot literally, giving back what you gave them in the story-telling. There will be no honest feeling; imitation will be rampant; and the inexperienced children will interrupt their playing with "I don't know what to do. What do I say next?"

If they come to a stop, do not intrude on the improvisation. That is, do not show how one character may be played or tell what another character may say. Rather, direct a few well chosen questions at the player, questions which relate to the play and to the particular unit he is acting:

"What is the Emperor like inside of him?

"What does he want at this moment?

"Does he want the robes very much?

"What does he do to get them?

"How do the Minister and the court feel about this?

"Will they try to help the Emperor choose the robes or will they try to get him away from this foolish business?"

As for the irrelevant material that creeps in—bits of fairy tales, movies, television programs—let it pass without discussion. The scene-by-scene playacting to come will show that it has no bearing on the story plot. On the other hand, horseplay is best stopped well before it gets out of control.

Playmaking Scene-by-Scene

With the initial free playing over, your attention is next directed to the scene-by-scene development of the script. Where previously you were interested in stimulating the children into creative play, your goal now is to channel their creativity into the construction of a play that can be presented informally.

Start with the very first scene of your outline: the Emperor tries to select a costume, while the Minister presses him about his duties. The children have already run through the incident superficially. Now they are ready to dig into its dramatic possibilities.

As always, there is a *preliminary discussion*. Since this is the beginning of the play, you ask, "What must we let the audience know?" You explain that the first exposition must tell the spectator (1) who the main characters are, (2) what their relationships are to each other, (3) what they want (objective), and (4) who opposes them (obstacle). In brief, you seek general information about the leading personnae (the Emperor and the Minister) and the possibility of a sharp conflict to come. In the short play for children, such information should be given quickly, in terms of a dramatic tug-of-war.

To create the first scene, you question the group along such lines as: "How do we show that the Emperor is too fond of fine clothes?"

The children may answer, "Let's show the Emperor fussing over a costume for the parade."

"How do we show that the Minister worries about the way the King neglects his people?"

"The Minister argues with the King to help the people who are starving."

Having determined the general action of the scene, you ask: "Who *else* is in the scene besides the Emperor and the Minister? Is someone showing him various robes or materials?"

"Would the Minister be the person to show these to him?"

"Who else might do this?"

"The Jesters!" shout the children. Weavers or merchants could fulfill this function equally well, but the children who worked on the dramatization in this book were enchanted with the idea of the Jesters.

"When should the parade be held? Let us make it as soon as possible."

"Next week," could be the answer to this question.

How the conflict in the scene between Emperor and Minister ends is also clarified at this time. The Emperor cannot find material suitable for the processional robes, and the Minister cannot get the Emperor to think about his People.

"Where do we show the Emperor and the Jesters fussing over the robes? Where does it happen?" you ask here. Their improvisations lead the players not only to decide on the Throne Room as background for this scene, but also to assemble chairs and other props defining the throne itself, the dais on which it rests, and the entrance to the room where two Guards stand. The children are just as quick to suggest hand props for the characters: a fan for the Emperor; a large appointment book for the Minister; wisps of material for the Jesters; scimitars for the Guards.

Now the *first cast* of volunteers gets up and *plays the scene from beginning to end*. Never stop an improvisation to offer criticisms. Such an interruption destroys the child's involvement in the character and the story, and his creative flow will suffer.

If the player gives up of his own accord, there are several ways to help him. Drop the acting and analyze, again, the traits, the objectives, the activities, and the conclusion of the scene. Or, if the characterization bothers the child, let him concentrate on his role while he enacts a part of the scene in pantomime.

In extreme cases, you may step into the improvisation yourself, not as the teacher, but as a character in the episode. At all times avoid showing the inhibited child what to do or telling him what to say. The resourcefulness he can develop on his own will astonish you.

Evaluation

Before the playing of the same incident by a second *cast*, take the time to evaluate the work that has just been done by the first. Probe for additional values inherent in the action and the characterization. The boys and girls take to this phase of activity as the well-known duck to water. Most often, your opening queries, "How did you like the scene? What do you think of it?" will evoke not praise but negative comments. "Joel turned his back on the audience." "Helen didn't speak loud enough."

Acknowledge the defects with a brief comment, "That's true but right now, it's not important. Later, if we act out the play for an audience, we shall watch out for these things. At the moment, what we want to know is did the playing tell the story clearly."

With the plot outline for your guide, lead the group into an analysis of the scene's essentials: plot growth, characterization, and pertinent dialogue. To help the group do this, you ask guiding questions, such as the following, after each playing of a scene:

"Is this part of the plot clear? Would you, if you were hearing and seeing the scene for the first time, understand what is happening?

"How much of it would you be able to follow if it were acted in pantomime? How much of the story is clear without words?

"Is there enough information about the *who? where? what? why? when?* How can you bring in more exposition naturally, without just talking?

"Is there a conflict, a fight here? What is its high point? Do you have to make the fight sharper, the crisis bigger? What can we do to make it so?

"Do we need a fresh character or another scene not already in the outline to make the conflict more exciting?

"Can anyone think of one thing we could add or change or do differently to make the scene itself better?"

After each question, you always advise the children, "Take a few moments to think."

For the dramatization in this book, the players decided to write-in a short scene of conflict between the starving People and the Emperor's Guards. It was meant to illustrate visually the state of the kingdom.

"Did you believe in the *characters?*" you question further. "Did they seem natural, truthful? Were they the kind of people we had decided upon?

"Did their actions and words result from their inner attitudes and objectives?

"Do you believe they acted the way they did because it was the only way they could act under the circumstances?

"What was at stake for each one? Did each show this urgency in the scene?

"What was his mood before he entered the scene?

"How did he affect his partners in the scene?

"What did he want to do to them?

"What did they want to do to him?"

Such probing is applied to every character in the scene. If you feel that the boys and girls have lost sight of their original understanding of the characters, refer to the outline for clarification.

Incidentally, be sure to address a child by his character's name during discussion and playacting. This device will keep him involved in his role, and will make the story come alive for the rest of the group.

"Is it natural?" You are talking of the *dialogue* now. "Is it in keeping with the characters who speak it, that is, would they really speak the way our players did?

"Did the dialogue tell us something of what the characters are like inside?

"Did it give necessary information or advance the story?

"Was it to the point or did it wander? Did it become talky, repetitious?"

And last, "Was the speech clear?"

Naturally, how far you pursue the exploration and how you conduct it will depend on the age and maturity of the children who play the scene. Dramatization through group playmaking cannot be rushed. Many meetings are needed to discuss, to improvise on, and to evaluate the playmaking; and many more before the final script is ready.

Improvement

Do not criticize harshly. Discuss each comment quickly but tactfully with "That's a good idea too, but don't you think that doing it Carol's way will make your point stronger?" When a child insists on his interpretation, let him try it out on stage to see if it works.

Sum up all the good suggestions before another cast plays the scene. Ask these children to add the two or three best ideas to their improvisation.

Apply the whole playmaking treatment to every scene in the outline, and where you aim for fine detail, apply it also to the smaller units which make up a scene. Follow this process until the play grows in depth and clarity, and the players are content.

And make notes. On the dialogue, the bits of scenes, the twists of characterization, the gestures each player invents. Make notes.

chapter 11

DIRECTING THE PLAY

There is a dream that almost every boy and girl share—to wear a costume and act in a play. It is this dream and its realization that transform the process of play performance into a valuable and creative experience.

Let us suppose that you and the young players have just finished the first group dramatization. A short, "actable" play lies before you, complete with the flexible dialogue they have contributed during many sessions of playmaking. Now you ask the group, "Shall we put it on before our friends? We can make up our own words and movements while we act it. Or we can rehearse the play, memorizing the dialogue and movements that are in it now."

The short plays, in Part Two of this book, were presented not only in the two styles suggested above, but also in a third. The third manner of presentation pertains to scripts that can be narrated. After telling and discussing the play carefully, the leader acts as Narrator, and the young people perform in pantomime. Such an approach needs little preparation.

Once the form of playing is chosen, your work as director begins. To help you follow the material in this chapter, you will find here a recapitulation of some basic information on creative dramatics as applied to the production of a play.

The Director and the Play

The functions of a director are many. Among them you may list:

(a) Preliminary work before rehearsals.
(b) Casting the play.
(c) Rehearsing the play.
(d) Staging the play.

All four factors enter into your preparation of the play. A working knowledge of stage techniques (sets, costumes, lights, sound, etc.) is more essential to the formal performance than to the informal.

The formal script, as you know, is usually played on the proscenium stage of a theater or school auditorium. And because tickets are sold, it relies heavily on beautiful sets and costumes, intricate lighting, and sound effects to hold the interest of the audience during the presentation. Even the choice of the play depends in part on the size of the stage, the stage equipment available, and the budget allotted for production.

The informal play, on the other hand, is elastic and may be produced in a simple but inventive manner. You can give it in a large living room, arena style, or at one end of the room with the acting area marked off from the audience by a sheet strung up as a curtain. Your own interest lies in the informal approach where individual expression is placed above slick professionalism.

Director's Preliminary Work

If the play to be staged is unfamiliar, you as director must study it beforehand until you have a clear understanding of its theme, the characters, and the development of the plot—act by act, scene by scene.

Before your first rehearsal try to visualize the total effect you want to achieve, the style of presentation the script needs. The kind of play to be presented—a religious play, a fantasy, a folk tale, or a here-and-now story— determines the choice of sets, costumes, lights, and sound. The religious play, for instance, may be played against a background of sky and Gothic arches, with the children in costumes designed to convey peace and dignity through their long, flowing lines. Your image of the finished form, however, is not imposed upon the group. It serves as a guide for the discussions to come.

How elaborate your production will be, depends upon your objective in putting on the play. Before the sets for the formal, long play are built, they are drawn to scale, and color sketches are made of the various scenes. These backgrounds may also be projected in three-dimensional models of plywood or cardboard. Entrances, windows, and furniture are marked on the drawings or models so that the players may understand the layouts at once, and adjust easily to their story world.

The drawings and models also help you *block* (map) the stage movements before rehearsals begin. As an experienced director of children's plays, you write marginal notes on the script about the major bits of stage action—important crosses, entrances, and groupings. You depend upon the players to create the minor movements as they act. The new director, like some professionals, often blocks out the entire movement to give himself a sense of security when he rehearses.

In either case, the blocking is never fixed. It is left in a state which allows the introduction of any new movements (*stage business*) that the children themselves may suggest in their playing. Blocking is used not only to achieve pictorial effect on stage, but, more important, it is used to highlight the dramatic points of the story.

When your preliminary work is prepared, read or tell the play to the children. If it is unfamiliar to them, go over the play with the group— the theme, the characters, the plot, etc.—in the same way that you previously studied it.

Casting the Play

Casting is approached in much the same manner as described in active playmaking. Where the children have shared in the dramatization of the play, they will understand the characters. They will know what the role needs, and the capabilities of a fellow player to fill it; therefore, you may safely ask the children to cast the play. Impress upon them, however, the importance of basing the choice of an actor on his talent, on his sense of responsibility, and on his spirit of co-operation.

If the young people are hearing a play for the first time, discuss it in detail. Then ask for volunteers to act out characters and representative scenes. The boys and girls will then be ready to select the cast.

Many instructors who lack a background in creative doing use the tryout system to cast a production. Such a "one-shot" audition is unpleasant and ineffective. It does not reveal ability. The aggressive child shines at the expense of the sensitive one. Too frequently, the aggressive child fails to live up to the promise of talent he displayed in the tryout. Even Broadway producers distrust the tryout and avoid it whenever they can.

The advantages of casting two complete sets of actors for the play outweigh the burden of the double rehearsals. Double casting enables many children "to wear a costume and act in a play," and it also supplies an understudy for the player who falls victim to measles or mumps at the last minute. One cast performs before classmates during the daytime hours. The second cast makes its debut at night, before parents and adult friends. This arrangement has been followed successfully in camps and schools. Two casts are almost essential for the production of the long play.

When you want to use only one cast, choose a play that permits improvisation and the introduction of crowds, dancers, and singers. The play should be so written that several characters are carrying the story line. In a number of the scripts here, two characters perform the same dramatic function, for which only one is actually needed—the two Jesters, for instance, in *The Emperor's New Clothes*. If one of the Jesters becomes ill the night before performance (and this has happened!) the other Jester can improvise the scene and carry on the continuity of the play. Though last-minute cuts plus a run-through are necessary, the poise of the remaining player will delight you.

A child can adapt to a new situation with an ease his adult colleague may envy. Perhaps this is so because the child, who has participated in creative dramatics, does not feel compelled to impress his audience. Thus free from stage-fright, he becomes completely involved with the character and with the plot he is projecting. At the end of a performance of

A Christmas Story, a critical mother fretted, "The children were too relaxed. You could see they were having fun!" Consider such an observation as a mark of success!

Rehearsing the Play

When the play is cast, creative rehearsing starts. Set up and follow a rehearsal schedule such as the one below:

(a) *First script reading by the cast.* Here, the whole play is given an oral reading by the players as they sit in a semicircle facing the director. No movements are attempted at this reading. Its purpose is to help the children to "get the feel" of the play and to communicate with each other. "Listen, react, then reply" is the key now (Chapter 6).

Discussions follow, during which you dig deeper into plot values and character interpretation. The set, or sets, for the play may be talked about in a general way.

(b) *Scene rehearsals.* The play is now broken down into sections of one or more scenes that can be rehearsed creatively at a single meeting. Only the children who are involved in these scenes need attend this rehearsal. Start off by asking the players to read the scene for the second time, encouraging them to get up and move as the action suggests. This will release tensions and facilitate the child's identification with the role and its acting needs. These movements may, or may not, contribute to the blocking of the play.

At this time, the players may improvise on their lines as long as they keep to the story and the flavor of the written dialogue.

If yours is to be an improvised presentation, you will encourage extemporizing until it flows, rich and alive, at performance time. In the play to be memorized, you will discover that improvisations gradually lead to a knowledge of the written lines—the players begin to associate certain words with certain situations and general movements. Memorization is also facilitated by frequently using or referring to the important lines, the key lines, during every discussion of the play.

Each rehearsal of a section of the play may start in the same way—with a reading of the scene and with improvisation. To refresh the children's recollection of the story, give them, or ask one of them to give, a quick synopsis of what has happened in the play so far.

The problem of directing the young players creatively needs elaborating. Since spontaneity is what you are most interested in achieving, bear in mind these few "do nots":

Do not hurry the player through an interpretation or a movement.

Do not demonstrate how a character should act or how a line should be said.

Do not drill.

A hollow, imitative performance presented by tense, stilted children will be your only reward.

Instead, be alert to the truth that each one of us visualizes a character or an action in the light of his own experiences, real or imaginary.

Help the young person to visualize an idea of his own.

Help him to avoid the conventional, the cliché.

Through patient, skillful questioning, lead him to express an emotion or to execute an activity in his particular way.

"Who am I?" Joel is urged to ask himself in the role of the Emperor. "What was I like as a little boy in the fisherman's hut? What did I feel inside when I had nothing but rags to wear? How was I found by the old Emperor, my father? What do I want today? What will happen if I do not get what I want? Who stands in my way of getting it? What must I do to get it?"

Gradually and naturally, through digging and improvisation, the player assumes the character of the Emperor as he sees him—in a form that is truthful to the child.

When the inner attitudes of the role are understood, the physical characteristics, such as speech or gesture, can be acquired by improvising situations other than those in the play (Chapter 7).

Explain, too, the importance of assuming a character before making an entrance on stage, and of holding the characterization and mood until after the exit. And remember to call each player by the name of his character. It helps.

If a child becomes bored or "frozen," stop the rehearsal and discuss interpretation again with the group. Ask for some suggestions to improve the scene. Pantomime, fresh improvisations, musical accompaniment, and encouragement will do much to reawaken interest and to stimulate imagination.

(c) *Establishing the set temporarily.* After group discussion of a particular scene, use temporary props, such as chairs and tables, to define the set's boundaries—the walls, the windows, the entrances, and the furniture groupings.

(d) *Rehearsals for blocking.* Tell the cast to say or improvise their lines while moving about, but without their scripts, if possible. Introduce the movement you have blocked out in your preparatory study.

Include any practical suggestions on blocking that the boys and girls make as they work. When a suggestion is impractical, do not criticize or discard it without discussion. If this does not convince the inventor, let him try out the movement while acting. He will discover for himself what makes, or does not make, for good stage movement.

All movement must be motivated. It must stem from an emotional impulse or a physical need. A piercing scream may alarm a person and make him jump out of his chair; or it may root him to it, powerless to move (emotional impulse). A knock on the door compels another person to cross the stage to admit the knocker (physical need). Avoid gestures and crosses that signify nothing. They blur the dramatic picture.

Stage terminology may be used even with the young players. A simple vocabulary can include words such as *downstage* (toward the audience); *upstage* (away from the audience); *offstage* (the portions of the stage invisible to the audience); *right* and *left* (the actor's right and left); the *apron* (the lip of the stage that extends into the audience beyond the front curtain); *cyc* (the cyclorama or draperies that cover the back wall only, or the back and the side walls); *properties* or *props* (the movable articles on stage, such as small pieces of furniture as well as the articles carried by the actors themselves). *Cross, entrance* and *exit* are self-explanatory. The glossary in this book defines other stage terms you may encounter during dramatization.

(e) *Short run-throughs.* After the cast has worked on several scenes, have the players run through all of these scenes consecutively before you proceed to the next new scene. This procedure helps to keep the play alive for the children. Continue with your work on interpretation, character, and motivated movement.

The long, formal play also needs one or two run-throughs, just for the lines. During such a run-through, do not burden the players with any acting problem other than that of knowing their lines.

(f) *Polishing rehearsals.* Now your goal is to put the entire play into a shape suitable for presentation. The formal play needs a longer finishing process than does the informal. Run-throughs of the entire play are given to focus attention on picking up cues quickly, on achieving a variety of tempi, and on working for climactic tension, clear-cut movement, and audibility.

(g) *Technical rehearsals.* At least one rehearsal on stage is needed to correlate and check sets, costumes, lights, props, music, and sound effects. A backstage crew, composed of adults or group members, has been working on these physical problems. Any changes in the play that affect the physical arrangements should be made at the technical rehearsal.

(h) *Dress rehearsals.* The whole process of the preparation of a play comes to an end with one or two dress rehearsals on stage. The players in costumes and make-up, the props, sets, lights, music, and sound merge, and become a single unit. A warning—at this time, make no attempt to alter characterization, interpretation, or major blocking. It will serve only to confuse the players.

Staging the Play

The techniques needed for a formal production are intricate, and their execution requires taste and experience in stagecraft. If you, as a director, are interested in the formal approach and require technical detail, you will find many excellent books (several of which are noted in the bibliography of this book) that give such information. At the moment, it is sufficient to say that any production, elaborate or not, offers an exciting challenge to the director.

A *set,* for instance, need not be realistic; it can "suggest" rather than "show." A screen or two, some hand and stage props (appropriate to the staging), levels, builder's paper, crêpe paper or heavy wrapping paper, and paints—these materials can be used to create an imaginative impression of a background.

A *Christmas Story* had for its setting a fireplace which was painted on a screen covered with builder's paper, a couch, a round table with a chair near it. The first set of *The Emperor's New Clothes* (the Throne Room and the Hall outside) was created by using levels, screens, and lanterns, imaginatively. A high-backed chair placed on a small level served as His Majesty's throne, and three lanterns that the children had made dangled over the chair to form a charming design. A screen, covered with builder's paper and painted to resemble bamboo, was placed downstage right. A flowering tree, arranged downstage left, balanced the picture. The tree, fragile and pink, was fashioned from a tall, dead branch to which dozens of tiny crêpe paper blossoms were attached. In *Where the Sea Breaks*, a reclining mermaid, a sea serpent, and several fish were cut out of cardboard and then painted in blues, greens, lavenders, and rust. These were strung on a wire over the heads of Neptune and his Court.

Original designs like these, which cost very little, can give hours of artistic pleasure to the young people who do the pasting and the painting.

Costumes, like sets for the creative play, need not be realistic. However meager the budget, however limited the time at your disposal, do try to dress up the players. By wearing a costume, the child finds a quick identification with the character he is portraying, and forgets self-consciousness. And costumes are fun.

Burlap bags, old curtains, sheets, and clothes forgotten in the attic have often been transformed into the most glamorous of wardrobes. A maroon bathrobe saw valiant service in many a play, sometimes as Daddy's robe, often as an old nobleman's gown. For the latter, the bathrobe was decorated with ermine, made of white felt and black paint.

Avoid the use of crêpe paper for costumes. It does not cling to the lines of the body, and it tears too quickly.

Do not overlook *make-up*, even in the smallest of "auditoriums."

And remember that every one of these elements—sets, costumes, lights, and sound—must contribute to the meaning and mood of the play. Your aim is to create an artistic whole, harmonious in color and interpretation.

Now the stage is set. The players are waiting. The moment is here.
Relax. Doing through drama is a part of the child's world.
And because of this, even his beginning efforts have meaning for you.

NOTES FOR PART ONE

The quotations used in this book have been reprinted from the following sources with the kind permission of the publishers.

PREFACE

Pg. XII.   1, 2,   Winifred Ward, *Playmaking with Children*, revised edition, 1957, D. Appleton-Century Co., Inc., reprinted by permission of Appleton-Century-Crofts, Inc., New York

Pg. XIII.   3,   ——, *ibid.*

CHAPTER 1

Pg. 4.   1,   Peter Slade, *Child Drama*, 1955, The Philosophical Library, New York

CHAPTER 2

Pg. 13.   1,   The sea was the topic of one such subject, with the drama unit creating the play *Where the Sea Breaks*, included in Part Two of this book

CHAPTER 3

Pg. 6.   1,   Geismer and Suter, Editors, *Very Young Verses*, 1945, Houghton, Mifflin Co., Boston

Pg. 23.   2,   E. Johnson, C. E. Scott, and E. R. Sickels, Compiled by, *Anthology of Children's Literature*, 1948, Houghton, Mifflin Co., Boston

Pg. 25.   3,   The Association for Childhood Education, Editors, *Sung Under the Silver Umbrella*, 1935, The Macmillan Co., New York

Pg. 26.   4, Michael Chekhov, *To the Actor*, 1953, Harper & Brothers, New York

CHAPTER 8

Pg. 64.   1, Kenneth Thorpe Rowe, *Write That Play*, 1939, Funk & Wagnalls Co., New York

Pg. 69.   2, ——, *ibid.*

CHAPTER 9

Pg. 74.   1, Winifred Ward, *Stories to Dramatize*, 1952, Children's Theatre Press, Anchorage, Ky.

CHAPTER 10

Pg. 78.   1–6, Hans Christian Andersen, *Fairy Tales;* translated by Mrs. Edgar Lucas, Children's Illustrated Classics (American Publishers—E. P. Dutton & Co., Inc., New York; English Publishers—J. M. Dent and Sons Ltd., London

Pg. 79.   7, 8, ——, *ibid.*

Part Two

THE PLAYS

INTRODUCTION

The short, non-royalty plays given here vary in subject matter, age of players, length of playing time and manner of presentation. Information on these points precedes each script, together with a cast list and a description of the set involved. Brief staging suggestions follow each play. They pertain to casting, preparation of sets and costumes, use of music and sound effects. Included is a list of properties required by the characters in the play.

Occasionally, simple "freeing" exercises for the children are described. Using rhythms, moods and characterization, these exercises are designed to relax tensions and to stimulate the imaginations of those members of the cast who have not had experience in creative dramatics. The exercises will help the boys and girls to "open up" during the discussion and the playmaking that accompany all creative rehearsing (Chapter 11).

Should the group improvise or memorize the play? Should the young people invent their own words on the theme and plot at performance time or give the lines of the script as previously written? You can arrive at the manner of presentation best suited to your children only after weighing the group's dramatic purpose, the time of rehearsal at its disposal, and the experience and maturity level of its members. Younger boys and girls, naturally, are not required to memorize a script. They enact it through pantomime or improvisation of dialogue or both pantomime and improvisation. And they use a Narrator, acted by an older child or an adult, to give the audience certain expository details without which the story is incomprehensible.

Such information tells where and when the play is taking place, who its main characters are, reveals their individual objectives, and describes their interdependent relationships. In *How the Snowman Got His Broom*, for instance, the Narrator informs his audience that the Old Woman lives in a cottage at the edge of the forest, that she and her friends, the Birds, hate the winter, and that the Broom possesses a peculiar attribute. The Narrator also supplies the story continuity which not only clarifies the plot as the children improvise but also serves to remind the performers of each action just before it occurs.

The older players who wish to extend their experience by doing more formal productions will find the dialogue of these scripts easy to memorize (Chapter 11). For them, the role of the Narrator may be retained or omitted. In *A Real Birthday Present*, Mrs. Fields may appear both as Narrator and in her part as Judy's defender. Or, with some script changes, she may be dropped as Narrator and kept as Judy's friend. In *A Christmas Story*, the role of the Narrator, Miss Warren, may be eliminated in the same way.

Before memorizing the more difficult *A Midsummer Night's Dream*, ask your players to act out the meaning of the lines in their own words. When they understand the script and feel at ease in its situations, they may proceed to the original poetry. Such an approach will enable them to absorb Shakespeare easily, naturally and to develop a feeling for his language—its beauty and its form.

There will be times when you will wish to and should retain the Narrator to bring about an audience participation. The Narrator of *Where the Sea Breaks* achieves it when he addresses his spectators directly and even asks the children among them to recite the nursery rhyme "There was an Old Woman who lived in a shoe." At a recent performance of the play, spectator interest was so high that one listener, aged eight, not only recited the entire rhyme, but contributed a stanza which he had created on the spot. And good it was too!

Among the scripts you will find an outline for a play, *Bank Notes and Music.* Your experienced groups may enjoy using its suggested characters and story plot as the basis for a playmaking adventure.

All staging suggestions, by the way, are just that, suggestions. Consider them as a means to stimulate the fertile imaginations of your children to originate their own sets and costumes and, ultimately, a production that will be creatively and uniquely theirs (Chapter 11).

Introduce music at the spots designated in the scripts and at your discretion. It enhances a performance, especially one that is simply staged.

Sound effects, too, add to the value of the presentation. A sound may be recreated vocally, mechanically, or by commercial sound effects records. For instance, you can reproduce the sound of the Snowman crashing through the forest in *How the Snowman Got His Broom* by crushing cellophane offstage.

Lighting directions have been generally omitted since complete stage lighting requires special equipment and technical knowledge. A well-lit stage will be sufficient for most informal plays, whether their backgrounds be indoors or out.

The notes on casting suggest when and in what areas the number of players may be increased or decreased to fit the needs of your group. The sex of a role may be changed: Grandma may become Grandpa.

And please, please dress up everyone in a costume, even the Narrator. It adds to the excitement of the performance and the joy of its performers.

HOW THE SNOWMAN GOT HIS BROOM

A NONSENSE FANTASY

Playing Time   10—15 minutes approximately

Age   5—10 years

Manner of Presentation   Narrate with pantomime
or
Narrate with improvisation
or
Narrate, improvise and memorize

Staging Suggestions   See end of play

Cast   The Narrator (a pompous professor)
Professor Doodlebug (an inquiring professor with cowboy inclina-
tions)

The Old Woman (who hates the winter)
The Maple Tree
Snowflakes
Birds
Children
The Snowman (last winter's Snowman without any arms)

Time The beginning of winter in a magic time

Place A garden

Scene The curtain opens on the Old Woman's garden located at the edge of a forest. The forest occupies the back and left side of the stage. The garden is still green even to the leaves on the big Maple Tree standing upstage center. The front of the Old Woman's cottage can be seen downstage right. A gaily-colored broom leans against the right wall of this cottage in full view of the audience. A small bench stands downstage left.

Entrances are from the cottage, from the forest behind the Tree, from the forest, upstage left corner, and from the forest, downstage left.

When the play begins, the NARRATOR, *in the character of a stern-faced professor inclined toward pomposity, walks on, apron left. There are several heavy volumes under his arm. As he walks slowly across the apron, engrossed in a book, he shakes his head at what he reads and mutters in a discouraged manner.*

NARRATOR: Mmm, it's not in this book. (*He lets the book drop and opens a second volume, flipping through its pages.*) This volume may possibly—possibly—(*He shakes his head and lets this book drop too.*) No, nothing here either. (*He opens a third and scans its pages quickly. He is about to discard this too, when he stops himself.*) Wait—(*He looks through the pages again, stops at one, reads and exclaims in excitement.*) Yes—yes—yes! This is it! (*He waves the book at audience.*) The information I've been hunting for, yes. And now our lecture can commence. (*Standing stage center, he looks at the audience sternly.*) No squirming in your seat, sir—and no chewing gum either! Ready? (*He gives a brief smile.*) Good. We can begin. Now, our lecture for today is entitled . . . uh . . . entitled . . . (*he glances at the book*)—hm, entitled *How the Snowman Got His Broom.* (*He moves toward stage right.*) As you know, there are many theories about the origin of this interesting phenomenon—

(PROFESSOR DOODLEBUG *who is seated in the audience jumps up. He is dressed in cowboy suit and high hat.*)

DOODLEBUG: What does that word mean? Phe—phe—phe-nome-non?

NARRATOR: Did I hear anyone ask what the word means?

DOODLEBUG (*drawing his guns belligerently*):   I did!

NARRATOR: Hm. Well, phenomenon means any fact or event of scientific interest. (DOODLEBUG *sits.*) To continue, the eminent Professor Ipswitch— you've heard of him, of course—he's the renowned anthropologist, geologist, biologist—(*becoming interested in the game of seeing how many 'ologists' he can remember, he ticks them off on his fingers*)—archeologist, psychologist, zoologist, pathologist—(*he is stuck for a moment*)—neurologist— (*stuck again*)—sociologist and—and—monologist! (*He holds up his tenth finger in triumph.*) I made it! (*Regaining his dignity, he clears his throat.*) Hmm—hmm—well, now—the esteemed Professor wrote an article claiming that the Snowman acquired the instrument in question, that is, his Broom, during the first Glacial Period when the Ice Cap, moving down from the North, pushed it right into the Snowman's arms.

DOODLEBUG (*jumping up*):   What's an Ice Cap?

NARRATOR (*glaring at him and continuing*):   However, this theory was disproved in another article by Professor Blam, the equally renowned—(*he counts on his fingers again as* DOODLEBUG *jumps up on each count*)—biologist, zoologist, anthropologist, geologist—(*he struggles through the rest*) —archeologist—psychologist—sociologist—monologist—neurologist—and— and pathologist! (*He mops his brow.*) Phew. . . . Now, Professor Doodlebug made a very pertinent point. He asked—you can get up now, Professor.

DOODLEBUG (*jumping up*):   Where did they find a broom in the Ice Age? (*He pulls out his guns.*) Where, I ask you?

NARRATOR: Thank you, Professor. You may sit down. (DOODLEBUG *does so.*) Now, since no one could answer that question, we were forced to search elsewhere for the solution to the puzzle, "How did the Snowman get his broom?" And—(*he taps the book he holds*)—today I have found it! Yes!

It seems that—(*looking at the book, he walks to far right as the curtain opens and remains standing at this point throughout the play*)—once upon a time, there was an Old Woman who lived at the edge of a forest. This book doesn't tell you just when it was but one point is certain—it was a time when all things magical could happen and *did* happen. Well—(*The* OLD WOMAN *comes out of her cottage and begins to dig in her garden.*)—the Old Woman loved to clean her snug little cottage and plant in her garden. Oh uh—oh yes—this is her house—(*he points to stage right*)—and this is her garden right at the edge of the forest. (*He points to center.*) The Old Woman has cleared all of the brush, as you can see, except for that nice big Maple Tree standing over there towards the back. Now the Old Woman would be perfectly happy if it were not for one thing. The Winter. She hates the Winter. It keeps her from her cherished planting—(*The* OLD WOMAN *returns to her cottage.*)—and makes her very, very cold. Yes. Well, one night while the Old Woman is sleeping in her cottage, the Snow falls.

(*To snow music accompaniment, the* SNOWFLAKES *dance in from downstage left and fall to the ground.*)

It's long past autumn, you see, and high time that Winter were here. It's a soft, pretty Snow but when the Old Woman comes out of her cottage next morning, she doesn't like it one bit. No indeed!

OLD WOMAN (*enters right, yawning*):   Oh dear, oh dear, I shouldn't have slept this late. The turnips have to be planted and—(*She sees the* SNOW *and is shocked.*) Snow! By my toe, Winter's come during the night. And now it will be cold—cold—

(*She shivers and draws her shawl about her.*)

NARRATOR: She knows, you see, that Winter often follows the first Snow and hating the cold as she does, she tries to think of a way to brush the Snow away and so keep Winter from getting into her garden.

OLD WOMAN (*hobbles about the garden, murmuring*):   I've got to keep that mean old Winter out of my garden. By my big toe, I've got to keep that mean old—(*She looks down at the* SNOW.) Now, if the Snow were swept away, Winter wouldn't dare show his face here, would he? No, he couldn't. Only how is a weak old woman to do that? How is a stiff old body to sweep all this Snow away? (*She sits down on the bench.*) Oh dear, oh dear.

NARRATOR: She thinks and thinks and thinks to no avail. But just as she is about to give up, she remembers the Magic Broom standing outside her cottage door. (*He points at it.*) This Magic Broom can sweep the Snow away.

OLD WOMAN (*hobbling to the* BROOM, *excited*):   The Magic Broom! That will do the trick! By my toe, that will do the trick just fine!

NARRATOR: Now this Broom is magic because no one can lift it—no one, that is, except the Old Woman and one other person. We'll learn who he is by and by. Yes. Well, the Old Woman lifts the Broom but when she tries to sweep the Snow away, she finds that she is not strong enough to do it.

OLD WOMAN: I'll pick it up—like this—and I'll push it along like—I'll push—I'll—(*She cannot sweep.*) Oh dear, oh dear, my poor arms are too frail to push the Broom. Who will help me? Who in the world will—why, my friends! The Birds! They will help. (*She hurries to upstage entrance behind the* TREE.)

NARRATOR: So she calls out to her friends, the Birds.

OLD WOMAN: Oh darling Birds! My good, little Birds! Come to me! Come to me quickly!

NARRATOR: And the Birds, alarmed by the worry in her voice, fly to her at once, not knowing what to think.

BIRDS (*flying in from upstage center*):   What is it, Old Woman?—Are there any hunters about?—Did you see the cat?—Are the boys throwing stones at you?—

OLD WOMAN: No—no—no! But all this Snow came during the night! And where there's Snow there's Winter! You don't like Winter, eh? Nor do I. (*She whispers like a conspirator.*) Now, if we could only sweep the Snow away with my Magic Broom, Winter will have to stay out of the garden. What do you think? Will you help me push the Broom, eh?

BIRDS (*improvising*):   Winter! We hate the Winter!—Winter hides all our food—We must fly away South to keep warm—Of course we'll help you, Old Woman—We'll all get behind you and push.

NARRATOR: And since the Birds hate the Snow and Winter as much as the Old Woman does—the Snow covers up all their food on the ground and they must fly South to keep warm—they get behind the Old Woman and her Magic Broom and push and push and push until the Snowflakes, twirling and tumbling, are swept out of the garden.

  (*Forming a line behind the* OLD WOMAN *who holds the* BROOM, *the* BIRDS *push with great effort. The* SNOWFLAKES *twirl and tumble out, downstage left. As the snow music fades away, the sweepers hear a sad moan.*)

BIRDS and OLD WOMAN: Did you hear that?—It sounded like someone crying

—What can it be?—Is anyone hurt?—Maybe it's one of the Bird babies— Where did the cry come from?—

(*They search behind every bush and tree.*)

NARRATOR: But no matter how carefully they search, they cannot find where the moan came from. So the Birds decide they had mistaken the passing of the wind for a cry and saying good-bye to the Old Woman, they fly back to their nests.

BIRDS: Oh well, let it go—It must have been the wind—We'd better get back to our nests—Our babies are hungry—They're crying for their breakfasts—

OLD WOMAN: Oh dear, yes. And I have to cook a chicken for lunch. Thank you, my good little Birds, my darling little Birds, thank you, thank you.

(*They say good-bye and fly back to the forest, upstage center. The* OLD WOMAN *returns the* BROOM *to its place and enters her cottage.*)

NARRATOR: The Old Woman puts the Magic Broom back in its place and goes into her cottage to cook herself a potted chicken for lunch. Now who should come running out of the woods but the Neighbors' Children. (*Running and leaping in glee, the* CHILDREN *enter, upstage left corner.*) Dressed in ski togs and hauling skates and sleds, they swarm into the garden for a morning's fun in the Snow.

CHILDREN (*improvising happily*):   Hurry up, Margie, we want to have a snow fight!—Says you! Bob and I are going to skate—It's too early for ice, silly—Have you got your sled?—I can hardly wait to play in the Snow— Hurry, everyone, before the Snow melts!—

NARRATOR: They rub their eyes in astonishment. There is no Snow!

CHILDREN: Oh look!—The Snow! It's gone!—What happened to it?—The Snow's disappeared!—It was here this morning!—How did it vanish?— Maybe it melted away—Not that quickly!—Now we can't skate or go sledding or anything!—

NARRATOR: They are staring at the ground when suddenly there is a crashing noise at the edge of the forest. (*Noise offstage left.*) And who should stalk out of it but a big, clumsy Snowman. (*An armless* SNOWMAN *stalks in from upstage left corner.*) He is such a funny-looking Snowman too. His top hat is punched in, his white coat is spotted with mud and his two arms are missing!

CHILDREN: Who's that?—It's a Snowman!—A Snowman now? There isn't any Snow.—Just look, he has no arms!—No arms? I never saw a Snowman without any— (*They crowd around him curiously.*)

(NARRATOR *or* SNOWMAN, *or both, may carry the story line.*)

SNOWMAN or NARRATOR: I'm a left-over Snowman, a last winter's Snowman. My arms were melted away by the summer's sun. When I heard the Snow was falling, I rushed over here hoping the Old Woman would make me a pair of arms. But she and the Birds have swept the Snow away with the Magic Broom. And Winter can't come into the garden. And now I won't have any arms! Do you hear? I won't have any arms!
    (*He weeps.*)

NARRATOR: The Children comfort him as best they can. "The Magic Broom? What is that?" they ask him.

CHILDREN: Don't cry, Mr. Snowman—You've got us. We'll try to help you— But first you better tell us about the Magic Broom—What is it?

NARRATOR: The Snowman points to the Broom near the cottage door and several boys and girls run over and try to lift it.

SNOWMAN or NARRATOR: It's that Broom over there. Only no one can lift it except the Old Woman and me. Now if I could only hide it from her, she wouldn't be able to sweep the Snow away any more. But how can I hide it when I haven't any arms with which to pick it up? (*He stamps about the garden.*) I ask you—how can I?

NARRATOR: The Children grasp the problem and being smart as a two-month-old puppy, hit on the solution quickly. "Next time Winter comes," they tell the Snowman, "we shall go into the garden early and grab enough Snow to make you a pair of arms."

CHILDREN: I know what to do!—I know!—I know!—Next time Winter comes, we'll come to the garden early and grab enough Snow to make you some arms.—Don't worry.—We'll be here before the Birds.—

NARRATOR: So promising to help, the girls and boys run off to their homes where their mothers are waiting with some hot noodle soup and frank-furters. And the Snowman stamps back into his forest.

CHILDREN (*running off, upstage left*):   Come on, everybody.—We might as well go home.—There is no Snow.—My mother promised me some noodle soup and hot dogs.—Oh boy, can I have lunch with you?—Good-bye, Mr. Snowman—good-bye—good-bye.—
    (*The SNOWMAN stamps off after them.*)

NARRATOR: A week later, the Snow falls again. (*The SNOWFLAKES dance onto stage as before.*) The Old Woman leaves her ironing and hurrying into the garden calls to her friends, the Birds.

OLD WOMAN (*hobbling in from right*):   By my big toe, here is the pesky

Snow again! Well, I know what to do about it this time! (*She hobbles upstage.*) Oh darling Birds! My good, little Birds! Come to me! Come to me quickly!

(*She returns, right, and picks up the* BROOM.)

NARRATOR: Twittering in shrill excitement, the Birds fly to her at once.

BIRDS (*flying in, upstage center*): What is it, Old Woman?—Has Winter come again?—So soon?—Form a line, everyone, quick!—There's no time to lose!—Ready?—One—two—three—push!

NARRATOR: And moving in perfect drill order, the Birds get behind the Old Woman and the Magic Broom and push and push—(*The* SNOWFLAKES *twirl and tumble to music*)—when all at once there is a loud outcry and the Children and the Snowman come storming into the garden—too late!

CHILDREN and SNOWMAN (*storming in from upstage left corner*): Are we in time?—I ran all the way!—Stop that sweeping, Old Woman!—You can't sweep away the Snow!—We need the Snow!—Quick, Bob, Steve, Sue, everybody! Let's get the Magic Broom away from the Old Woman!—Come on, pull-pull-pull!

NARRATOR: The Children hurl themselves at the Magic Broom to pull it away but though they pull with all their might, they cannot budge it. Only the Snowman may lift it but *he* has no arms.

CHILDREN (*to the* OLD WOMAN): Don't you understand? We want the Snow to play with—

SNOWMAN: And to make a pair of arms for me.

OLD WOMAN: Well, I'm sorry. You'll just have to do without. The Birds and I hate the Snow. My very bones ache with cold.

BIRDS: The Snow hides all our food and chills our nests.—Our babies can't keep warm.—We have to leave our homes.—

NARRATOR: The disappointed Children and the Snowman are forced to leave again without any Snow for the Snowman's arms. (*The* CHILDREN *and the* SNOWMAN *stamp off.*) And the Old Woman, aided by the Birds, finishes her sweeping. (*The* SNOWFLAKES *dance off, left.*) But just as they are about to return to their homes, they hear that mysterious moan again. (*The* NARRATOR *asks the audience.*) Can you hear it now?

OLD WOMAN and BIRDS: Listen!—There's that moan again!—It came from this bush.—No, it came from the forest.—No, it came from the cottage!—

NARRATOR: They hunt for its source just about everywhere—around the stumps and under the stones and among the bushes—but it's no use. They can't find where that lonely sound came from. And completely baffled a second time, they go off to their separate affairs—the Old Woman to her ironing, the Birds to their little ones.

BIRDS: Oh well, I've got to go home now.—My babies need their flying lessons—I'm late enough as it is.—When you teach, do you swoop up or do you swoop down?—

OLD WOMAN: Oh dear, my ironing's piled up on the kitchen table.
        (*She puts the* BROOM *back, downstage right, and enters her cottage. The* BIRDS *fly away, upstage center, amid many good-byes.*)

NARRATOR: A few days later, the Snow falls again. (*The* SNOWFLAKES *dance in, left.*) This time the Children and the Snowman are waiting right outside the garden and when it comes, they sneak in quickly before the Old Woman appears. (*The* CHILDREN *tiptoe in, upstage left corner, shushing the* SNOWMAN *who finds it difficult to move quietly.*) They pile some Snow onto their sleds and manage to get back into the forest just a moment before the Old Woman walks out of her cottage. (*The* CHILDREN *snatch some snow and return to the forest just as the* OLD WOMAN *enters.*) The small amount of Snow surprises the Old Woman but shrugging her shoulders, she calls again to her friends, the Birds.

OLD WOMAN: Oh my toe, just look at this little bit of Snow. I could have sworn more fell. . . . Well, no matter. (*She hobbles upstage and calls.*) Oh darling Birds! My good, little Birds! Come to me—come to me quickly!

NARRATOR: The Birds arrive amid a flurry of wings and forming a line behind her and her Magic Broom, start to push—and push—and—when there is that crashing noise and the Snowman stalks into the garden proudly swinging a pair of brand new arms! The boys and girls troop after him! (*The* SNOWMAN, *followed by the* CHILDREN, *stalks in; he is the proud possessor of two arms.*) The Snowman orders the Old Woman to stop her sweeping and let the Snow remain where it is. But the Old Woman refuses.

SNOWMAN: Hey, Old Woman! Stop! You can't sweep the Snow away!
        (*The* CHILDREN *echo his words.*)

OLD WOMAN: No, by my big toe, no! It's too cold and my poor bones ache so.

BIRDS: The Snow goes or we have to go!

NARRATOR: And though they argue and argue, the Old Woman refuses to change her mind. Instead she and the Birds continue sweeping. Seeing this, the Snowman flexes his new arms and grabs hold of the other end of the Magic Broom. He tries to pull it out of the Old Woman's hands. The Birds get behind the Old Woman to help her and the Children get behind the Snowman to help *him*! (*The* OLD WOMAN *and the* BIRDS *form a line on one side of the* BROOM: *opposing them are the* SNOWMAN *and the* CHILDREN.) There is a real tug of war. Yes. Each side tugs and strains to free the Broom from the other side's grasp. To no avail. One side is as strong as the other. Yes. Soon everyone is out of breath and the Old Woman cries a halt to the struggle.

EVERYBODY (*improvising*): Pull!—Harder!—They're gaining on us!—Can't you pull more?—Watch it, the Broom's slipping away!—I've got it! Now pull!—More!—They're gaining again!—PULL! HARDER!—

OLD WOMAN (*her groans overlap the above*): Oh dear, my arms!—They're breaking!—I can't hold the Broom any more!—I can't catch my breath!—I've got to rest!—Everybody rest!—Stop! Everybody! Let's rest a minute! Stop! Stop!

NARRATOR: They obey the Old Woman gladly. Releasing the Broom, they start to breathe in deeply when they hear that strange, strange moan again. It is louder this time, so loud in fact that the Birds are able to trace it right to its source—right to that big Maple Tree standing over there at the back of the garden!

BIRDS: There's that moan again!—We've got to find where it comes from!—Spread out!—Hurry!—Spread out—spread out—

OLD WOMAN (*discovering the source*): Oh my toe, it's my Maple Tree! Oh dear, oh dear! My Maple Tree is moaning!

SNOWMAN: Why are you crying? You have all your arms!

NARRATOR: Everyone is astonished to see a Maple Tree crying and all crowd around her to find out why. "I'm so tired," the Maple Tree explains.

MAPLE TREE (*sighing*) or NARRATOR: I'm so tired. I want to sleep so much. But how can I sleep if you sweep the Snow away and keep our Winter out of the garden? How are my brothers and sisters going to sleep? Don't you see? As long as it's sunny and warm, the Trees and the Bushes and the Plants have to keep right on blooming. After a while, we'll all be so weary we shall die. Oh please, please, let the Winter come so we can sleep. *Please. . . .*

NARRATOR: The Old Woman and the Birds feel sorry for the Maple Tree. And so ashamed of themselves too. They did not realize what harm their sweeping could do. After all, they can always keep warm in spite of the cold weather. The Birds can take their families South in search of food, and the Old Woman can light a nice, hot fire in her stove to warm her bones. But the poor, tired Trees can do neither. And they do need the Winter-time to rest in.

OLD WOMAN and BIRDS: We did not realize we were hurting you.—We don't want to do that! Ever!—We love the Trees and the Bushes and the Plants. —You are our friends.—

BIRDS: We can always fly to the warm lands for our food.

OLD WOMAN: And I can build a nice, hot fire in my stove to keep me warm. Oh dear, I'm so sorry, so ashamed.

NARRATOR: The Old Woman and the Birds apologize to the Maple Tree for what they've done and agree to let the Snow remain in the garden.

BIRDS: We'll never sweep the Snow away again. Never!

OLD WOMAN: Never, never! By my big toe, I promise you that!

NARRATOR: Now the Old Woman remembers the Magic Broom in her hand. ' Oh my toe, what am I to do with this Broom?" she asks.

OLD WOMAN (puzzled), or NARRATOR: Oh my toe, what am I to do with this Broom? If I leave it here, someone is bound to try to pick it up and get into mischief. And I won't need it any more.

NARRATOR: Her eye falls on the Snowman and before you can say, "Well, how did the Snowman get his broom?", she pops the Broom into his arms and everyone thinks he looks so strong and proud with the Broom in his arms, they all agree he ought to keep it there forever.

OLD WOMAN (thrusting the BROOM into the SNOWMAN's arms):   Here, you hold it, Mr. Snowman!

CHILDREN: Oh, doesn't he look handsome!—Just like a soldier!—Tell you what, let him keep the Broom!—Forever!—He'll be our handsome Snowman!—And stay with us till Summer comes!—Yes, yes! And stay with us till Summer comes. . . .

NARRATOR: And catching hands, the Children start to jump and dance around him in great excitement. (The CHILDREN join hands and dance around the SNOWMAN singing as the BIRDS and OLD WOMAN exit to their various homes.) And if you listen carefully, you'll hear them singing the Snowman's song.

> (The curtain closes on the singing and dancing CHILDREN. Now the NARRATOR, open book in hand, clears his throat and addresses the audience from his position, apron right.)

NARRATOR: Hmm—an interesting theory, don't you think? "How the Snowman got his broom?"—Uh, do you believe it's true?—I do. (But he begins to doubt it.) That is—(he clears his throat again and says firmly)—hmm— YES!

> (He shuts his book abruptly and stalks off the apron.)

STAGING SUGGESTIONS

Cast

Increase or decrease the number of BIRDS, CHILDREN and SNOWFLAKES according to your needs. Avoid overcrowding the stage. If the group is very large, players may impersonate the various plants, etc. in the garden.

If there are not enough players in your group, suggest rather than enact the arrival and departure of the SNOWFLAKES. You may do this by playing appropriate music or simply through the NARRATOR's references, such as "The Snow falls again."

Cast the older, more mature children in the main roles, as leaders of the different crowds and as the MAPLE TREE. When the play is being pantomimed by young players, you may take the part of the NARRATOR.

If the group is all male, the OLD WOMAN may become the OLD MAN. Incidentally, young boys enjoy being SNOWFLAKES every bit as much as girls do. PROFESSOR DOODLEBUG may be eliminated.

Set

This may be left entirely to the audience's imagination with the NARRATOR indicating through gestures the forest, the garden and the cottage. However, place a real broom against the proscenium arch and a bench or stool downstage left.

For a realistic set, paint a forest background on drawing, wrapping or builder's paper and stretch it across the back and left side of the stage. Remember to cut out entrances, please. Painted screens or cardboard cutouts of individual trees can be placed in strategic positions to suggest the forest. Add bushes and flowers and stones to mark the garden plantings. Several lengths of picket fence borrowed from your local lumber yard may define the boundaries of the garden.

The front side of the OLD WOMAN's cottage may be created in the same way. Allow for her entrance on stage.

Costumes

In one production, the OLD WOMAN wore a shawl over a costume that consisted of a long skirt, blouse, bodice and apron. The other characters stirred the players into truly imaginative designing.

The SNOWFLAKES were dressed in white jerseys, shorts and slips, to which were sewn bits of the sparkling white cotton used for Christmas decorations. Cardboard stars made out of glitter and glue formed their headdresses, and spangled snowballs hung from wrists and ankles.

The BIRDS wore brown crêpe paper hoods over their heads to which yellow beaks had been attached. Brown cardboard wings were pinned to their crêpe-papered bodies. Dyed, long, winter pajamas, wings and mask will also transform a child into a BIRD.

The SNOWMAN, a black top hat of cardboard on his head, was enveloped in a long white sheet with two side slits through which his arms finally emerged. The sheet covered a small pillow strapped around his middle.

The MAPLE TREE's body was wrapped in green crêpe paper, and irregular green strips tipped with leaves hung from her outstretched arms. A circlet of green leaves for her hair completed the outfit.

The NARRATOR and PROFESSOR DOODLEBUG were costumed in nonsensical fashion—the NARRATOR in pince-nez, high collar, flowing tie and old-fashioned suit; DOODLEBUG in cowboy attire topped by a high hat!

The CHILDREN used their own snow outfits, many carrying skates, skis and sleds. The last provided an unexpected bit of improvisation at the performance. When it came time to make off with some snow for the SNOWMAN's arms, the CHILDREN trapped a few SNOWFLAKES after a merry game of tag and plopped these on their sleds. They then dragged the captives across the good, hardwood floor of the stage!

Props

A kitchen broom painted in vivid colors for the MAGIC BROOM; three big books for the NARRATOR; two guns for DOODLEBUG.

Sound

Appropriate music accompanies the movements of the BIRDS and the SNOWFLAKES.

If possible, herald the SNOWMAN's entrances with offstage, crashing noises. Experiment with newspaper, crumpling and rustling it with your feet. Or borrow a recorded sound effect.

Frosty the Snowman was the song used in the production.

Freeing Exercises

Ask *all* the children to perform a series of activities with which they are familiar—first as they themselves would do these, then as the characters in the play would. Precede these exercises by a thorough discussion of the ways in which activities are affected by age, sex, physical ailment, etc.

For the OLD WOMAN: "You wake up in the morning and get out of bed. You wash and dress yourself. You hang up your night clothes and make the bed. You sweep the floor. You weed the garden."

For the SNOWMAN, tape yardsticks to the legs of the players and tie arms to body, then ask them to walk, sit, bend and run. Encase their feet in oversize shoes or galoshes to bring out additional clumsiness. Later, remove yardsticks, cord and oversized shoes and ask the players to repeat the previous, stiff movements.

For the BIRDS and SNOWFLAKES, play appropriate music to stir the children into rhythmic patterns of their own creation. With the music for background, stimulate imaginations still more by telling them of the tiny tree bud that blossoms into a leaf and how, once grown, it insists on leaving its Mother Tree to look at the big, big world. This it does during the very first rainstorm even though Mother Tree begs it to stay within the warm safety of her leafy arms.

The sun and the soft breezes which follow the first rain excite the baby leaf and it soars into the air high above the houses and the lakes and the church spires and the mountains, its young delight growing with every gentle rise and fall of the wind. Until one day—the sky darkens, the clouds puff over their edges, the wind cuts cruelly and the baby leaf, wet and cold and frightened, soars and tumbles, twirls and stumbles faster and faster with each wild whistling of the wind. And the rain, no longer friendly, warm no longer, beats hard upon the shivering leaf until it drives it down, down, down into the wet, slippery mud. Down—down—down—.

WHERE THE SEA BREAKS

A NONSENSE FANTASY IN PROLOGUE AND ONE ACT

Playing Time   15 minutes approximately

Age   5—10 years

Manner of Presentation   Narrate with improvisation
or
Narrate, improvise and memorize
or
Memorize

Staging Suggestions   See end of play

Cast   The Narrator
The Old Woman (who lived in a shoe)

The Old Man (her husband)
Their Quarreling Children (among them Mary, Humpty Dumpty, Simple Simon, and Miss Muffet)
Neptune (an easily irritated monarch)
His Minister (a timid, stuttering creature)
His Mermaids (among them Silver Tail, Pearly Fins, and Coral Eyes)

Time   Once upon a time

Place   The sea

Scene   This is an unusual spot where one can see both the surface and the bottom of the ocean at the same time. A houseboat bobs gently, upstage right. The bottom of the sea, downstage left, is occupied by Neptune and his Court.

While the curtain is still closed, the NARRATOR, *in beach attire, runs onto apron right. He glances over his shoulder as though he were escaping from something unpleasant. He is! The sea breakers which caught him resting at the water's edge are now lapping at his heels.*

NARRATOR: These pesky waves! (*He brushes imaginary sand off his legs.*) They're always dashing up and wetting you when you least expect it. (*He addresses the audience.*) Haven't you noticed that? There I was lying on the sand at the water's edge—(*he points off right*)—feeling the sun hot on my face, when suddenly—(*he grimaces*)—all that salt water rushes into my mouth! It's always like that at the seashore. No rest from these waves, never! Not even on the calmest of days when there isn't a sign of a cloud or a bit of a breeze anywhere. Not even today! Have you ever wondered why it's so? I mean, why we always have sea breakers, rain or shine? *I* have. In fact, last week I went to the Marine Library down here at the beach and tried to read up on it. And what do you suppose I found in the encyclopedia? It's the craziest story you ever heard! I don't know yet whether to believe it or not!

The story tells of the Old Woman who lived in a shoe. You remember the Mother Goose rhyme, "There was an Old Woman who . . . (*he gestures to the audience to recite it with him*)—lived in a shoe. She had so many Children she didn't know what to do. So she gave them some broth without any bread, and whipped them all soundly and sent them to bed." Now you listen to this and see what you think.

As time went by, so the encyclopedia said, the Old Woman and her husband, the Old Man, continued to have more and more Children, so many in fact, that a shoe couldn't hold them any more and they had to find another place to live. . . .

(*The* OLD WOMAN *enters, left, weeping into her apron.*)

OLD WOMAN: Oh, what are we going to do? What are we going to do?

OLD MAN (*hurrying in after her*):   What's the matter, Wife? Why are you crying so hard?

OLD WOMAN: We have so many children—Mary and her lamb, and Simple Simon and Humpty Dumpty and darling Miss Muffet and . . . oh—oh—oh—

(*She weeps harder than ever.*)

OLD MAN: Will you *please* stop this foolish weeping and tell me what's wrong?

OLD WOMAN: Where are we going to put them all? Every nook and cranny is filled. You're their father. You've got to find them a new home.

OLD MAN: All right, all right! I'll find them a home. (*He thinks a moment as the* OLD WOMAN *wails.*) Stop crying! Now, you remember Captain Hook, the pirate, don't you?

OLD WOMAN: That monster!

OLD MAN: Well, I heard from reliable sources that Hook has been captured by Peter Pan and clapped into jail.

OLD WOMAN: What has that got to do with us? (*She wails.*) Oh, my poor, homeless children!

OLD MAN (*losing all patience*):   Stop crying! You'll fill the shoe with your tears and drown us all! Now listen. Since Captain Hook is in jail, his boat is up for sale, isn't it? Well—

OLD WOMAN: You mean—?

OLD MAN: Exactly! We will buy his boat.

OLD WOMAN (*rushing off, left*):   Mary, Humpty, Muffet, Simon, Children! Start packing right away! Your Father is buying us a beautiful new home. Mary, Humpty, Children—

OLD MAN (*moving off, right*):   While you pack, I'll go buy the boat. (*He counts his money.*) Ten dollars—twenty dollars—fifty—ninety—a hundred dollars—

NARRATOR: That was how the Old Woman and her husband, the Old Man, and all their Children came to live in a boat on the sea.

(*Now the curtain opens slowly revealing a houseboat bobbing gently on a blue-green sea. The houseboat, upstage right, is filled with the* OLD WOMAN'S CHILDREN. *They are standing and sitting in the boat. On the ground, downstage left, their heads buried in their laps, sit* NEPTUNE, *his* MINISTER *on his left, his* COURT *of* MERMAIDS *spread out behind him. They are sleeping.*)

NARRATOR: Now, in those days, there were no such things as sea breakers. The sea was always as smooth as a pane of glass. And quiet. That is, until the Children came along. And then everything changed! All day and night, the Children cried and screamed and fought among themselves. Listen—

MARY: It's my turn to steer the boat, Humpty.

HUMPTY DUMPTY: Aw, go chase your little lamb.

MISS MUFFET: Wait a minute. Mary and you had turns yesterday while I was eating my curds and whey. It's my turn now.

SIMPLE SIMON: No, it's mine, Muffet. But if you give me your curds, I'll let you steer.

(*The* CHILDREN *scream and push each other.*)

MISS MUFFET: Mama, Simon wants to eat my curds!

MARY: Get away, Humpty, or I'll push you off the wall!

HUMPTY DUMPTY: I'll tell Mama on you. Mama! Mama! Mary is pushing me off the—

OLD WOMAN (*hurrying onto boat from right*): What's the matter, children?

OLD MAN (*following her*): Oh, a man can't get any rest in his own family.

HUMPTY DUMPTY: Mary won't let me steer.

MISS MUFFET: Mary and Humpty had their turns. It's my turn now.

HUMPTY DUMPTY: Be quiet, Muffet, or I'll put a spider down your back.

(MISS MUFFET *wails.*)

SIMPLE SIMON: Mama, I'm hungry. Can't I have a piece of pie now?

OLD WOMAN: Stop screaming! Simon—Muffet—Children!

OLD MAN: Stop! Or I'll whip you all soundly—

OLD WOMAN: And send you to bed!

(*The* CHILDREN *continue their fight in pantomime as the* NARRATOR *speaks.*)

NARRATOR: The screaming was so loud that the noise reached down to the bottom of the sea, all the way down to the very Court of Neptune himself. Neptune, as you know, is the King of the Sea, and he and his Minister and his Mermaid Attendants were trying to get some sleep after a whole month of Spring cleaning the bottom of the ocean. The noise awakens them.

NEPTUNE (*an easily irritated monarch given to roaring and shaking his fists*): What's that racket? I can't get any sleep!

MINISTER (*a timid creature who stutters when he's scared*):   I d-d-don't hear anything, Your Majesty.

NEPTUNE: WHAT!

MINISTER: I m-m-mean, I hear it now. It's the Mermaids, c-c-combing their hair.

SILVER TAIL (*a sleepy mermaid who yawns all the time*):   We're not combing our hair, Your Majesty.

NEPTUNE: NO!?

MINISTER: It's the f-f-fishes, Sire, working on their scales.

PEARLY FINS (*a mermaid who sings her words*):   Oh no, Your Majesty. The fish are away at school. It's test time now.

NEPTUNE: SCHOOL!?

MINISTER: Remember y-y-your blood pressure, Sire. The doctor said you had to be c-c-calm.

NEPTUNE (*shaking his fists*):   CALM!?

CORAL EYES (*a mermaid given to sneezing*):   It's those children, Sire, who've come to live on the sea.

SILVER TAIL: They used to live in a shoe.

PEARLY FINS: But then they moved to Captain Hook's houseboat.

CORAL EYES: And now they're always quarreling about who should steer the boat.

NEPTUNE: So *they* are making the racket, eh? I've got to stop them. But how? Now let me think.

(*As* NEPTUNE *thinks, the* CHILDREN *become audible again.*)

MARY: Mama, Humpty took my fishing rod.

HUMPTY DUMPTY: Muffet did, to stir her curds!

MISS MUFFET: That's a fib! Simon used it to spear a cherry pie.

SIMPLE SIMON: I did not! Mary's lamb was playing with it and broke it in two.

(*The* PARENTS' *scolding and the* CHILDREN'S *whimpering subside into pantomime as* NEPTUNE *talks.*)

NEPTUNE: I've got it! (*He calls.*) Silver Tail—Silver Tail!

SILVER TAIL (*yawning*):   Yes, Sire, I'm coming—I'm coming.

NEPTUNE (*holding his voice down*):   Silver Tail, you swim over to the boat and ask the Old Woman and her Children to stop their racket. Tell them nicely—tell them—(*roaring*)—I WANT TO SLEEP!

MINISTER: Didn't y-y-you hear what Neptune said, sleepyhead? Hurry!

  (SILVER TAIL *"swims" over to the boat, to accompanying music.*)

SILVER TAIL (*addressing the* CHILDREN *politely*):   Neptune, King of the Sea, requests that you stop quarreling, if you please, so he can go to sleep.

MARY (*rudely*):   Neptune? Who is he?

HUMPTY DUMPTY: Never heard of the baby.

MISS MUFFET: Some nasty, old spider, I guess.

SIMPLE SIMON: Can he make pies?

SILVER TAIL: Neptune can do anything he likes.

MARY: He can? Then tell him he can let us alone.

  (*She pulls* SILVER TAIL's *hair.* SILVER TAIL *starts to cry.*)

HUMPTY DUMPTY: Tell him to go row his boat!

  (*He pulls* SILVER TAIL's *hair.*)

MISS MUFFET (*pulling hair*):   Tell him—

SIMPLE SIMON (*pulling hair*):   We'll make as much noise as we want!

CHILDREN: And if he doesn't like it, let him try and stop us!

  (*Crying,* SILVER TAIL *swims back to the* COURT *as the* CHILDREN *resume their quarreling in pantomime.*)

SILVER TAIL (*to* NEPTUNE):   I gave them your message, Sire. But they laughed at you and pulled my hair.

NEPTUNE: WHAT!?

MINISTER: I'm s-s-sure they didn't mean that, Sire. Silver Tail made a m-m-mistake.

SILVER TAIL: I didn't. They laughed at you and pulled my—

NEPTUNE: THEY LAUGHED AT ME!?

MINISTER: Sire, your b-b-blood pressure.

NEPTUNE (*calling*):   PEARLY FINS! WHERE'S PEARLY FINS?

PEARLY FINS (*always singing*):   Here, Sire, waiting—waiting.

NEPTUNE (*controlling himself*):   You swim over and tell them to stop their yelling. If they won't, tell them that I, Neptune, will set the waves rolling and make them seasick. Tell them—(*roaring*)—I WANT TO SLEEP!

MINISTER: Stop that s-s-silly singing now and hurry.

  (PEARLY FINS *"swims" over to the boat, to accompanying music.*)

PEARLY FINS (*addressing the* CHILDREN *politely*):   Neptune, King of the Sea, requests that you stop quarreling. If you don't, he will set the waves rolling and make you seasick.

MARY (*rudely*):   Neptune? Who is he?

HUMPTY DUMPTY: Never heard of the baby.

MISS MUFFET: Some nasty, old spider, I guess.

SIMPLE SIMON: Can he make pies?

PEARLY FINS: Neptune can do anything he likes.

MARY: He can? Then tell him he can let us alone.

(*She pulls* PEARLY FINS' *hair.* PEARLY FINS *starts to cry.*)

HUMPTY DUMPTY: Tell him to go row his boat!

(*He pulls* PEARLY FINS' *hair.*)

MISS MUFFET (*pulling hair*):   Tell him—

SIMPLE SIMON (*pulling hair*):   We'll make as much noise as we want!

CHILDREN: And if he doesn't like it, let him try and stop us!

(*Crying,* PEARLY FINS *swims back to the* COURT *as the* CHILDREN *resume their quarreling in pantomime.*)

PEARLY FINS: I gave them your message, Sire. But they laughed at you and pulled my hair.

NEPTUNE: HOW DARE THEY! HOW-HOW-HOW DARE THEY! I'LL—I'LL—

MINISTER: S-s-sing, Pearly Fins, and m-m-make His Majesty relax.

(PEARLY FINS *sings amid her tears as she rejoins the* MERMAIDS.)

NEPTUNE: HOW DARE THEY! H-HOW-HOW-HOW DARE THEY! (*Controlling himself.*) Well, I'll show them! (*To his* COURT) All of you. When I say "Blow," blow! Now, get ready—set—BLOW!

(*The whole* COURT *blows in unison, the boat rocks, the* CHILDREN *begin to feel seasick.*)

NARRATOR: They blow—and blow—and blow until the waves begin to roll and the boat begins to rock. And it isn't long before the Children turn green from seasickness. Not liking this one bit, they shout to Neptune that they will be good.

OLD WOMAN: Forgive them, Your Majesty, they're only children.

OLD MAN: Brats—(*corrects himself*)—children, dear, little, darling children.

MARY: We'll be good. We won't fight any more. I promise.

HUMPTY DUMPTY: May I fall off the wall if we do.

MISS MUFFET: You may take my curds away.

SIMPLE SIMON: And my cherry pie.

CHILDREN: We'll be good—we'll be good—

NEPTUNE (*gesturing to his* COURT *to stop blowing*): Listen. (*There is no sound anywhere.*) Quiet, at last! Now I can settle down to a nice, long nap.
  (NEPTUNE *and his* COURT *bury their heads in their arms and go to sleep.*)

NARRATOR: No sooner are Neptune and his Court asleep when the naughty Children, their seasickness forgotten, start to fight and yell all over again. (*The* CHILDREN *quarrel as before.*) Neptune wakes up with a start. This is the last straw! Roaring with rage, he summons a third Mermaid.

NEPTUNE: AGAIN!

MINISTER: I d-d-don't hear a thing, Sire. Oh, a b-b-bit of a squeal, maybe.

NEPTUNE: CORAL EYES! (*Sneezing,* CORAL EYES *swims over to* NEPTUNE.) STOP THAT SNEEZING!

CORAL EYES: I have a bad cold, Your Majesty. I caught it washing the sea shells.

NEPTUNE: I DON'T CARE WHERE YOU CAUGHT IT! (*Controlling himself.*) Now, swim over to that noisy group and tell them to stop fighting. Tell them if they won't stop this time, I'll wreck their boat! Tell them— (*roaring*)—I WANT TO SLEEP!
  (*Still sneezing,* CORAL EYES *swims over to the boat, to accompanying music.*)

CORAL EYES (*addressing the* CHILDREN *politely*): Neptune, King of the Sea, requests that you stop quarreling. If you don't, he'll wreck the boat!

OLD WOMAN: Wreck the boat!

OLD MAN: The good fairy preserve us! Now will you be quiet?

MARY (*rudely, as before*): Neptune? Who is he?
  (*She pulls* CORAL EYES' *hair.* CORAL EYES *starts to cry.*)

HUMPTY DUMPTY: Never heard of the baby.
  (*He pulls hair.*)

MISS MUFFET: Some nasty, old spider, I guess.
  (*She pulls hair. Sneezing and crying,* CORAL EYES *swims back to the* COURT *as the* CHILDREN *laugh.*)

CORAL EYES (*to* NEPTUNE): I gave them your message, Sire, and they laughed at you and—

NEPTUNE: WHAT!? THEY STILL LAUGH! (*To his* COURT.) All of you, when I say "blow," BLOW! Get ready—set—BLOW!—HARD!—HARDER!—HARDER!!—HARDER!!!—
  (*As the* COURT *blows in unison, the boat rocks, the* CHILDREN *groan. This continues for a few moments.*)

SILVER TAIL (*suddenly*): Look! Look at the boat! It's still afloat!

NEPTUNE: BLOW!

PEARLY FINS: I can't blow any more!

NEPTUNE: BLOW!

CORAL EYES: But nothing is happening! The boat's still there!

NARRATOR: Coral Eyes is right! Although the Court blows as hard as it can, although the waves dash furiously against the side of the boat, NOTHING HAPPENS! For this is no ordinary boat, you see. Nor are these boys and girls ordinary children but—a boat and children that live in the pages of Mother Goose and you can't wreck *them*. Mother Goose's people go on living forever! Now Neptune is really in a state! How is he ever going to stop those Children?

NEPTUNE (*spluttering*):   What shall I do? How shall I stop them? How am I going to make my sea quiet again?

MINISTER: Sire, why don't we wish a c-c-case of the hiccups on the Children?

NEPTUNE: WHAT?

MINISTER: If they are busy hiccuping, they c-c-can't quarrel!

SILVER TAIL: You can't do both at one and the same time, can you?

NEPTUNE: I'll try anything! ANYTHING! Ready, Silver Tail? Pearly Fins, ready? Coral Eyes?—All right then. Get ready—set—WISH!

COURT (*rocking in unison*):   I wish—I wish—I wish—
     (*This continues for a few moments.*)

NARRATOR: Suddenly, one Child starts to hiccup—then another—and another—then everyone, even the Old Woman and the Old Man, is hiccuping away. Neptune is all smiles now and, at his signal, the Court and he lie down to sleep. Barely are they asleep when—oh no! The Minister is hiccuping now!—And Silver Tail!—And Pearly Fins!—And Coral Eyes! And —and—and Neptune himself! Neptune himself is hiccuping now! Hiccuping and roaring to beat the band! And since everyone is so busy hiccuping, there is no one left with enough breath to *wish* they could stop!—And so Neptune and his Court and the Children and their Parents are still hiccuping to this very day, to this very moment! And can you guess what all this hiccuping does to the ocean? It sets up a rolling motion in the sea which, in turn, starts the waves moving until they grow into mountainous peaks of force and foam! And that is why, on the nicest and calmest summer days, when there isn't a sign of a cloud in the sky or a bit of a breeze anywhere, you will still find sea breakers slapping and crashing madly against the very edge of the shore. At least, that's what I read, and if you

don't believe me—(*The* NARRATOR *starts to hiccup! Startled, he apologizes*)
—EXCUSE ME! (*He exits hurriedly*

as the curtain closes.)

STAGING SUGGESTIONS

Cast

Increase or decrease the number of MERMAIDS and CHILDREN to fit the needs of your group and stage space.

Cast the more mature players in the roles of the NARRATOR, the OLD WOMAN, the OLD MAN and as leaders of the MERMAIDS and the CHILDREN.

Encourage your boys and girls to create characters other than the MERMAIDS and CHILDREN listed.

Set

The boat may be one-dimensional, its side cut out of cardboard or painted **on** eight feet or more of drawing, wrapping or builder's paper. This, in turn, **may** be tacked onto a wooden frame which is supported at each end either by chairs or by the CHILDREN themselves. The players stand, sit or crouch behind this framework. The CHILDREN at its two ends can rock the boat at will.

The sea may be cut out and painted in bold waves of blue-green. Sea strips of different heights and lengths can then be placed in front and back of the boat with artistic discretion. Drapes of blue-green gauze may suggest the sky, and scattered sea shells and fish cutouts will contribute color. In one production, the group cut out and painted a reclining mermaid and fish of different shapes and colors. These were all attached by thread to a thin wire strung across the stage.

Costumes

The OLD WOMAN, the OLD MAN and their CHILDREN may wear anything the players design, from simple peasant costumes to those suggested by the "Mother Goose" drawings. Do not forget the apron for the OLD WOMAN.

NEPTUNE dresses as befits a sea king. In the production mentioned above, his long robe was made out of a plastic tablecloth to which Christmas glitter had been glued. An aluminum foil crown, necklaces of pearls and sea shells and a silver trident (a cardboard cutout covered with foil) completed his costume.

The MINISTER wore a long rust-colored robe. Since his portrayer saw him as deaf, he used a large sea shell as an ear trumpet.

The MERMAIDS were wrapped in tails cut out of gray, glittering lining. Aluminum foil "scales" were sewn to these tails. Pearls and sea shells gleamed in their loosely-worn hair. One attractive MERMAID pasted glitter to the nails of her fingers and her toes! Long hair, incidentally, may be created out of yarn, string, crêpe paper or veil strips.

The NARRATOR was in modern beach attire.

Music

Music may be played throughout the performance—a sea breaker motif when the NARRATOR talks, a swimming motif for the MERMAIDS, and a rolling motif for the "blowing" episodes.

Props

Stage money for the OLD MAN.

Freeing Exercises

Ask all the children to perform a series of activities with which they are familiar—first as they themselves would do them, then as the characters in the play would. Precede the exercises by a thorough discussion of the ways in which activities are affected by age, sex, physical ailment (Chapter 7).

For the CHILDREN and their PARENTS: "You are a family, consisting of Mother, Father and several children, and you all live in a house with one bathroom. One morning the alarm clock fails to ring. All of you wake up about the same time and make a wild dash for the bathroom. Result—turmoil and tears."

To bring on an understanding of seasickness, ask the players to work freely on this: "One day, you are lucky enough to find a five-dollar bill on the street. You pick it up and run to the corner candy shop where you gorge yourself on the sweetest, stickiest goo you can find. You then manage to eat some double ice-cream pops, a jelly apple or two, some of that pink, sugar-spun cotton and drink a bottle of soda pop to wash it all down. Only it doesn't stay down! Then, when Grandpa comes along and insists on buying you those licorice sticks you adore, well—"

For NEPTUNE's reactions: "Mother must go out shopping and tells unwilling you to mind Wee Brother, a bit of mischief if ever there is one. No sooner does the front door close on Mother than Wee Brother starts right in living up to his reputation. He teases, he whines, he messes up your belongings, he crayons over your library book and ends by breaking your favorite record. Your anger builds and builds until finally you let go and—"

Extend this exercise to work on Wee Brother's reaction to the explosive rage. How would he react if he were a timid soul like the MINISTER?

DREAM NO MORE, MY DARLING

A DREAM PLAY

Playing Time   10 minutes approximately

Age   5—9 years

Manner of Presentation   Narrate with improvisation
or
Narrate, improvise and memorize
or
Memorize lines with or without Narrator

Staging Suggestions   See end of play

Cast   The Narrator
Mother
Amy (an eight-year-old who is afraid to sleep)

The Bad Dreams (among them Scalpface the Indian, Bobby the Bandit, and Rocky the Robot)

Time The present: bedtime

Place A bedroom

Scene A young girl's bedroom. Its important pieces of furniture are a bed, left, an armchair, downstage right, and a table with lamp, upstage center.

A screen stands behind the armchair. The entrance into the room is upstage, to the left of the table.

While the curtain is still closed, a clock is heard striking the hour offstage— one—two—three—four—until eight is reached. On the fourth chime, the NAR-RATOR *appears on apron left. He counts the chimes as he looks at his watch.*

NARRATOR: —five—six—seven—eight. Eight. Right on the button. Eight o'clock on the night of—(*current month, day and year*)—tonight, this time, now. Now and—(*he looks at audience*)—time for John and Wendy and Peter and all of you to put down your comics and tear yourselves away from the television and—

MOTHER'S VOICE (*heard from behind the curtain*): Amy, it's eight o'clock, dear. Why don't you do what I told you? Turn off the television—

NARRATOR (*to audience*): Shhh—listen.

AMY'S VOICE (*heard from behind the curtain*): Yes, Mom, in a minute.

MOTHER'S VOICE: Amy, I've called you three times. It's time for bed. Turn off that horror movie!

NARRATOR (*to audience*): Sounds familiar, doesn't it?

AMY'S VOICE: But, Mom, I'm right in the middle!

MOTHER'S VOICE: Turn it off! I've told you that again and again! You know I don't like you to look at such trash!

AMY'S VOICE: It isn't trash! It's wonderful! It's about Bobby the Bandit and his pal, Scalpface the Indian, and they're just tying the Sheriff to the railroad tracks and . . .

NARRATOR (*to audience*): The same old argument, too—

MOTHER'S VOICE: The railroad—I've heard enough!

AMY'S VOICE: Don't turn it off, please, please! It's the most exciting part!

MOTHER'S VOICE: No wonder you have bad dreams every night!

AMY'S VOICE: I don't have bad dreams. I—

MOTHER'S VOICE: Never mind what you have. Get ready for bed.

AMY'S VOICE: But—

MOTHER'S VOICE: GET READY FOR BED!

NARRATOR (*to audience*):   Practically the same words. You hear them all the time at my house. Mother says the horror movies and comics give Brother nightmares and Brother keeps crying that they don't. Yet when it comes to bedtime, he doesn't want to go to sleep. He's scared although he won't admit it. I wonder if Amy's scared too. What do you think?—Tell you what. If we keep very quiet, I can creep up to Amy's bedroom window and peek in and tell you what's happening. Shall I?—All right then, but remember—SHHHHHHHHHHHHHHHHHHH. . . .

> (*The* NARRATOR *tiptoes to the center of the curtain. He picks up its right edge and holding it, crosses to apron right as the curtain opens.* AMY's *bedroom is revealed. It is empty except for the* BAD DREAMS *huddled in their capes behind the screen. They are invisible to the audience.*)

AMY (*enters. She is dressed for bed. Arguing*):   But I'm not sleepy, that's all.

> (MOTHER *enters as* AMY *climbs into her bed.*)

MOTHER: You will be once you get under the blankets. (*She tucks her in and kisses her.*) Now dream no more, my darling.

> (*She turns to leave.*)

AMY (*sitting up in bed, scared*):   I forgot to brush my teeth.

MOTHER (*tucking her in again*):   You brushed them.

> (*She turns to leave.*)

AMY (*sitting up*):   I want some water. I'm thirsty.

MOTHER (*tucking her in*):   You've had enough water to float a battleship. Lie down.

> (*She turns to leave.*)

AMY (*sitting up*):   My foot hurts—

MOTHER (*tucking her in*):   Lie down! Oh, if you'd only listen to me and give up those horror movies and comics. Then you wouldn't be afraid to go to sleep. Those silly things give you bad dreams. (*She kisses* AMY.) Well, good night, darling, and sleep well. I'll be in the next room reading in case you want me.

> (*She is about to turn off the lamp.*)

AMY: Mom, leave a small light on. I don't like it when it's dark.

MOTHER: All right, a small light.

    (*She adjusts the lamp and leaves.*)

NARRATOR: No sooner has Mother gone out of the room, than Amy sits up and looks about her fearfully. She is sure there are strange, black shapes creeping out of the corner of her room, behind her cozy armchair—(*The* BAD DREAMS *crawl out slowly.*)—clumsy, crawling creatures with bloodshot eyes. She can even hear them whispering among themselves.

BAD DREAM 1:   Is she asleep?

BAD DREAM 2:   No, but she will be.

BAD DREAM 3:   What'll we Bad Dreams do to her tonight?

BAD DREAM 4:   Let's do something awful, something new. Think.

BAD DREAMS (*they huddle and whisper even during* NARRATOR's *words*): Think—think—think—think—think—

NARRATOR: They are Amy's Bad Dreams. They have been haunting her for a long, long time and tonight they are trying to think of an especially bad nightmare with which to frighten her.

BAD DREAM 1:   Let's take all her candy and hide it.

BAD DREAM 2:   No. We've been doing that for years.

BAD DREAM 3:   Let's put pepper in her food.

BAD DREAM 4:   No—no. Think—think—think—think—

NARRATOR: It's not easy to be a Bad Dream. It's very hard to think of something that will scare boys and girls today.

BAD DREAM 1:   Let's put her on an island—

BAD DREAMS: No.

BAD DREAM 2:   Let's put a pumpkin on her nose—

BAD DREAMS: No.

BAD DREAM 3:   Let's change her into a mean, old witch—

BAD DREAMS: No—no—no. THINK—THINK—THINK—

BAD DREAM 1 (*raising his voice in excitement*):   I got it! I got it!

BAD DREAMS: SHHHHHHHHHHHHHHHHHHH! (*Whispering.*) What is it?

BAD DREAM 1:   As soon as she's asleep, we'll creep onto her bed and grab her and scalp her just like—

BAD DREAM 2:   —Scalpface the Indian did in the movie she watched tonight!

BAD DREAMS (*in excitement*):   WHAT FUN! WHAT FUN! WHAT— SHHHHHHHHHHHHHHHHHHHHHHHHHH!

    (*The* BAD DREAMS *inch toward the bed.*)

AMY (*sitting up quickly*): I'm not asleep!

BAD DREAM 1: Hey, that's not fair. You're supposed to be sleeping. Lie down!

AMY: I won't!

BAD DREAM 2: How'll we haunt you then? Lie down!

AMY: I won't and you can't make me!

BAD DREAMS (*inching nearer*): We'll make you—we'll make you—we'll—

AMY: MOMMY! MOMMY! MOMMY!

MOTHER'S VOICE: Here I am, darling, in my room. Do you need me?

AMY: Mommy, they're coming nearer! My Bad Dreams! They're going to scalp me! Help me!

MOTHER'S VOICE: I'm coming. Oh, I can't open your door! It's blocked! Your crime comics are blocking the door!

AMY: Help me!

MOTHER'S VOICE: Push the Dreams away!

AMY: I can't! They'll hurt me!

MOTHER'S VOICE: They can't—they're just silly ideas that the movie put in your head tonight. They're not real—they're just air! Push them away!

NARRATOR: Now, as Amy cries for help, one Bad Dream starts climbing over the edge of her bed. It is Scalpface the Indian, his knife in his hand.
(*Discarding his cape,* SCALPFACE *crawls toward* AMY.)

SCALPFACE: I'll cut off your hair—I'll cut off your hair—I'll—(*He yells as he scratches himself on the bed.*) Ouch! I've scratched myself on the bed post! (*He cries like a baby.*) Oh, my knee, oh! It's bleeding! It hurts! It hurts—Oh—oh—oh—

AMY (*calming him*): It's only a tiny scratch.

SCALPFACE: Scratch! That's what you say! Oh—oh—oh—
(*He weeps as he crawls back to the* BAD DREAMS.)

AMY (*not believing her ears*): You're afraid of a little scratch? You can't be! You scalp cowboys all the time! I've seen you on TV.

NARRATOR: Now, another Bad Dream moves forward—Bobby the Bandit.
(*Discarding his cape,* BOBBY *runs toward the bed, brandishing a gun with one hand and twirling a lasso with the other hand.*)

BOBBY (*shouting*): I'm Bobby the Bandit and I'll shoot you! I'll—
(*He tries to shoot.*)

AMY: MOMMY! MOMMY! BOBBY THE BANDIT IS SHOOTING—

MOTHER'S VOICE: Push him away! Push him away!

BOBBY: I'll shoot you! I'll—(*Unable to work the gun, he flings it from him.*)
Aw heck, I'll never learn to work this gun! I hate the stupid thing!

AMY: You can't shoot a gun? But Bobby the Bandit can hit a sheriff at a thousand paces! I've seen you do it—in the comics—

BOBBY (*returning to the* BAD DREAMS): Heck, that's only make-believe!

NARRATOR: The Bad Dreams try once more. They send out Rocky the Robot, huge, heavy, powerful.

(*Discarding his cape,* ROCKY *strides forward, roaring.*)

ROCKY: Where are you? I'll tickle you till you cry! I'll tickle you till—

AMY (*screaming*): MOMMY! THE ROBOT IS HERE! HE'LL TICKLE ME! HE'LL—

MOTHER'S VOICE: Push him away! Push him away! Push him—

(*Frightened,* AMY *flings out her arms blindly and pushes* ROCKY *who falls to his knees.*)

ROCKY (*wailing*): Don't hurt me! Please don't hurt me! I couldn't bear it!

AMY: *I* hurt Rocky the Robot who crushes rocks with his bare hands?

ROCKY: But it isn't true! I couldn't crush a leaf! That's only what the comics say.

(*He returns to the* BAD DREAMS.)

AMY: "The comics say?" Then it isn't true? None of it is true? You're a cry-baby and Bobby the Bandit hates guns and Scalpface the Indian is afraid of a tiny scratch and—and—MY MOTHER'S RIGHT! She said you were all just plain silly!

(*At this,* AMY *jumps out of bed and runs toward the* BAD DREAMS, *swinging her arms. The* BAD DREAMS *scamper back to their hiding place.*)

AMY: That's what you are! SILLY! And I'm never going to believe in you anymore or watch you either! Or even read about you! Go away, you silly things! GO AWAY! GO AWAY!

(*When the* BAD DREAMS *vanish,* AMY *climbs back into her bed and falls into a restless sleep.* MOTHER *hurries in.*)

MOTHER: Amy, are you all right? I heard you moaning.

AMY (*sitting up, dazed*): Where are they? Where did they go? I thought they were—

MOTHER: Who?

AMY: The Robot and Scalpface and— Oh. They must have been part of a dream I just had—a bad dream.

MOTHER: Again? Amy, I told you not to look at that crime movie tonight.

AMY: You won't have to tell me anymore, Mommy. I'm not going to look any more, I promise. I'm not going to look at the horror movies or—(*she starts to yawn*)—the crime programs—(*she is getting sleepier*)—or at the silly—silly—comics.

(*She is almost asleep.* MOTHER *tucks her in for the last time.*)

MOTHER (*kissing* AMY):   Dream no more, my darling.

(*She starts to tiptoe out.*)

AMY: And, Mommy, you can turn off the lamp now—I'm not—afraid—any more—I'm not—any—

(*She falls asleep. Smiling,* MOTHER *turns off the lamp and exits softly.*)

NARRATOR (*he talks as he moves toward the center and the curtain closes*): And you know something? I'm sure Amy is going to keep that promise too. Who wants to be bothered by bad dreams when there are lovely, lovely dreams just waiting to come and visit you. That is, they will visit you if you let them come through to you. And this you can do by promising never, never, NEVER to look at horror movies and crime comics again. Promise?

STAGING SUGGESTIONS

Comments

You may be interested to know that the horrors which the BAD DREAMS thought of were improvised by the players themselves. In this way, the play served as a legitimate outlet for the children's tensions and fears!

Cast

Increase or decrease the number of BAD DREAMS to fit the needs of your group and stage space.

Encourage your boys and girls to create characters other than SCALPFACE, BOBBY THE BANDIT and ROCKY THE ROBOT.

The sex of the characters may be easily changed—AMY and MOTHER may turn into JACKIE and FATHER for instance.

Cast the more mature players in the roles of the NARRATOR, MOTHER, AMY and the leader of the BAD DREAMS.

Set

A few pieces of furniture—the bed, table, lamp, armchair and screen—are sufficient to suggest the background. The bed can be improvised with orange crates or chairs. The main function of the screen is to serve as a hiding-place for the BAD DREAMS.

Costumes

The NARRATOR, MOTHER and AMY wear present-day dress.

The BAD DREAMS are dressed according to their individual characterizations —SCALPFACE wears an Indian costume, BOBBY a cowboy outfit with bandana mask. ROCKY's attire can be made out of two cartons—a large one for his body, painted red, black and silver and resting on his shoulders, a smaller carton for his head, similarly painted, with holes cut out for eyes, nose and mouth. All the DREAMS wear masks on their faces, dark leotards or long pajamas. They cover themselves with dark capes made out of crêpe paper or sheets. These capes are cast off when the DREAMS emerge as specific characters.

Props

A watch for the NARRATOR; a knife for SCALPFACE; a gun and lasso for BOBBY THE BANDIT.

Sound

The chiming of the clock may be reproduced by a commercial record or by striking a triangle. Play appropriate music to accompany the movements of the BAD DREAMS.

Lights

If your stage has the electrical equipment to "build and dim" light, bring down the bedroom light to a dream-like effect when AMY falls asleep. Throw a special green spot on the BAD DREAMS when they come into view. Black out the light when all the DREAMS vanish and AMY returns to her bed. Then bring the light up again as MOTHER enters for the last time.

ROBIN HOOD

A SHORT ADAPTATION IN TWO ACTS*

Playing Time   15 minutes approximately

Age   7–10 years

Manner of Presentation   Improvise lines
or
Memorize lines

Staging Suggestions   See end of play

Cast   Robin Hood
Little John

* The author acknowledges her indebtedness for several incidents used in this script to the formal, three-act play, *Robin Hood*, by James Norris, published 1952, by the Children's Theatre Press of Anchorage, Kentucky.

Will Scarlet
Friar Tuck
The Sheriff of Nottingham
Sir Guy of Gisborne
The Sheriff's Henchmen
A Trumpeter
An Archer
King Richard
A Companion to King Richard
People at Nottingham Fair

Time   In the days of King Richard, the Lion-hearted

Place   England

Scenes

ACT ONE   A clearing in Sherwood Forest
ACT TWO   A corner of the Nottingham Fair

ACT ONE

Scene   The clearing in Sherwood Forest is dotted with bushes, right, trees, upstage center, and a boulder, downstage left. *Robin Hood* and his men hide behind these objects when occasion demands.

Entrances to the clearing are upstage and downstage right, upstage and downstage left, and back center.

When the curtain opens, the clearing is empty. ROBIN HOOD *hurries in from downstage left, looking behind him. Finding no sign of life, he whistles three times.*

ROBIN HOOD (*whispering*):   Come out, my lads. It's Robin Hood. (LITTLE JOHN, *a big, broad-shouldered man, creeps out from the forest, back center.*) It's all right, Little John. No one's about.

LITTLE JOHN: Did you find the Sheriff and Sir Guy?

ROBIN HOOD: They're heading this way with four Henchmen. They'll be here any minute. Where's Friar Tuck? (WILL SCARLET *creeps out, upstage right.*) Will, did you see Friar Tuck?

WILL: He's behind a tree, no doubt—sleeping.
(*The three men search through the clearing until they discover the fat* FRIAR *asleep, downstage right. He is snoring peacefully. They remove the branches that cover him.*)

ROBIN HOOD: Just look at the old bear. Shh! Don't wake him yet.
(*He finds a branch and tickles the* FRIAR's *nose with it. The* FRIAR *reacts then turns on his side and snores some more.* LITTLE JOHN *removes the* FRIAR's *sandal and* ROBIN HOOD *tickles the sleeping man's foot.* FRIAR TUCK *wakes up roaring and ready to fight. The others laugh.*)

ROBIN HOOD (*bowing with exaggeration*):   I hope you slept well, good friend.

FRIAR TUCK: Slept! I never sleep! I was lying here—thinking.

LITTLE JOHN: Well, you'd better stop thinking. The Sheriff of Nottingham and Sir Guy of Gisborne are riding here to hang us.

WILL (*homesick*):   I wish we were home again. I wish we weren't outlaws.

ROBIN HOOD: So do we all, my good Will. But you know why we're called outlaws and forced to live like this in Sherwood Forest.

LITTLE JOHN: Aye, that we know. The thieving Sheriff took our lands for taxes, stole our very homes and, when we protested, he tried to hang us.
(*He clenches his fist in rage.*)

ROBIN HOOD: Courage, lads. Good King Richard is our friend. When he returns to England, he'll make short shrift of the Sheriff. He'll give us back our homes.

FRIAR TUCK: In Nottingham 'tis said the King is back. But no one knows for certain.

ROBIN HOOD (*holding up his hand to quiet them*):   Listen! The Sheriff! Hide, all of you! Quick!
(ROBIN HOOD *hides, upstage left,* LITTLE JOHN *and* WILL, *back center,* FRIAR TUCK, *upstage right. The* SHERIFF *and* SIR GUY *enter, downstage left. The* SHERIFF, *a mouse of a man, looks about him anxiously.* SIR GUY, *a tall bully, pushes forward. Four* HENCHMEN, *bows drawn, follow them into the clearing, treading fearfully.*)

SHERIFF: This must be Robin Hood's hiding place. Can you see trace of him, Sir Guy?

SIR GUY: Not yet, Sheriff, but when I do, I'll—

(*He makes a plunging movement with his sword.*)

SHERIFF (*trembling*):   What if he sees you first! N-n-no! Never mind answering! (*He calls out to his* HENCHMEN *without looking at them.*) Men! Spread out there! Search behind every tree, under every bush! Don't be afraid. Your Sheriff's here. (*He quivers.*)

(*Unnoticed,* ROBIN HOOD *sneaks out of his hiding place. He hits the end* HENCHMAN *with his stave and drags him offstage as the* SHERIFF *and his party inch slowly from left to right.*)

SIR GUY: You're not afraid of this outlaw?

SHERIFF: I? Afraid? I should say not!

(LITTLE JOHN *creeps forward, hits another* HENCHMAN *and drags him offstage. The* HENCHMAN'S *groan causes the* SHERIFF *to start.*)

SHERIFF (*still without looking at his men*):   Here, fellows, don't spread out so far. Keep closer to me. (*He addresses* SIR GUY.) As I was saying—(FRIAR TUCK *and* WILL *creep out, hit and make off with the remaining* HENCHMEN.) I'm not afraid of any outlaw, though he be as strong and shrewd as Robin Hood. (*The* HENCHMEN'S *groans startle him.*) What was that?

SIR GUY: I didn't hear anything.

SHERIFF: I thought I—well, never mind. As I was saying, let Robin Hood show his face before me and I'll—

(*He tries to imitate* SIR GUY'S *sword movement and trips over his robe.* ROBIN HOOD *emerges from the forest and watches him, laughing.*)

SIR GUY: I said that.

SHERIFF: *I* did.

SIR GUY: You didn't. *I* did.

SHERIFF (*stamping his foot like an enraged child*):   You didn't! I did! I did!

ROBIN HOOD: Masters—Masters—

(*The* SHERIFF *and* SIR GUY *ignore the interruption which they assume comes from a* HENCHMAN.)

SIR GUY (*drawing his sword*):   I did! And I'll prove it to you!

ROBIN HOOD: Masters, no fighting, please.

SHERIFF (*without looking at* ROBIN HOOD):   Keep quiet, you!

SIR GUY (*to the* SHERIFF):   Draw your sword!

SHERIFF (*tangling in his robes*):   In just a minute—

ROBIN HOOD: Please, Masters, it isn't seemly.

SHERIFF: I thought I ordered you to keep—(*Turning around, he sees* ROBIN HOOD. *He drops his sword.*) Robin Hood!

SIR GUY (*running in the wrong direction*):   Robin—! Where?—Where?

SHERIFF: Here, you fool! (*He calls to his nonexistent* HENCHMEN.) Men, grab him!—Ah, Robin Hood! I've got you at last!

(ROBIN HOOD's *men emerge from their hiding places, bows drawn.*)

ROBIN HOOD (*pretending fear*):   Oh Sheriff, mercy!

SHERIFF: Come on, men. Pin his arms back. (*To* ROBIN HOOD) Kneel, knave. Your last hour has come.

ROBIN HOOD (*falling on his knees*):   Oh Sheriff, please, please don't hang me!

SHERIFF: Hanging's too good for you. I'll tie you to a horse and drag you all the way to Nottingham, then I'll—(*He turns to his men.*) What's the matter with you fools? Didn't I tell you to—

(*He recognizes the outlaws and squeaks.* SIR GUY *sees them now.*)

SIR GUY: We're surrounded! Where are our fellows?

ROBIN HOOD (*jumping to his feet*):   Fast asleep, Sir Guy. They were so tired, you know, after their long walk through the forest. (SIR GUY *raises his sword.*) Oh, don't do that. Little John has a new arrow and he's eager to shoot it—between your ribs!

SHERIFF (*knees knocking*):   W-w-what are you going to do with us?

ROBIN HOOD: Nothing, Sheriff.

SHERIFF: Nothing? (*He regains his courage.*) Well, then, how dare you—

ROBIN HOOD (*interrupting the* SHERIFF *as he signals to* WILL *and* FRIAR TUCK *to lift the* SHERIFF's *arms*):   —only relieve you of some excess weight.

(*He searches for and finds the* SHERIFF's *money bag. In the process, he tickles the* SHERIFF.)

SHERIFF: My money!

ROBIN HOOD: The Widow May's money, you mean. You left her and her babes to starve. (*He pockets the bag.*) Thanks, Sheriff. I'll return this to her tonight.—All right, my lads. Let us go.

(*The outlaws start moving right.*)

SHERIFF: Hey, you can't take my money!

ROBIN HOOD: Hold on, Sheriff. I don't want to hurt you—either of you. Turn your backs, both of you. Lift your arms. Now, start counting and don't turn around until you've reached one hundred. Start.

(*As the* SHERIFF *and* SIR GUY *count, the outlaws run off, right.*)

SHERIFF and SIR GUY: 1—2—3—4—5—6—

SHERIFF (*peeping over his shoulder*): —7—8—9—10—11—(*he whispers to* SIR GUY)—are they gone?—12—13—14—

SIR GUY (*glancing around quickly*): They're gone—15—16—

SHERIFF: —17—18—you're sure?—19—

SIR GUY: Sure.

SHERIFF (*lowering his arms and bragging*): That Robin Hood! That knave! If he hadn't had a hundred men here, I'd have run him through! (*He tries to disentangle his sword.*)

SIR GUY: What are we going to do? How can we capture him now?

SHERIFF (*pulling a parchment out of his sleeve*): With this. My second plan in case the first one failed.

SIR GUY: What is it?

SHERIFF: Listen. (*He unrolls the parchment and reads.*) "Hear ye! Hear ye! A great shooting match will be held tomorrow at Nottingham Fair to which all and sundry are invited to come. He who proves himself best archer will receive a golden arrow and will be hailed greatest archer in all the land."

SIR GUY: How will this catch Robin Hood?

SHERIFF: Like a trap will catch a rabbit. Robin Hood brags he is the finest archer in all England, does he not? Well, he won't let anyone else take the prize. He'll come to the Fair to win it, see if he doesn't. And when he turns up, in that green jacket of his, I'll have him seized and hanged.

SIR GUY (*bowing*): You are a master at ruse.

SHERIFF: Now, I'll tack the notice to this tree—(*he does so*)—and we shall see who is the smarter man—Robin Hood or the Sheriff of Nottingham. (SIR GUY *laughs uproariously and claps the* SHERIFF's *shoulder as they exit, downstage left. A moment later,* ROBIN HOOD *and his men re-enter.* ROBIN HOOD *walks over to the tree and removes the notice.*)

LITTLE JOHN (*laughing*): Did you ever hear of such a stupid trick?

FRIAR TUCK: The Sheriff takes you for a baboon. He thinks you'll fall for it and go to the Fair.

WILL: What will you do, Robin?

ROBIN HOOD (*calmly*): Go to the Fair.

HIS MEN (*exclaiming*): Go—Fair—You'll be hanged!

ROBIN HOOD: If the Sheriff catches me. But he won't.

LITTLE JOHN: How will you escape him? He knows you.

ROBIN HOOD: He knows Robin, the outlaw, in his jacket of green. But does he know poor old Raymond, the Beggar? (*He assumes a beggar's pose and bleats.*) Alms. Alms. Give a poor, old man alms. Alms, noble sir—

HIS MEN (*laughing*):   By my troth, he is a beggar!—A beggar, indeed!—

LITTLE JOHN: If Robin's a beggar, then I'm a country bumpkin.
      (*He assumes a gaping pose.*)

WILL: And I a boy.
      (*He jumps over several imaginary rocks.*)

FRIAR TUCK: Come to your mother, boy.
      (*He pulls* WILL's *ear.*)

THE OUTLAWS (*entwining arms, they skip off left*):   And thus we go, beggar, bumpkin, mother, boy, all to the Fair at Nottingham.

                                                   (*The curtain closes.*)

ACT TWO

Scene   Simple but colorful booths designate a corner of the Nottingham Fair. Shields, banners and branches decorate them.

Entrances are back, right and left. The target for the archery contest is offstage, down left.

When the curtain opens, people are milling about the Fair, happy and excited. The SHERIFF, gloomy, is walking up and down in great agitation while SIR GUY is examining the faces around him.

SHERIFF: Do you see any sign of Robin Hood?

SIR GUY: Not yet. But it's early.

SHERIFF: Maybe he didn't see the notice.

SIR GUY: Maybe he's out there—(*he looks at the audience*)—beyond the gates and is afraid to come in.

SHERIFF: You think so? (*He shouts.*) Here, Trumpeter. (A TRUMPETER *enters left and bows.*) Go to the gates and blow your trumpet. When you have the crowd's attention, read them this notice. (*He hands the man a* parchment.) Speak loudly so all can hear. Go. (*The* TRUMPETER *bows and walks to front center. The* SHERIFF *turns to* SIR GUY.) Now, we'll stand at the side gate and see who enters.

(*The* SHERIFF *and* SIR GUY *walk to stage right.*)

TRUMPETER (*blowing his trumpet then reading*): "Hear ye! Hear ye! A great shooting match is about to begin here at Nottingham Fair in which all and sundry are invited to compete. He who proves himself best archer will receive a golden arrow and will be hailed greatest archer in all the land."

(*A tall, regal-looking man enters, right. He is dressed as a poor traveler. A companion, similarly dressed, follows him. The* SHERIFF *inspects them and shakes his head. Other men enter and are inspected by the* SHERIFF. *Now a* BEGGAR—ROBIN HOOD—*enters.*)

ROBIN HOOD: Alms, noble sir, alms for a poor, old man.

SHERIFF: Begone, Beggar, before I throw you into the tower.

(ROBIN HOOD *hurries upstage center.* LITTLE JOHN, *his mouth open, comes in. He bumps into* SIR GUY *deliberately.*)

LITTLE JOHN: Pardon, madam. A million pardons, madam.

SIR GUY: Phew. Away with you, bumpkin. You smell of pigs.

(LITTLE JOHN *joins* ROBIN HOOD. FRIAR TUCK, *dressed as a fat woman, arrives. He is pulling* WILL *by the ear.* WILL *is eating a hunk of bread.*)

FRIAR TUCK: Now you behave yourself, you mischief, or I'll have your father switch you with his stoutest stave.

WILL: Yes, Mama. I will, Mama. (*The* FRIAR *pulls his ear.*) Ouch, Mama! (*They join their friends.*)

SHERIFF (*to* SIR GUY): He didn't come. That rascal, Robin Hood, dare not come after all.

SIR GUY: We cannot wait any longer. We must start the contest now.

SHERIFF: You're right. (*He shouts.*) Trumpeter. Announce the contest rules.

TRUMPETER (*stepping forward to the audience and blowing his trumpet*): Attention, pray you. The greatest contest in the history of England is about to begin. The archery contest. (*The crowd exclaims.*) Each man will shoot three arrows. (*He demonstrates with his fingers.*) One—two—three. He will shoot at a target—(*Two* HENCHMEN *jump forward and display a round target*)—to be placed at a distance of five hundred yards over yonder. (*He points to offstage left.*) Whoever hits the center of our target most often wins the golden arrow.

SHERIFF: Let me present to you good people England's great marksman,

Sir Guy Gisborne. (SIR GUY *nods and several people cheer.*) Good. Now, who will be the first to shoot against Sir Guy? (*An* ARCHER *steps forward and bows.*) All right, fellow, take your place. Over there.

(*The* ARCHER *and* SIR GUY *stand facing offstage left. A* HENCHMAN *hands them bows and arrows. The* ARCHER *shoots one arrow offstage. The crowd watches closely and voices disappointment.* SIR GUY *shoots an arrow and several people cheer.*)

PEOPLE: He hit the outside circle.

(*The* ARCHER *shoots a second arrow. The crowd is disappointed.* SIR GUY *shoots a second arrow.*)

PEOPLE: He hit the middle circle!

(*The* ARCHER *shoots a third arrow.*)

PEOPLE: It fell to the ground. (SIR GUY *shoots a third.*) The middle circle again!

(*The* ARCHER *acknowledges his defeat with a bow.* SIR GUY *waves to the crowd. Several people cheer.*)

SHERIFF: Excellent, Sir Guy, excellent. Now, who will be the next challenger?

ROBIN HOOD (*stepping forward*):   I, noble sir.

SHERIFF: You! An old beggar!

ROBIN HOOD: A mighty archer, your honor, none better.

(*The* SHERIFF *and* SIR GUY *laugh.*)

SIR GUY: I won't compete with a filthy beggar.

SHERIFF (*whispering to* SIR GUY):   Why not? It will be sport for the crowd. (*He turns to* ROBIN HOOD.) Step forward, Beggar, and take your place.

(ROBIN HOOD *stands facing offstage left, an arrogant* SIR GUY *beside him. A* HENCHMAN *brings them bows and arrows.*)

SHERIFF: You first, Sir Guy.

(SIR GUY *shoots.*)

PEOPLE: The middle circle. (ROBIN HOOD *shoots. The crowd is astonished.*) The middle circle too! The Beggar hit the middle circle too! (SIR GUY *shoots a second time.*) He almost hit the bull's eye. (ROBIN HOOD *shoots. The crowd becomes excited.*) The Beggar's arrow is next to Sir Guy's! (*Furious,* SIR GUY *shoots a third time.*) Bull's eye! Bull's eye! (ROBIN HOOD *shoots. The watching crowd murmurs in disappointment then, suddenly, turns wild with joy.*) Bull's eye! He knocked Sir Guy's arrow down and hit the bull's eye! The Beggar wins! The Beggar wins!

SIR GUY (*furiously*):   An error! An error!

SHERIFF: An error! The Beggar's arrow lies on the ground. Sir Guy's sticks in the target. (*The crowd murmurs in anger.*) Sir Guy, give me your hand. Allow me to hail you best archer in all the—

THE TALL MAN (*interrupting quickly*): One moment, Sheriff. The people are angry. They want fair play. (*He signals to his* COMPANION *who exits, offstage left.*) My man will fetch the target here so we can see whose arrow quivers in the center. (*The* SHERIFF *is about to protest, but the crowd's angry voices keep him silent. The* COMPANION *returns with the target. The* TALL MAN *examines it.*) It is the Beggar's arrow. The Beggar wins the prize. (*The crowd cheers.*)

SHERIFF (*ungraciously*): Well, come, Beggar, quickly, and receive the golden arrow. (ROBIN HOOD *steps forward to get it.*)

SIR GUY (*enraged*): Not so fast, Beggar! Let us shoot another match. Not so fast. (*He grabs the* BEGGAR *and, in so doing, tears off his robe.* ROBIN HOOD *stands revealed in his outlaw's green jacket. The crowd exclaims. His men drop their disguises and stand ready to defend their leader.*)

SHERIFF (*to his men*): Seize him! Seize the outlaws!

(*A fight ensues.*)

SIR GUY: Stop! Let me tackle Robin Hood alone. He is my prize. Mine alone.

ROBIN HOOD: And you mine. If the Sheriff will withdraw his fellows, I'll withdraw mine.

SHERIFF: Men, stand back!

ROBIN HOOD: Now, Sir Guy.

(*He and* SIR GUY *wrestle. The* SHERIFF *whispers to his* HENCHMEN. *Just as* ROBIN HOOD *is about to win, the* SHERIFF *shouts.*)

SHERIFF: Seize him, fellows! Seize the outlaws!

(*His* HENCHMEN *spring into action and pin down the outlaws.*)

ROBIN HOOD: That's a blackguard's way with treachery, Sheriff.

SHERIFF (*hopping in jubilation*): Talk, talk. What care I for your talk? Nor will you need to care much longer. Sir Guy, draw your sword. (SIR GUY *obeys.*) Good. You know what to do with it.

(SIR GUY *lifts it and is about to plunge it through* ROBIN HOOD *when* THE TALL MAN *interferes again.*)

THE TALL MAN (*in a ringing voice*): Put your sword away! Untie these men!

SHERIFF: What! You dare to interfere! I'm the man who gives the orders! I'm the Sheriff of Nottingham, your Sheriff!

THE TALL MAN (*throwing off his cloak and revealing his royal attire*): And I the King of England, your King! I order you to let these men go!

(*All exclaim and bow before the* KING. *The* SHERIFF *and* SIR GUY *are terror-struck.*)

ROBIN HOOD: Mercy, Sire. Mercy for my lads and me.

SHERIFF (*sniveling*):   Mercy.

KING RICHARD: Mercy you shall have, Robin, you and your brave and sturdy friends. I have been back in England but a week and already have I heard of the injustices this sniveling coward has worked in my name.

SHERIFF: Mercy, S-s-sire.

KING RICHARD: Henchmen, take this mouse away and put him in his hole until the time I pass judgment on him. Take Sir Guy with you. (HENCHMEN *drag the two men off right.*) Now, Robin Hood, never have I seen such courage as you have shown today. What say you? Will you be my man and serve your King?

ROBIN HOOD: I will, my lord. Your right good man and true. From this day on and ever more.

LITTLE JOHN: I, too, my lord.

FRIAR TUCK and WILL: And we, my lord.

THE FOUR OUTLAWS: Your men from this day on and ever more.

KING RICHARD: Then outlaws you have ceased to be,
I, King Richard, do this decree;
And lands and goods restored will be
To you and all your men.
Give me your hand.

ROBIN HOOD (*grasping the* KING's *hand*):   Gladly, Sire.

LITTLE JOHN, FRIAR TUCK, WILL (*cheering*):   KING RICHARD! KING RICHARD! KING RICHARD!

PEOPLE (*cheering*):   ROBIN HOOD! ROBIN HOOD! ROBIN HOOD!

(*The curtain closes.*)

STAGING SUGGESTIONS

Cast

Increase or decrease the number of OUTLAWS, HENCHMEN, and TRUMPETERS to fit the needs of your group and stage space. Cast the mature players in the key roles.

Set

Trees, bushes and boulders may be realistic or suggested. A painted cloth thrown over a level, chair, stool or orange crate becomes a huge rock. To make effective-looking bushes and trees, you can cover hatracks with chicken wire and push green branches into the holes. Cardboard, cut out in the desired shapes then painted, will also serve your purpose.

Cardboard, again, may be cut out to represent the booths of Act Two. These cutouts are nailed to chairs or table fronts. Decorate the booths with banners and shields—painted cutouts—to give a festive air.

To shorten the time required for the set change, place the booths of Act Two on stage at the beginning of the play, then hide them with the trees and bushes of Act One.

Costumes

ROBIN HOOD, LITTLE JOHN, WILL SCARLET, the HENCHMEN and the ARCHER wear short tunics over long-sleeved jerseys. A tunic may be made out of Daddy's old shirt. Remove the collar and neckband, trim the sleeves and shirt bottom appropriately. Dye the garment in the desired color and add a wide belt. Tights (or long stockings) and sandals complete the costume.

Elves' hats will distinguish the OUTLAWS from the folk around them.

FRIAR TUCK wears a monk's robe and hood, made out of an old bathrobe, sheet or coat lining.

For Act Two, ROBIN HOOD gets a long, tattered garment to transform him into a beggar, and FRIAR TUCK a bonnet.

The SHERIFF has a long robe—Daddy's old bathrobe again. It may be trimmed with felt or bits of fur to make it look elegant. Fashion his jeweled belt out of ribbon and the shiny, copper pads Mother uses to scour pans. He has a long sword.

SIR GUY's costume consists of a tunic, long-sleeved jersey, tights and sandals. The tunic is embroidered with imitation jewels, copper pads and Christmas glitter. He carries a long sword.

KING RICHARD is also attired in a rich tunic. Necklaces appropriate to his rank hang around his neck. A long, drab cloak with hood serves as his disguise at the Fair. His companion has a similar cloak.

The TRUMPETER may wear a longer tunic. He carries a trumpet. This is shaped like a flaring bell at one end of a long tube.

The PEOPLE at the Fair are clothed in gaily-colored garments.

Sound

Commercial recordings of the trumpet call are available.

Props

A branch, stave, bow and arrows for ROBIN HOOD; staves and daggers for LITTLE JOHN, WILL SCARLET and FRIAR TUCK; bows and arrows for the HENCHMEN; sword, money bag and two parchments for the SHERIFF; sword for SIR GUY; a trumpet for the TRUMPETER; a target.

A CHRISTMAS STORY

A COMIC FANTASY

Playing Time   13 minutes approximately

Age   8—12 years

Manner of Presentation   Narrate and improvise
or
Memorize

Staging Suggestions   See end of play

Cast   Miss Warren (Narrator)
The Kent Children (Abby, Sue and Kay)
Mrs. Gordon (a fretting mother)
Grandma Gordon (a wise but crotchety old lady)
Janie Gordon (a selfish ten-year-old)

Jeanie Gordon (her selfish sister, a year younger)
Anna (a sensitive immigrant from Hungary, Jeanie's age)
Three peculiar Doctors (very peculiar)
Dolls

Time   The day before Christmas. Late afternoon

Place   The Kent library

Scene   The curtain opens to reveal the library of the Kent home. The main decoration is a large Christmas tree, upstage right. At its base are gift packages and dolls without wrapping. A fireplace, gaily decorated for the holiday, is found upstage to the left of the trees. A hassock is in front of it. A comfortable studio couch, decked with afghan and pillows, stands left center. More gifts are lying on the couch. Downstage right, there is an occasional table with a club chair at its right. This table acts as a sort of screen between anyone sitting in the chair and the rest of the room.

There are two entrances—one in the right wall above the chair which leads to the outside foyer, and one in the left wall above the couch, leading to the rest of the house.

When the curtain opens, the KENT CHILDREN *are busy decorating the Christmas tree.*

ABBY (*standing on hassock*):   Hey, Kent, do you think we have enough balls on the tree now?
SUE (*kneeling*):   Better put some on this side. It looks kind of droopy.
ABBY: Maybe the woodpeckers had themselves a feast.
SUE: Won't Mom and Dad be surprised when they find the tree ready for tomorrow?
ABBY: Quit gabbing and hurry. We promised to make some Christmas cookies and it's getting dark.
KAY (*entering, left*):   Who came in, kids?
SUE: Who?
KAY: I heard the doorbell ring.

MISS WARREN (*the* NARRATOR, *calling from offstage right*):   Hi there! Anyone home?

CHILDREN: It's Miss Warren—From the Settlement House—I'd know her voice anywhere—

> (*They dash to entrance right just as* MISS WARREN *appears, laden with packages. The children cling to her affectionately as they greet her.*)

CHILDREN: Hello—We didn't hear you come in—Did you ring?

MISS WARREN (*a thoroughly nice person*):   I certainly did. But no one came so I walked right in. Is Mother home?

ABBY: No, but she'll be back any moment though.

SUE: I know why you're here.

KAY: Bet I know too.

ABBY: You're collecting Christmas gifts—

SUE: For the kids at the Settlement House.

KAY (*poking* SUE):   Genius at work!

MISS WARREN: You may all go to the head of the class!

ABBY: Mommy prepared a lot of packages for you—

SUE: And left them on the couch.

KAY (*getting packages*):   Here they are.

> (*The children give them to* MISS WARREN.)

MISS WARREN: All these! It's wonderful of you girls to share your gifts like this. I'll take them now and, you'll say "thank you" to Mother for me, won't you?

ABBY: But you can't go yet.

SUE: Not before you tell us a story.

KAY: Like you always do, a story!

CHILDREN: A story, YEAH! A story, YEAH!

> (*They surround her.*)

MISS WARREN: But I have so many things to do. It's the day before Christmas.

CHILDREN: We won't give you the packages!—Not before you tell us a story! —A story!

MISS WARREN (*gives in, laughing*):   A story it is. Only I can't say a word if you're going to smother me! (*She places her parcels on the table.*) Here, let me sit down in this chair and you make yourselves comfortable on the floor, around me. (*The children group themselves at her feet.*) Okay. Now, let's see. What shall the story be?

ABBY: Tell us about those two girls. You know who.

SUE (*correcting*):   Whom.

KAY: Those two sisters. You know, the ones who were spoiled and selfish.

MISS WARREN: Those girls! But didn't I tell you that one before?

CHILDREN: No.—We haven't heard it.—You promised to tell it one day.

MISS WARREN: Okay, the spoiled sisters it is. Janie and Jeanie Gordon. And they lived in a house such as this one, with their Mother and their Grandma. And they were rich, very, very, in everything—toys, clothes, camps, cars—

ABBY: Boy, were they lucky!

MISS WARREN (*continuing*):   —everything, I should say, except in one of the most important things of all. Can you guess what that is?

CHILDREN: Skates?—A hamster?—A fish tank?

SUE: I know, bubble gum!

MISS WARREN (*laughing*):   No, no, no. Just simple sweetness and kindness such as you have. In knowing how to get along with all kinds of people and sharing. Especially sharing. They didn't know what the word meant. Because they were—well, very selfish.

SUE (*poking* KAY *playfully*):   Just like you.

MISS WARREN: Now, one Christmas day—it was a brisk, clear day, the kind the weatherman has promised us for tomorrow—Mother Gordon was in the library arranging some gifts for Janie and Jeanie under the tree—

> (MOTHER GORDON, *laden with packages, enters, left and hurries over to the tree.* GRANDMA *hobbles in after her on her cane and sits down on the couch. The lights dim on* MISS WARREN *and the* KENT CHILDREN *while the rest of the stage—where the story is being enacted—grows brighter.*)

MISS WARREN (*continuing without a break*):   —while Grandma, a wise, old lady if ever there was one, leaned on her cane and shook her head at what Mother was doing.

GRANDMA: I tell you, you're spoiling those girls.

MOTHER (*smiling*):   Now, Grandma, it's Christmas and Christmas always means presents for the young ones.

GRANDMA: Then every day's Christmas for those children. It's time they received a different kind of present!

> (*She shakes her cane vigorously as though she would thrash the girls with it.*)

MOTHER (*laughing*):   You old bear, you know you'd never use your cane on them. You never did on me.

GRANDMA: You were a sweet child, friendly with everyone, unselfish. You shared your things. (*She walks over to the tree and pokes at the dolls with her cane.*) Now, just look at all this rubbish.

MOTHER: Dolls, Grandma.

GRANDMA: Dolls. Do you think if a poor child were to walk into this room, Janie or Jeanie'd so much as let her play with one? I tell you again, you should give them another kind of a present!

(*Shaking her cane, she reseats herself on the couch.*)

MISS WARREN: And while Mother was laughing, who should walk into the room but Janie and Jeanie themselves, fighting as usual—over a belt, of all things.

(*JANIE and JEANIE enter, left, fighting over a red belt.*)

SISTERS: Let go!—You let go!—It's mine!—No, it isn't!

MOTHER (*separating the SISTERS*): Janie, Jeanie! What's it all about?

SISTERS: She said this belt is hers!—You got it for my new skirt, didn't you, Mom?—Tell her it's mine!—Let go or I'll pull your hair!

MOTHER (*trying to distract the SISTERS*): Come over here, girls, to the Christmas tree. Look what Santa's brought you.

(*The SISTERS "stroll" over to the tree.*)

JANIE (*kicking at the dolls, bored*): Dolls again.

MOTHER (*holding up a doll*): Don't you think this one's pretty? It's from Aunt Martha. (*JEANIE grabs it and pokes out an eye. MOTHER holds up another.*) Or this? You can put her in the big doll house.

GRANDMA (*shaking her cane at the SISTERS*): Or THIS!

MOTHER (*as SISTERS mistreat the dolls*): Janie! Jeanie! Put them down! Stop it! Put them—(*There is a knock at the door, right.*) Shhh, someone's here. (*The SISTERS quiet down.*) Come in. (*ANNA enters timidly. She is poorly dressed. MOTHER greets her warmly.*) Why, it's Anna. Come in, dear.

GRANDMA (*warmly*): Are you frozen, little one?

(*While the women fuss over ANNA, the SISTERS stand apart, stage left, and inspect the girl disdainfully.*)

MISS WARREN (*speaking during the greetings*): Anna was a little girl who came here from Hungary when her mother died over a year ago. Her father worked for the Gordons as a handyman.

ANNA (*shyly*): Papa cannot come to work, Missus. He has a big pain in chest. He said I come work for you in his place.

MOTHER (*hugging* ANNA): You'll do nothing of the kind. Nobody works today. It's a holiday, Christmas. But now that you're here, you can take home a big basket of goodies I'll pack for you. And I'll add some medicines for Papa's cold. Girls, will you play with Anna while I get them for her.
(*She exits left.*)

GRANDMA: I'll put in my own mustard plaster. And you tell your father, child, to put it on his chest. Nothing better.

JANIE: Mustard plaster huh! They use antibiotics now.
(GRANDMA *shakes her cane at* JANIE *and hobbles off, left.*)

MISS WARREN: Now, while the grownups were preparing the basket, Anna smiled shyly at Janie and Jeanie and tried to be friendly. But did those spoiled sisters smile back?

ABBY: Not those meanies!

SUE: They stuck out their tongues.

KAY: They teased her.
(*The* SISTERS *walk slowly around* ANNA, *poking at her clothes.*)

JANIE: Jeanie, just look at her dress! Did you ever see such a funny, old thing? Bet it's a hand-me-down.

JEANIE: And her shoes! They've holes in them!

JANIE (*arrogantly*): Listen, you! What's your name?

ANNA: You know. Anna.

JEANIE: Anna-banana! She can't even say it properly!

JANIE: She's a foreigner—what can you expect?

ANNA (*holding back her tears*): I go home now.

JANIE (*stopping her*): No, you don't! You've got to wait for the basket.

JEANIE: And you've got to work! In your father's place. That's what you came for. Remember?

JANIE: And you can start in right now!

MISS WARREN: And then those two silly girls started ordering Anna around, bossing her as—well, as the mean, old stepsisters bossed Cinderella.
(*The* SISTERS *give poor* ANNA *many, contradictory orders which she tries to obey.*)

SISTERS: Scratch my back!—Pick up my doll!—Tidy up the presents!—Not at the fireplace, stupid, at the tree!—Pick up my belt!—
(*During this teasing,* JANIE *whispers into* JEANIE's *ear, following which* JEANIE *hides a doll behind the couch.*)

JANIE: Jeanie, my Mama doll is missing!

JEANIE: I bet Anna took it! Let's search her! She may be hiding it under her coat!

(*The* SISTERS *ruffle up* ANNA's *clothes. Weeping,* ANNA *sinks to the floor. The* SISTERS *laugh as* MOTHER *and* GRANDMA *return with the basket.*)

MOTHER: Why are you crying, Anna? What's wrong?

ANNA: Nothing.

MOTHER: Did anyone hurt you?

ANNA: No one.

GRANDMA: No one person, you mean, but two persons. And I know who they are.

(*She glares at the* SISTERS. MOTHER *eyes them thoughtfully as she raises* ANNA.)

MOTHER: Girls, since you have so many dolls, wouldn't you like to give one to Anna? It would make a lovely Christmas present.

SISTERS (*clinging to the dolls, protesting*):   No, no!—They belong to us!—We want them.—Let her work and buy her own.

MOTHER: But you didn't care for them a moment ago!

GRANDMA: Ha! What did I tell you?

(*She swings her cane.*)

MOTHER (*hiding her disappointment*):   Never mind then. Time to bring this nice, big basket to your father, Anna. I'll drive you home and see how he's feeling.

(*Picking up the basket,* MOTHER *starts to walk out, right, with* ANNA.)

MISS WARREN: When Janie and Jeanie saw their Mother leaving with Anna, they didn't like it one bit. They wanted their Mother to pay attention to no one but them. So they thought of a trick to make her stay with them.

SISTERS (*doubling up and moaning*):   Oh—oh—oh—it hurts something awful!—My stomach hurts!—I feel dizzy!—I'm going to be sick!

MOTHER (*running back to the* SISTERS):   What is it? What hurts? Show me! Grandma, their foreheads feel hot! It may be the virus! (GRANDMA *watches the scene skeptically.*) My poor babies! Here, lie down on the couch. Grandma, phone the doctor while I get some aspirin! Hurry, please! (GRANDMA *starts to exit right but stops at the door.*) My poor darlings, don't you worry, you'll be all right. (*She covers the* SISTERS *with the afghan.*) Just you stay covered. I'll be right back. Grandma, watch them until I get back. Give them some dolls to play with.

(*She hurries out, left.*)

MISS WARREN: Grandma didn't know what to make of the whole business. She wasn't convinced that the girls were ill. She suspected that they were faking. She hobbled over to the head of the couch, leaned over the sisters and studied their faces carefully. Now, there was one person Janie and Jeanie feared—their Grandma—because they knew they couldn't fool her for long. So, while she examined them, they lay very quietly, not daring to move, not even to cry. They closed their eyes tightly and pretended to fall asleep. And then a very strange thing happened. Grandma stared at the girls, nodded her head quickly as though she had just thought of a secret and, smiling mysteriously, hobbled out to the foyer.

(GRANDMA *exits, right.* ANNA *remains at the fireplace. The* SISTERS *sit up quickly.*)

JANIE (*in a scared whisper*):   Where did Grandma go?

JEANIE (*equally scared*):   To the front door. She's up to something!

JANIE: Do you think she's going to thrash us with her cane?

JEANIE: Stupid! She wouldn't have left us, would she? She must have gone to get the doctor.

JANIE: The doctor! Now we are in trouble. (*The* SISTERS *moan.*)

MISS WARREN: And frightened as they were, what do you suppose happened to Janie and Jeanie?

ABBY: They got sick!

MISS WARREN: Yes! Really sick! Fear can double up your stomach, you know.

SISTERS (*groaning*):   Jeanie, I'm sick!—I've got a sharp pain!—Why doesn't Mommy help us?—SHH! I hear Grandma coming back! Lie down and keep quiet or she'll cane us!

(*They lie down and cover themselves.*)

MISS WARREN: In the midst of this moaning, Grandma returned, beckoning to someone behind her. (*Smiling with satisfaction,* GRANDMA *hobbles in, right, beckoning behind her.*) And in came the oddest creature you ever saw. (*A strange-looking* DOCTOR *enters. He is dressed in top hat, mittens, muffler, much-too-large overcoat and carries a suitcase. He looks about him cautiously as though he expects an ambush then beckons behind him, shushing the* SECOND DOCTOR.) In came two of the oddest—(*A* SECOND DOCTOR *similarly dressed, enters in the same cautious way and takes his place behind the* FIRST DOCTOR, *shushing and beckoning behind him.*) No! In came three—yes, THREE of the oddest creatures you ever did see! (*A* THIRD DOCTOR, *similarly dressed, rushes in, stumbles, shushes loudly and* takes his place behind the SECOND DOCTOR. Now, the THREE DOCTORS look around the room slowly. They move at the same time, in drill formation. They advance a few steps, stop, look around, advance, stop, advance again until they reach stage center. Here, they put their suitcases down, face front and announce themselves, roll call fashion.)

MISS WARREN: The odd creatures introduced themselves.

FIRST DOCTOR: Doctors Mustard—

SECOND DOCTOR: Custard—

THIRD DOCTOR: Flustered.

ALL DOCTORS: At your service.

(They make an awkward bow, still facing front. MOTHER enters and crosses to the couch.)

MOTHER: Doctors, I'm so glad you came!

(The THREE DOCTORS turn with precision toward MOTHER and bow.)

FIRST DOCTOR: Where's the patient?

SECOND DOCTOR (quickly):   Where's the—?

THIRD DOCTOR (quickly):   Where?

GRANDMA (pointing to the couch and leering):   There they are, Doctors. There are the plump, little chickens.

FIRST DOCTOR (removing his hat, he passes it on to the SECOND DOCTOR quickly. The second DOCTOR is at his right):   So here you are!

SECOND DOCTOR (passing on his hat and the first hat to the THIRD DOCTOR at his right):   So here you—

THIRD DOCTOR (dumping his hat and the other two hats on GRANDMA):   So!

FIRST DOCTOR (hanging his muffler around the neck of the SECOND DOCTOR): Hiding from the doctor!

SECOND DOCTOR (hanging his muffler and the first muffler around the neck of the THIRD DOCTOR):   Hiding from the—

THIRD DOCTOR (dumping his muffler and the other two mufflers on GRANDMA): Hiding!

ALL DOCTORS: Naughty, naughty—tch, tch! (Suddenly, the DOCTORS whirl around. The first pounces on MOTHER, the second on ANNA, the third on GRANDMA. They think these individuals are their patients. Please note that, this being a dream, all the characters act in a slightly stylized or exaggerated manner, especially the THREE DOCTORS. The DOCTORS are in continuous movement. When the hat of the FIRST DOCTOR is off, he works at his muffler. The SECOND DOCTOR starts on his hat the moment the FIRST DOCTOR has his off. The THIRD DOCTOR starts on his, the moment the SECOND DOCTOR has removed his. The effect is that of doing "Three Blind Mice" without music!)

FIRST DOCTOR (trying to subdue the struggling women): We'll cure you or kill you!

SECOND DOCTOR: We'll cure you or kill—

THIRD DOCTOR: We'll KILL YOU!

MOTHER: Doctors, it's the children who are sick! Not us!

ALL DOCTORS (releasing the women): The children?

(They form their line, stage center front, again.)

FIRST DOCTOR: Doctors Mustard—

SECOND DOCTOR: Custard—

THIRD DOCTOR: Flustered.

ALL DOCTORS: We're sorry.

(They bury their faces in their right arms and weep.)

MOTHER (pleading): DOCTORS! Look at my babies! Please!

FIRST DOCTOR: Yes, yes, we're coming. Just as soon as we get our thermometers—

(All open their suitcases and remove oversized thermometers.)

SECOND DOCTOR: And remove our mittens—

(All remove their mittens.)

THIRD DOCTOR: And—

(Whirling around, they stick their thermometers into each other's mouth.)

MOTHER: Doctors, please! The children are turning green! Save them!

ALL DOCTORS: Sorry—so sorry.

(Separating, they count off in drill fashion as they turn left and march over to the girls. The SISTERS try to hide under the afghan.)

FIRST DOCTOR: So there you are. Nothing to cry about.

SECOND DOCTOR: Nothing to cry about.

THIRD DOCTOR: Nothing.

(The DOCTORS bend over the girls to examine them. There is an ominous silence. Even GRANDMA is anxious. Eventually, the DOCTORS straighten up. Their faces are grave as they walk toward center with a slow, funereal step.)

FIRST DOCTOR: A very serious case. Almost fatal, wouldn't you say?

(He turns to the SECOND DOCTOR chummily.)

SECOND DOCTOR: Almost fatal, wouldn't you say?

(He turns to the THIRD DOCTOR chummily.)

THIRD DOCTOR (*almost singing the words*): Almost fatal, I should say. Almost fatal, I should say.

(*All* THREE DOCTORS *join hands and dance to the chant, "Almost fatal, I should say."* MOTHER *and* GRANDMA *stop them.*)

MOTHER: What can it be? Tell me!

FIRST DOCTOR: It's a disease peculiar to spoiled children.

SECOND DOCTOR: Not catching—

THIRD DOCTOR: But serious.

MOTHER: Can you cure it?

FIRST DOCTOR: Only one thing can cure it.

SECOND DOCTOR: Only one thing—

THIRD DOCTOR: One.

FIRST DOCTOR: A dose of their own medicine. That's what will cure them!

SECOND DOCTOR: At them, Anna!

(*He pushes* ANNA *in the direction of the* SISTERS.)

THIRD DOCTOR: At them, Dolls!

(*He grabs the* DOLLS, *alive and life-size now, and pushes them toward the couch.*)

MISS WARREN: Anna and the Dolls, alive and life-size now, pulled the Sisters off the couch and treated them as the girls had treated the Dolls earlier. They scratched Janie's arms! They pulled Jeanie's hair! They poked at their faces and kicked their legs! They twirled them around until the girls were dizzy!

ANNA and the DOLLS: Will you be good?—Will you be GOOD?—WILL YOU BE GOOD?

(JANIE *and* JEANIE *break away and run back to the couch, sobbing.*)

SISTERS: We'll be good! We'll be good! We promise!

(*No sooner do the* SISTERS *promise than the* DOCTORS *vanish, right, the live* DOLLS *disappear behind the tree and* MOTHER *exits left. Only* GRANDMA, ANNA *and the* SISTERS *are left on stage.* GRANDMA *is hovering over the girls as they lie on the couch. The dream has come to an end. Now* MOTHER *hurries into the room, bringing aspirin and a glass of water.*)

MOTHER: Grandma, why are the girls crying?

GRANDMA (*genuinely concerned*): I don't know. They fell asleep for a little while and then they woke up crying. Oh dear, they're really sick.

SISTERS (*clinging to* MOTHER): We're not sick, Mommy! (MOTHER *feels their foreheads.*) We swear we're not! We were just pretending before because—because we didn't want you to go away with Anna and leave us.

MOTHER (*confused*):　I don't know what to think.

SISTERS:　We're sorry we were mean to the dolls—and to Anna—we want to help her now—and share our toys with her! (*They run to* ANNA.)

ANNA (*frightened*):　I go. I do not wait for basket.

SISTERS:　Don't go!—Not yet, not until we—(*Each sister picks up a doll and holds it out to* ANNA.) Here! Take our dolls—as Christmas presents.

(*When* ANNA *hesitates, the* SISTERS *put the dolls into her arms.*)

MOTHER (*beaming*):　That's my girls! I knew you'd make me proud of you one day! Tell you what, why don't we all bring this basket to Anna's father?

SISTERS:　Swell!—Come on, Janie, I'll race you to the coat closet!

(*Talking and laughing, the* SISTERS *run out, right.* MOTHER *and* ANNA *follow them. Surprised at this turn in events,* GRANDMA *looks after them then turns to look at the audience.*)

GRANDMA:　Well! Now, I've seen everything!

(*Shrugging her shoulders, she hobbles out, right. Lights dim on the center area and build on* MISS WARREN.)

MISS WARREN:　And that is how Janie and Jeanie Gordon, once known as "THOSE SELFISH SISTERS," came to be the nicest, friendliest girls on the block, rich in everything now—in friends, in sweetness and in the joy of sharing! (*The singing of carols is heard offstage.*) Listen! Do you hear the carol singers? They've started! And I haven't delivered these parcels yet! (*She rises, collecting her packages.*) Good-bye, girls. Thank your mother for the Christmas packages, will you? And a Merry, Merry Christmas to you all.

CHILDREN (*They troop after* MISS WARREN *as she exits right, improvising their good-byes*):　Merry Christmas, Miss Warren—Thank you for the story—Merry Christmas—Merry—

(*The singing swells*

　　　　　　　　　　　　　　　　　　　　　　　　　as the curtain closes.)

STAGING SUGGESTIONS

Cast

In all-male groups, MISS WARREN may become MR. WARREN, MOTHER may become FATHER, the DOLLS may be transformed into TIN SOLDIERS, etc. In all-female groups, there should be no difficulty in asking the girls to impersonate the THREE DOCTORS. Girls often enjoy impersonating masculine characters. If they object, change the sex. There are women doctors too!

Increase or decrease the number of KENT CHILDREN and DOLLS to fit the needs of your group and stage space. The cast may be cut down to MISS WARREN, one KENT CHILD, MOTHER, GRANDMA, JANIE, ANNA and TWO DOCTORS. If you use only one KENT CHILD, the curtain opens on her decorating the Christmas tree. MISS WARREN enters immediately. JANIE alone can carry the continuity of the story. There is an advantage, however, to retaining the two SISTERS. In case of illness, one or the other carries on. While two DOCTORS may be used, *three* are funnier for the stylized routines.

Set

The couch may be constructed out of two benches, covered and decorated with pillows. The Christmas tree may be real or cut out of painted cardboard or made with chicken wire and crêpe paper. A comfortable chair for MISS WARREN, an occasional table beside the chair, and a hassock or stool on which the KENT CHILDREN stand to decorate the tree complete the set. The fireplace is a cozy touch but optional. It may be painted on wrapping or builder's paper, tacked to a screen or the back curtains of the stage. Or, for a more elaborate set, it may be made out of beaverboard, painted or covered with commercial red brick paper. Bookcases, lamps, radio lend a library atmosphere to the background.

Costumes

MISS WARREN wears outdoor, winter clothes, MOTHER wears a dress or a house-robe, GRANDMA a sweater. She carries a cane, of course. The KENT CHILDREN wear informal clothes, but JANIE and JEANIE are fussily dressed. ANNA has poor, outdoor garments that are too large for her and are, obviously, hand-me-downs. The THREE DOCTORS are dressed as described in the script. The top hats may be cardboard, painted black. Their noses are red putty, their eyebrows black and bushy. Mustaches add to the funny effect. The child-size DOLLS resemble actual dolls with their starched dresses, hair ribbons or bonnets and red spots on their cheeks.

Sound

If you wish, music may be introduced to mark the beginning and the end of the dream sequence. It also accompanies the "dance" of the live DOLLS. The singing of the carols may be real or recorded.

Props

Pillows, afghan and Christmas packages on the couch; more Christmas gifts, tree ornaments and unwrapped dolls under the tree; Christmas decorations for the fireplace; tree balls for ABBY; Christmas parcels for MISS WARREN; a red belt for JANIE and JEANIE; a basket, an aspirin bottle, a glass of water for MOTHER; oversized thermometers cut out of cardboard for the THREE DOCTORS.

Lighting

If the stage has technical equipment, open the curtain on a well-lit set then, as MISS WARREN begins the Christmas story, dim the light on her and the KENT CHILDREN while building it on that part of the stage where the story is being enacted. Later, when JANIE and JEANIE start to dream, introduce a dream-like quality to the lighting of this area. Bring up the regular lighting when the dream is over. At the end of the Christmas story, dim this area while building the light on MISS WARREN and her listeners.

Freeing Exercises

If older groups are giving this play, you may expect and work for detailed characterization. This is obtained by the discussion, questions and improvisation process already described in the first part of this book (Chapter 7).

Here is a simple situation with which to introduce the group to characterization. You walk into the library, cross to the Christmas tree in the corner and start to decorate it. One of the glittering balls falls to the ground and you stoop to pick it up. You then bring over a chair, climb on it and stretching, try to place a star at the top of the tree. Ask all the players to perform these simple activities, first, as they themselves would, then as an older person—Father—then, as a still older person—Grandma. In each case, discuss with the group how the body movements change with each character—the muscles become less elastic, the spine bends, the body slumps, the head juts out, the arms and legs feel heavy. Similar changes occur in the vocal tones and in the mental and emotional processes.

Your children may decide that Grandma is crotchety. After discussing what has made her so, ask them to improvise a situation like this: it is Halloween and several children, bent on teasing Grandma, keep ringing the doorbell and hiding whenever she comes to answer it. They keep this up until Grandma's energy and patience are worn thin and she seeks release in swinging her cane threateningly.

To project anxiety naturally, caution the players against playing the feeling itself. Do not say, "I am anxious therefore I shall act a person being anxious." Rather, think back to a time when your favorite pet—your parakeet or puppy —was lost. Recall where you were, in detail, when you learned about his disappearance. Try to remember everything about that moment. This will enable you to live it again. Then, let your feeling of anxiety come of its own accord. When you have to portray an anxious moment on stage, as MOTHER in the script does, the feeling will come naturally and truthfully (Chapter 5).

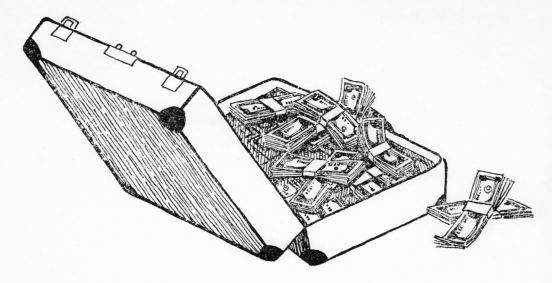

BANK NOTES AND MUSIC

A DRAMATIC OUTLINE FOR IMPROVISATION

Age   9–12 years

Manner of Presentation   Improvise lines

Staging Suggestions   See end of outline

Cast   The Narrator
The Mayor
The Policeman
Boys and Girls (among them Mike, Sleepy, Lynn and Betsy)
The Townspeople (among them a Laundrywoman and a Grocery-
man)
Three Robbers

Time   The present

Place   An out-of-the-way seacoast village

Scenes

ACT ONE   The town square. This can be set up on the apron of the stage. A park bench and a street lamp suggest the background. The town bell rests on a high stand to the left of the bench. Entrances are right and left.

ACT TWO   The kitchen of a beach house. This act is played on the stage proper. There is a cupboard, upstage right. The cupboard holds various kitchen and grocery items, among them a white towel, plates, pots, cutlery, a large container of pepper and food ingredients. A table and three chairs stand downstage, left of center. There is a window, stage right. It is boarded up. Entrances are upstage left and right.

ACT ONE

The NARRATOR, introducing the play, describes the small, out-of-the-way coastal village of which he is an inhabitant. It is a very quiet place, its main burst of activity occurring during the summer months when city people occupy the beach houses. Now that autumn is here, the beach houses are empty, their windows boarded up against the winter. The village itself is once again pursuing its old-fashioned way of living. The place is so old-fashioned that, in times of trouble, the MAYOR uses an old ship's bell to alert the villagers.

The bell is ringing now. As the NARRATOR exits left, the MAYOR, an imposing individual, stalks in right followed by the village POLICEMAN. The POLICE-MAN is ringing the bell and the MAYOR is scolding him. "It's too loud—no, no—it's not loud enough—no, no—make it more musical—stand near me—no, no, not in front of me!—Beside me, beside me!" As the MAYOR climbs up on the bench to a position of prominence,

The BOYS and GIRLS run in from both sides. Among them are MIKE, a mischievous lad, SLEEPY, a tired, fat boy, LYNN, a timid girl, and BETSY, a younger child who worships the others and trails after them, in spite of MIKE's protests.

MIKE, up to his old tricks, teases the MAYOR and rings the bell. There are a scuffle and a scolding before he is restrained.

The TOWNSPEOPLE, alarmed at the bell ringing, pour in. In the confusion, the LAUNDRYWOMAN's clean clothes are spilled, the GROCERYMAN's parcels dumped. MIKE, of course, is involved in the bumping and the tripping.

The MAYOR, on the park bench, now addresses the people in his flowery manner, "The bank at Seacove was held up this morning at 4:15 a.m.," he tells them, "by three robbers who escaped in a stolen car. When last seen they were heading this way and it is believed that they will go into hiding here. A reward of $5,000 is being offered for any information leading to their arrest. If any one of you has such information be sure to ring the town bell. I'll come running."

The MAYOR descends amid the buzz that follows the announcement. He and the TOWNSPEOPLE depart to attend to their separate affairs.

The BOYS and GIRLS, left behind, discuss the news. They are all excited about the reward, even BETSY. She tries hard to join in the chatter but MIKE keeps chasing her away. "She's only a baby," he teases. "Let her play with her dolls and sing *Frère Jacques* to them. That's all she knows anyway." And to prove his point, MIKE sings the English words, one line of which is "Go ring the morning bell." Delighted at what she thinks is a friendly gesture, BETSY sings along with him. This gives MIKE an idea for more mischief. Repeating "Go ring the morning bell," he urges BETSY, through pantomime, to ring the town bell which the POLICEMAN had left near the bench. Some of the CHILDREN protest. BETSY, however, anxious to please MIKE, rings the bell.

The MAYOR, the TOWNSPEOPLE and the POLICEMAN run back to the square. "What happened?" they ask. "Did you see the robbers?" When the MAYOR learns that BETSY rang the bell in play, he scolds her and she begins to cry. The people then return to their occupations.

Now LYNN wants to leave too. "These men are somewhere around," she wails, "maybe here." MIKE laughs but SLEEPY agrees with LYNN. "They may be hiding in one of the empty beach houses," he says and points to the drawn stage curtains behind him. To prove them wrong MIKE boasts he will search the houses. He dares the others to accompany him and, ashamed of their fears, they follow him. BETSY trails a distance behind MIKE.

ACT TWO

The curtain opens to reveal the kitchen of an abandoned beach house. Three ROBBERS *are sitting around the table.*

The ROBBERS are discussing the money they stole that morning and stowed away in an overnight bag. The bag is now lying on the table before them. "We'll stay here until dark," their LEADER says, "and then we'll make our getaway. We're safe in this house. No one comes here now. It's boarded up for the winter." A sudden noise at the door alarms them and pushing the money back behind the cupboard, they hide themselves behind the furniture, the curtains, etc.

The noise was made by the BOYS and GIRLS. They have found the door loose and forced it open. MIKE is the first to enter the kitchen and the others follow. Except BETSY. MIKE will not permit her to come in. "Go sing *Frère Jacques* to your dolls," he tells her. BETSY runs off but remains within calling distance of the house.

The CHILDREN look about them cautiously. Among other things, they notice the window that has been boarded up. When LYNN spies some cigarettes on the table, she wants to run home. MIKE laughs at her fears. At his suggestion, the BOYS and GIRLS tiptoe upstairs (*upstage left exit*) to explore the rest of the house. SLEEPY would prefer to stay in the kitchen and take a nap, but MIKE pulls him along. (MIKE *is not as brave as he pretends to be.*)

Now the ROBBERS emerge from their hiding places. They are worried. They must stay in the house without discovery until dark. But how are they going to do that when there are CHILDREN wandering about? They decide they will pretend to be ghosts and frighten the CHILDREN away. Grabbing the white towel and some pans, the men hide again.

SLEEPY is the first to return. He settles down at the table and is about to nap when the ROBBERS rattle the pans. He sits up in his chair, petrified. More rattling brings him out of his seat. A man sneaks out and moves the chair away. When SLEEPY tries to sit down, he falls to the ground and screams.

The BOYS and GIRLS come running. SLEEPY tells them of the ghosts. MIKE laughs. His laugh freezes when he hears a rattle and sees a ghostly arm emerge from nowhere—a man's arm wrapped in the white towel.

LYNN is so frightened that she tries to hide behind the cupboard. She disturbs the hidden money bag. This comes tumbling into the room, spilling its contents.

The ROBBERS, dropping towel and pans, dash out of their hiding places to retrieve the stolen money. They threaten the CHILDREN with their guns, "Don't try to leave the house or warn anyone through the boarded window!" (*One of the boards is loose.*)

The LEADER and a HENCHMAN run upstairs to see if there are any more CHILDREN there. The remaining ROBBER busies himself with stuffing the money back into the bag. "We've got to try to signal for help," urges MIKE. "Betsy is still outside. If we can distract the robber, we can signal to her with the white towel." MIKE turns to LYNN, "Lynn, you pretend to be sick. When he speaks to you, keep him busy until we have contacted Betsy."

LYNN starts to groan, the ROBBER comes to her side, MIKE grabs the towel and waves it out of the window. But BETSY is wary of MIKE and his tricks and ignores his frantic gestures. Just then the LEADER and his HENCHMAN return to the kitchen. MIKE quickly turns his gestures into those of an Indian war dancer while the other CHILDREN grab pots and pans and whoop it up in Indian fashion.

Now the LEADER feels hungry and orders the CHILDREN to prepare some food. As the BOYS and GIRLS busy themselves whipping up something to eat, there is a tapping at the window. "It's Betsy!" whispers MIKE who now wishes to frighten the little girl away so the ROBBERS cannot grab her and hold her captive too.

The ROBBERS notice the tapping and the CHILDREN hasten to drown the noise. They drop the plates with which they were setting the table, and when the men continue to be curious about the window, MIKE sprinkles the air with pepper until they fall into fits of sneezing. All this time, the CHILDREN are singing at the tops of their lungs—*Frère Jacques*—with special emphasis on "Go ring the morning bell." They have a forlorn hope that BETSY will not only go away but will ring the town bell and summon the MAYOR to the house.

But BETSY runs away without giving her friends any sign that she has understood their message. The CHILDREN are discouraged. Not only discouraged but frightened, because the ROBBERS have recovered from their sneezing and are discussing what they ought to do now. Should they remain in the house until dark as originally planned, or should they leave now? And what should they do with the CHILDREN? Take them along or tie them up and let them stay here, in the house, until discovered, until the following summer perhaps? The CHILDREN listen to the debate anxiously and protest when the ROBBERS decide to tie them up—which they proceed to do at once.

The MEN are gagging the last child when there is a great pealing of the town bell. As the ROBBERS make hasty preparations to leave, the MAYOR, the POLICEMAN, TOWNSPEOPLE and BETSY break through the boarded window and door and enter the house. The ROBBERS are put under arrest and the CHILDREN are reunited with their friends. BETSY explains that the ROBBERS' sneezing had made her suspicious, so much so, that she had rung the town bell after all. MIKE is so happy that he tells her she can play with the BOYS and GIRLS any time she pleases.

The MAYOR promises to split up the reward money among the CHILDREN and everyone, grabbing pots and pans, parades out of the house singing *Frère Jacques*.

STAGING SUGGESTIONS

Comments

Bank Notes and Music is an example of how play creativity grows out of a group situation or activity. The boys and girls who were involved in the dramatization had been learning folk songs, one of which was *Frère Jacques*. This occupation together with a strong interest in "shootin' " resulted in the above outline.

Cast

Increase or decrease the number of POLICEMEN, TOWNSPEOPLE and CHILDREN to fit the needs of your group and stage space. The mature members of the group play the main characters.

Set

In Act One, the park bench of the town square may be any bench with or without a back. If none is available, the MAYOR may carry a stool or an orange crate on which he will stand. The street lamp is optional. It may be a painted cutout pinned to the stage curtain.

In Act Two, you may "pretend" there are a boarded-up window and a door, stage right. The cupboard too, may be a painted cutout. The various props are then placed on a utility table in front of it.

Costumes

The players wear clothes of the current day.

Props

A big bell, a basket of clean laundry, several bags of groceries, an overnight bag with stage money, cigarettes, three guns, a white towel, dishes, cutlery, food ingredients, pots and pans, a large container of pepper, recognizable as such by the viewers.

A REAL BIRTHDAY PRESENT

A PLAY IN TWO ACTS

Playing Time   15 minutes approximately

Age   9—13 years

Manner of Presentation   Improvise lines
or
Memorize lines

Staging Suggestions   See end of play

Cast   Mrs. Fields (an understanding mother)
Cathy Fields (her ten-year-old daughter)
Cathy's Friends (among them Ricky, Joan and Rochelle)
Lynn (another friend—a spoiled girl)
Judy Hicks (an unhappy tomboy who tells fibs)
Esther, the Maid

Time   The present: early summer

Place   A garden

Scene   The entire action takes place in the Fields' garden. This has for its important piece of furniture a round garden table, upstage center. There are garden chairs on either side of the table, a garden bench, downstage right and a stool, left center.

A white picket fence, stage right, separates the garden from the street, offstage. The kitchen side of the Fields' home can be seen stage left. Shrubbery forms the back wall of the garden.

The street entrance is through a gate in the middle of the fence, right. The house entrance is upstage left.

ACT ONE

The curtain opens as MRS. FIELDS, *a pleasant, motherly woman, comes out of her house, upstage left. She is crossing to the table, a dustcloth in her hand, when she notices her neighbors.* (MRS. FIELDS *acts here as a narrator. The audience acts as her neighbors.*)

MRS. FIELDS (*crossing down to greet the audience*):   Hello there. I'm Mrs. Fields, your neighbor. You know—I live in this house with my family. We haven't been here long, but you must have noticed us fussing in our garden many times—that is, Mr. Fields, my daughter Cathy, and me.

  We love it here—thanks to you who have been so helpful and *friendly*. As a matter of fact, Mr. Fields and I were talking about it only last night— the friendliness of everyone in this town. It's wonderful, it really is, the way you all get along with one another, the way you *understand* one another. Even the children are like that. Why, they seem to understand problems you'd expect only grownups would. Just as in the case of Cathy's friend, Judy Hicks. The children were quick to see what was bothering Judy.

Oh, not at the very start, of course. She wasn't Cathy's friend then or anyone else's. "That tomboy!" they used to call her and poke fun at her whenever they got a chance. In fact, that was what they were doing the day of Cathy's . . . birthday party. (*Insert player's age.*)

It was the morning of her party, I remember, and I was in the kitchen— (MRS. FIELDS *starts walking to the house*)—putting chocolate icing on the birthday cake. Through the open window I could hear Cathy and her friends chattering away about the party. Judy wasn't there. . . .

(MRS. FIELDS *exits into the house as* CATHY *and* ROCHELLE *come skipping into the garden right.* JOAN *and* RICKY *follow them.*)

CATHY (*she is a very nice girl. As she skips rope, she talks enthusiastically*): And wait until you see my birthday cake!

JOAN (*a chubby girl fond of food. Eagerly*): Cake! Where is it?

CATHY (*stops skipping to sit on stool*): It's not ready, silly. My mother's in the kitchen icing it now. But you'll see it at my party this afternoon.

JOAN (*disappointed*): Who wants to see it?

ROCHELLE (*disapprovingly, as a well-mannered lady would*): Joan, can't you forget food for once?

JOAN (*rubbing her stomach and wailing*): I can, Rochelle. But my *stomach* can't.

RICKY (*a detective at heart, she lies on the grass, examining a bug through a magnifying glass*): Cathy, are you going to show movies?

CATHY: But natch, Ricky. *Silly Symphony* and—

RICKY (*interrupting*): Oh kid stuff! Why don't you show *Dick Tracy* or *The Man from Outer Space*?

ROCHELLE: Cathy, did you invite Judy Hicks to your party? She's been telling the whole block that you did.

CATHY (*concerned*): I didn't but do you think I should have?

ROCHELLE: I should say not! She's a thief!

CATHY (*jumping up, shocked*): Rochelle, you shouldn't say that!

ROCHELLE: Well, that's what Lynn calls her. Judy's always lying and sneaking behind your back and Lynn once told me . . .

(*A street commotion interrupts* ROCHELLE. *The* GIRLS *hear screaming, offstage right.*)

RICKY: Hey, there's Lynn now! And she's yanking Judy by the arm!

GIRLS (*improvising in excitement as they jump up to look*): Where? . . . Oh migosh! . . . They're coming this way! . . .

CATHY: What can be wrong?

ROCHELLE: Whatever's wrong, you can bet Judy's at the bottom of it.
(*At this moment,* LYNN, *a spoiled darling inclined to be unpleasant, pulls* JUDY *into the garden through gate right. Dirty, hair wild, her dungarees half up, half down,* JUDY *is holding on to a ragged doll while trying desperately to break out of* LYNN's *grasp.*)

JUDY (*kicking and screaming*):   Let go of me! Let go, I tell you or—

LYNN (*pulling her to center*):   Oh no, you don't!

CATHY (*trying to separate them*):   Judy, Lynn, stop it! Both of you!
(LYNN *grabs* JUDY's *doll.*)

JUDY: My doll! Give me back my doll!

LYNN (*holding doll out of* JUDY's *reach*):   NO! Not until you repeat what you said down the street!

GIRLS (*exclaiming*):   What happened, Lynn? . . . What did she say? . . .

LYNN (*prodding* JUDY):   Go on—repeat it.

JUDY (*sullenly*):   You can't make me. This is a free country!

LYNN: Then I'll say it for you! (*To the* GIRLS.) She's told everybody that Cathy invited her to the party!

JUDY: You're making it up!
(*She makes a grab for her doll again and regains it.*)

LYNN: You're lying! I heard you!

JUDY (*fighting* LYNN):   You take that back or I'll . . .
(*All the* GIRLS *but* CATHY *join in the fight.*)

CATHY: Stop it! Stop it, all of you! (*The* GIRLS *subside.*) Judy's telling the truth. I did invite her. (*The* GIRLS *exclaim.*)

LYNN: Oh, you're just saying that to help her. You're always helping her.

GIRLS (*improvising*):   Yes, that's what you're doing! . . . It's true, you're always taking her part! . . . You don't know what she's really like! . . . She's a liar and a thief! . . . (*Just then, they hear the ice cream vendor's bell, offstage right. Forgetting* JUDY, *the* GIRLS *dash to the fence.*) The popsicle man! Yum—yum! . . . I'm going to buy a pop—what about you? . . . Have you enough money? . . . I've a quarter and two pennies. . . . Maybe the popsicle man will let me owe him the money. . . . We shouldn't eat pops before lunch. . . . What will you buy? . . . I'm getting a doublestix. . . . Chocolate sundae for me. . . .

CATHY (*following the* GIRLS):   Ask him if he has orange—(*She remembers* JUDY *and turns back to her.*) Judy, don't you want a pop?

JUDY (*shakes her head. Then fidgeting with her doll while her foot traces patterns on the ground, she speaks awkwardly*):   Cathy—thanks.

CATHY: Thanks for what?

JUDY: For saying what you did—that you invited me.

CATHY: Oh that's okay, Judy.

JUDY: But Lynn was right. I *did* lie.

CATHY: It doesn't matter. I'm still inviting you. I want you to come.

JUDY (*overwhelmed*): You—do?

CATHY: Natch.

JUDY: Even though I—?

(JOAN, RICKY and ROCHELLE *trail back into the garden licking their pops.* JOAN *hands one to* CATHY.)

JOAN: Here's your orange pop, Cathy. Ten cents.

CATHY: I'll get the money from Moms. (*She is unwrapping her pop when she notices* JUDY *has none and impulsively offers hers.*) Here, Judy, you take it. I don't feel like having any after all.

(*Surprised at* CATHY's *kindness,* JUDY *accepts the pop after a little hesitation. She puts her doll down on the table and starts to remove the wrapper as* LYNN *returns to the garden.*)

LYNN: Watch out, Cathy! Judy's snitched your pop!

CATHY: Oh stop picking on her. I gave it to her. I feel sorry for Judy. She has no money.

JUDY (*her pride stung*): I have too! Lots of money—fifty dollars! Right here in my pocket! I can buy all the pops I want! Only I don't want to, that's all! Here, take your dirty, old pop!

(*Humiliated and angry, she throws the pop at* CATHY *splattering* CATHY's *dress.*)

CATHY: My dress! You nasty thing you! Look at what you did to my dress! After I was nice to you and invited you to my party!

JUDY (*horror-struck*): I—I—Cathy— Oh—oh—oh—

(*Forgetting her doll on the table,* JUDY *runs out of the garden, right.*)

LYNN: You see! I told you she's a horrible girl!

RICKY (*discovering the doll*): She forgot her doll.

JOAN: Do you think she stole that too?

LYNN: That old rag! No one would own it but Judy. She *loves* it!

ROCHELLE: It must be near lunch time. I'd better go home.

GIRLS (*improvising*): Gosh, I hope it isn't late, my mother will skin me! . . . See you this afternoon, Cathy . . . . Don't tell your mother you ate a pop. . . . See you, Cathy, at the party. . . .

CATHY: Come on time, will you? The party starts at three o'clock.

(*The* GIRLS *leave through the gate, right.* CATHY, *unhappy over the pop incident, wanders to the table. Picking up* JUDY's *doll, she looks at it curiously; then, angry again, she dumps it back on the table as* MRS. FIELDS *enters from upstage left.* MRS. FIELDS *is now a part of the play.*)

MRS. FIELDS: Don't be angry, Cathy.

CATHY: Oh Moms, you don't know what happened! Judy Hicks . . .

MRS. FIELDS: I know. I saw everything from the kitchen.

CATHY: Did you see her throw the pop at me? After I gave it to her! Did you hear her lie about the money? (MRS. FIELDS *nods.*) And I felt sorry for her!

MRS. FIELDS: That's why she did it. (CATHY *looks puzzled.*) You see—(*she stops and smiles*)—no, how could you see? Well, let me try to explain it so you'll understand. (*Thinking hard,* MRS. FIELDS *sits down on the garden bench and pulls* CATHY *down to the ground beside her.*) You see, darling, Judy is a very lonely girl. Her mother died when she was a baby and her father—

CATHY (*interrupting*): He's away on business a lot. I know. But she has a maid.

MRS. FIELDS: So have you—Esther. On and off, off and on. But would Esther take the place of Daddy and me?

CATHY: No.

MRS. FIELDS: Then how would you feel if you had to live without Daddy and me most of the time? If you didn't have us?

CATHY (*scared, she hugs her mother*): Oh Moms, don't ever leave me— you or Daddy.

MRS. FIELDS: We won't, darling. Only just imagine we had to. Just imagine you're Judy. How would you feel then?

CATHY: I don't know. Lonely and sad and—sort of scared. Of people, I mean.

MRS. FIELDS: Because you'd think no one loved you, wouldn't you? And how would you behave then?

CATHY: Shy maybe or—(*Stops.*)

MRS. FIELDS (*prompting*): Or—

CATHY: Mean and sneaky and—(*getting the idea, she jumps up*)—JUDY! Just like JUDY!

MRS. FIELDS: And all because you weren't sure that anyone cared to be your friend.

CATHY: But I wanted to—I gave her my pop!

MRS. FIELDS: Didn't you do it because you were sorry for her?

CATHY: Yes, but—

MRS. FIELDS: —And didn't you say so in front of the girls?

CATHY: Yes, but—

MRS. FIELDS: Well, that wasn't what Judy wanted to hear. You can be sorry for a person and still not care to be her friend—really care. Judy was hoping you gave her the pop because you *liked* her.

CATHY (*ashamed*): I didn't think—I didn't realize—

MRS. FIELDS (*hugging her*): Never mind, darling. We all make mistakes. Just as long as we see them and correct them. Just as long as we *try* to see them. Next time you meet Judy you'll know what to say and do. (*She rises.*) Now we'd better get started on that party of yours. Oh, before I forget— (*She takes a small package out of her apron pocket. It is wrapped in shiny red paper and glittering ribbon.*)—here's your birthday present from Daddy and me.

CATHY (*excited*): May I open it now?

MRS. FIELDS: Not now. At the party. But it's what you've been begging for.

CATHY: A wrist watch! You're swell! You and Daddy both! (*She hugs her.*) I'm so lucky to have you both.

MRS. FIELDS: Now come along and get the decorations. We want to fix the garden before your friends come.

(MRS. FIELDS *exits into the house.* CATHY *is following her when* JUDY *peeps into the garden, right. She has returned to fetch her doll. As she stoops to pick up her skip rope,* CATHY *sees* JUDY. *She calls happily.*)

CATHY: Judy!

JUDY (*on the defensive*): All right, all right, I'm going. I only came to get my doll.

CATHY: Don't go yet—please. I'd like to talk to you. You're my friend.

JUDY (*suspicious*): Friend?

CATHY: My friend. (LYNN, *entering from house, left, overhears the following.*) That's why I want you to come to my party. You are coming, aren't you?

JUDY (*surprised*): You *still* want me to? After what happened?

CATHY: Oh that. My dress was dirty anyway.

JUDY (*shyly*): Cathy, I—your pop—I shouldn't have thrown it.

CATHY: Forget it.

JUDY: It's just that I felt you—I thought—you really *want* me to come?

CATHY: But natch. I like you.

JUDY (*jumping into the air with joy*): You like me! Oh boy! Will I come!

Will I! Will—I! (*Hugging her doll,* JUDY *runs out of the garden, right, exclaiming.*) Oh boy—oh boy—oh—

CATHY (*calling after her*): It's at three o'clock.

LYNN (*coming forward*): What did you want to do that for?

CATHY: Lynn! Where did you come from?

LYNN: Your house. My mother sent me over with some glasses for the party. Why did you have to invite her?

CATHY: Because I wanted to. I like her.

LYNN: Like? Are you crazy or something?

CATHY: Judy's a nice girl.

LYNN: Are we talking about the same animal?

CATHY: She's nice when you understand her.

LYNN: Ha! You are crazy! I wouldn't invite her if she were the only girl in the world. She'll spoil your party.

CATHY: She won't.

LYNN (*leaving through garden gate*): She will. She will too.

CATHY (*tossing her head defiantly*): How much do you want to bet? (MRS. FIELDS *calls to her again and she turns and runs into the house.*) I'm coming, Moms—I'm coming—

(*as the curtain closes.*)

ACT TWO

MRS. FIELDS *enters now and crosses down to the audience. She speaks to them in her role of narrator. Behind the curtain, the garden is being decorated for Act Two. Balloons and streamers are hung to give a festive air. Gaily-wrapped packages are placed on the table.*

MRS. FIELDS: That's how matters stood the morning of Cathy's party. After I had explained to my daughter how much Judy needed a good friend, Cathy was determined to become that friend—despite Lynn's warnings that the tomboy was bound to spoil the birthday party. (*She asks the audience.*) What do you think? Did Judy spoil the fun? . . . To be frank, I wasn't sure myself whether Lynn was right or not. After all, it takes a long time to convince a girl who has been hurt as Judy Hicks had, that you really want to be her friend. A sensitive girl like Judy is so quick to imagine that people are teasing when they are not. Anyway, I was still worrying about the outcome of Cathy's invitation when three o'clock rolled around and—(*The curtain opens for Act Two.*)—the party began. Cathy and Esther, our helper, had decorated the garden with balloons and streamers, and there were a number of presents on the garden table, including the wrist watch her father and I had given Cathy. (*She points to the conspicuously-wrapped package lying on top of the other presents.*) You can see it right there on top of the others. It's the red one with the glittering ribbon. (*She crosses to the house.*) Some of the early guests were already in the house looking at the movies and others were arriving. . . .

(MRS. FIELDS *exits into the house as* ESTHER *passes her ushering two* GIRLS *on stage. They are carrying presents.*)

ESTHER: Better put your presents here on the table, girls. This is where Mrs. Fields said for them to go.

GIRL 1 (*placing her package*):   Look at all these packages!

GIRL 2:   Gee, I wish it were my birthday.

(*They return to the house.*)

GIRL 1:   You know what? Lynn told me Cathy invited Judy! Did you ever hear of such a crazy thing?

GIRL 2:   JUDY? NO!

(*They exit as three* GIRLS *enter from house carrying packages. They place them on the table and return to the house, talking all the time.*)

ESTHER: This way, girls. This is the present place.

GIRL 3:   I got her a paint set. What did you bring?

GIRL 4:   My mother picked a book. She never lets me do my own choosing.

GIRL 5:   You should see what I brought—lollipop panties!

GIRL 3:   Say, has Judy come yet?

GIRL 4:   Judy coming here? What does Cathy want to have—a party or a brawl?

(*The three exit into house as five more* GIRLS *enter, place their presents on the table and return to the house, talking.*)

ESTHER: Come on, girls. I collect the presents today.

GIRL 6:   Did you see the birthday cake?

GIRL 7:   I hope they give us ice cream with it.

GIRL 8:   What if they do? Judy Hicks is coming!

GIRL 9:   Judy, oh no!

GIRL 10:   She'll ruin everything—just everything!

ESTHER: Hurry, hurry. You want to miss all of *Silly Symphony*?

GIRL 6:   Well, if she comes, I'm going home.

GIRL 7:   Cathy will be sorry and how!

GIRL 8:   Oh forget Judy and—come on. I want to see the movies.

>   (*They exit into house.*)

ESTHER (*placing red package on top of others*):   My goodness, all these and a wrist watch too! What a haul! I bet there are enough presents here to open up a store. (*She exits into house.*)

>   (*A moment later,* JUDY *walks in through gate right. She has dressed for the party by brushing and rolling down her dungarees and by wearing an odd-looking hat. She is talking to her doll.*)

JUDY: You understand, don't you? It's not because I don't love you any more. Because I do—you know I do. (*She hugs the doll.*) I love you more than anybody in the whole world except—except Cathy. She's my friend. My first friend. She *likes* me. That's what she said. Honest. So you see, don't you? It's her birthday and a friend must give a very special present to a friend. Not any old thing you can buy in a store either. But a real birthday present, something you love and want to keep for yourself. Something like you. (*In a sudden realization of the parting, she hugs the doll then walks to the table.*) I guess this is where you go—with the other presents. I'll put you under this pretty red package and—

>   (*She is holding the red package when she sees people coming out of the house. Reacting with her usual fear, she flings the package into the bushes behind her.* MRS. FIELDS, *with candy dish, and* LYNN, *with present, enter.* LYNN *looks at* JUDY *suspiciously.* MRS. FIELDS *is now a part of the play.*)

MRS. FIELDS: Hello, Judy. Cathy was beginning to wonder if you were coming.

JUDY: I came the back way.

MRS. FIELDS: Put your present here, Lynn dear.

>   (LYNN *places her present on the table and returns to the house after throwing* JUDY *a meaningful look.*)

MRS. FIELDS: Don't you want to see the movies too, Judy? You missed part of them already.

JUDY: Yes, Ma'am, I'm going.

MRS. FIELDS: Won't you give me your hat?

JUDY: Oh no. I'd like to keep it on if it's okay.

MRS. FIELDS: It's such a pretty hat, I don't blame you.

JUDY (*pleased*):   It is?

MRS. FIELDS: You know, Judy, I've been wanting to talk to you.

JUDY (*breaking away, suspicious*):   To me?

MRS. FIELDS: Yes. I wanted to tell you that I'm glad you decided to be Cathy's friend.

JUDY: I—decided?

MRS. FIELDS: Cathy needs a friend like you. A real friend. You *will* be her friend, won't you?

JUDY (*overcome*):   Oh, Mrs. Fields, I am already. Just to prove it, look what I brought her as a present.

(*She points to her doll.*)

MRS. FIELDS: Your own doll? But isn't that what you love best?

JUDY: That's why I'm giving it to Cathy. To show her I'm a real friend. I was hiding it under the other presents to surprise her.

MRS. FIELDS (*hugging her*):   You're a darling. It's a beautiful surprise. Now, let's go and see the movies, shall we? (*They start to cross to the house.*) Oh, oh, I think we're too late. Here come the girls.

(CATHY *enters and walks to the table. She is accompanied by* LYNN, JOAN, ROCHELLE, RICKY *and the other* GIRLS.)

CATHY: Come on, slaves. I'm going to open the presents now. (*She sees* JUDY.) Oh, here's Judy. I'm glad you came after all.

(*The other* GIRLS *point at* JUDY's *hat and whisper.*)

MRS. FIELDS: You girls look at the presents while I set the dining room table for ice cream and cake.

(*She exits into house.*)

GIRLS (*improvising*):   Open them, Cathy. Let's see what you got. . . . Yes, yes, open them. . . . You sure *have* a pile. . . . On my birthday, I got only twelve presents. . . . Buy me a fish tank, someone. . . . I can't wait for my birthday, it's next week. . . .

CATHY (*standing at table*):   All of you sit in a circle and I'll start. (*Noticing that everyone ignores* JUDY.) Here, Judy, you sit near me. I need you to help. Now, let's see, which one shall I open first? Oh, the present my parents gave me, natch. (*She looks for the red package.*) Where is it?

ROCHELLE: Which one is it, Cathy?

CATHY: It's wrapped in red paper. I don't see it.

RICKY (*pulling out her magnifying glass, she examines the table*):   Is this the one?

CATHY: No, red paper.

JOAN: What was in it? Chocolates?

CATHY: No, a wrist watch.

LYNN: I got two of them on my birthday.

RICKY: Where was it last?

CATHY: I left it here on top of the other presents when we went in to the movies.

RICKY: If we could only find a clue.

GIRL 1:   I remember seeing it when I put my present there.

CATHY: What are you doing, Ricky?

RICKY: Searching for fingerprints.

JOAN: Do you think it was stolen?

GIRL 10:   Who could have stolen it? We—(*she points to the* GIRLS *who had been in the garden with her*)—saw it when we brought our presents and we were the last ones to come.

LYNN (*stands up, accusingly*):   The last—but one. (*She points at* JUDY.) Judy!

(JUDY *jumps up. She is shocked and on the defensive.*)

GIRLS (*improvising*):   Judy! . . . I knew it! . . . She's always stealing! . . . Didn't I say she'd spoil everything? . . .

LYNN: Your mother and I found her here alone when you were watching the movies. Weren't you, Judy? Weren't you here alone?

(JUDY *backs upstage defiantly and says nothing.*)

CATHY: Were you, Judy?

GIRLS (*encircling her*):   Were you?—Were you? WERE YOU?

(JUDY *remains silent.*)

LYNN: And she was holding the red package. I saw her as I came in. Weren't you, Judy? (JUDY *is silent.*) You see, she's afraid to admit it. She stole the watch and—

CATHY (*coming to* JUDY's *defense*):   That's a mean thing to say, Lynn!

LYNN: Then what was she doing with it? Ask her.

JUDY (*bursting out*):   I wasn't doing anything! I wasn't even near the table!

RICKY (*discovering* JUDY's *doll on the table and holding it up*):   Oh yes you were! You forgot your doll.

(JUDY *snatches her doll away.*)

LYNN: There's your evidence. What more do you need? She stole the watch.

CATHY (*disappointed*):   Oh Judy—

JUDY (*shocked by* CATHY's *acceptance of her guilt*):   You believe Lynn? You—You're not my friend after all! You're not! I hate you! I hate all of you!

> (*A battle ensues during which* JUDY *climbs on the table.* MRS. FIELDS *and* ESTHER *run out of the house to separate the children.*)

MRS. FIELDS: Girls, girls, girls! What's gotten into you?

ESTHER: Quit kicking! You'll hurt somebody!

> (*The* GIRLS *quiet down.*)

MRS. FIELDS: What happened? (*No one answers.*) Cathy?

CATHY: The wrist watch is gone!

LYNN (*breaking in*):   Judy stole it, Mrs. Fields!

MRS. FIELDS: Stole? Now, wait a moment, Lynn.

ROCHELLE: We saw it there when we went in to the movies and then Judy sneaked in here and—it's gone!

MRS. FIELDS (*firmly*):   Judy did not sneak in!

RICKY: Then what was she doing here alone? Why didn't she come through the house like the rest of us?

MRS. FIELDS: Tell them, Judy. (JUDY *climbs down from the table.* MRS. FIELDS *puts her arm around her.*) Go on, dear.

JUDY: I wanted to put my present here without Cathy's seeing it. It was to be a surprise.

MRS. FIELDS (*holding up the doll*):   Was this your surprise? (JUDY *nods.*)

CATHY (*happy*):   Then you didn't leave it there by mistake. You were *giving* it to me!

MRS. FIELDS: That's right. As for stealing the watch, it must be . . .

JUDY: I took the watch. (*Everyone exclaims.*) But I didn't steal it. I picked it up to hide my present under it and then you and Lynn came in, and I got scared so I threw it over there. (*She points to the bushes.*) I was afraid you'd say I was stealing it.

> (RICKY *hunts in the bushes.*)

CATHY: Oh Judy, why didn't you tell us right off?

JUDY: I was scared you wouldn't believe me.

RICKY (*finding package*):   Here it is! (*She hands it to* CATHY.)

CATHY: I'm sorry, Judy, for the way I behaved—(*she turns to the* GIRLS) —for the way we all behaved. We should apologize. Shouldn't we, Lynn?

LYNN (*mumbling*):   I'm sorry. . .

> (*The other* GIRLS *mumble their apologies too.*)

JUDY: That's okay.

CATHY: And I make a promise too. I'll never judge anyone again the way we did you. Never. (*She puts out her hand to* JUDY.) Shake?

JUDY (*a moment's pause then*):   Shake.

MRS. FIELDS (*all smiles*):   All right, girls, all right. Now let's go in and have the ice cream before it melts. We'll open the presents later.

> (*She exits into the house,* ESTHER *and all the* GIRLS, *except* CATHY *and* JUDY, *following her.*)

GIRLS (*improvising as they leave*):   Ice cream! . . . at last! Now the party really begins! . . . I'm starved. . . . But you ate three hamburgers for lunch! . . .

CATHY (*alone with* JUDY, *seriously*):   Judy, this morning I said something to you about being your friend. I didn't really mean it. Not then, that is. But I do *now*. Will you be my friend, Judy? (JUDY *looks at* CATHY; *then, smiling quickly, she holds out her doll.* CATHY *accepts it.*) You will? Oh Judy, that's the nicest present anyone can give me today. That's a real birthday present. (*She takes* JUDY's *hand just as the guests start to sing* "Happy Birthday" *offstage left.*) Oh gosh, the birthday cake! Judy, you should see the cake! Five pink, fat roses with chocolate icing and the most delicious little green buds all around the outside and to top it all . .

> (*Chatting, arm in arm, the two* GIRLS *walk into the house as the strains of* "Happy Birthday" *ring out joyously and*
>
> > *the curtain closes.*)

STAGING SUGGESTIONS

Comments

This play is an example of the way in which a child's own moods, interests and problems are used by a leader as the basis for creative work. How it actually originated is described in Chapter 9 of this book.

Since the play deals with a problem that appeals to older children, it has the conventional play form they prefer—that is, its lines may be rehearsed and presented as written. If the players wish to improvise all dialogue, keep MRS. FIELDS to one side of the stage where she can prompt in her role as NAR-

RATOR. She then moves into the play proper whenever her part as MOTHER requires it.

Cast

Increase or decrease the number of FRIENDS and PARTY GUESTS to fit the needs of your group and stage space. If your group is small, reduce cast number by having ROCHELLE, RICKY and JOAN of Act One act as the guests who open up Act Two. ESTHER may be replaced by a FRIEND or omitted.

If the dialogue is improvised, the all-girl players are easily changed to a mixed or all-boy cast. The boys will add their own masculine flavor to the lines.

Cast the mature players in the roles of JUDY, CATHY and MRS. FIELDS. JUDY must be portrayed carefully to have point and meaning.

Set

The garden may be suggested simply with table, chairs, stool and several cutouts of shrubbery placed against the back curtains of the stage. For a more elaborate set, the white picket fence may be painted on drawing, builder's or wrapping paper and tacked onto the side curtains. You may be able to borrow a real fence from your local lumber company. Cardboard cutouts or screens may be used instead of the fence. Remember to leave an opening in the center for the "gate."

The side of the house, if retained, may be produced in the same way. Paint flowers at its base. Cutouts or screens to which real green branches have been tacked may be placed as shrubs at the back of the stage.

For Act Two, balloons and streamers decorate the garden. The table is laden with gifts.

Costumes

The GIRLS wear hot weather play clothes—shorts, shirts, cotton dresses—in the morning and party dresses in the afternoon. CATHY wears a dress in the morning as well as in the afternoon. JUDY is dressed like the disheveled tomboy she is—dirty or patched dungarees, a torn T-shirt and tangles in her hair. For the party she combs her hair, washes her face, cleans up her dungarees and puts on an odd-looking hat—perhaps a big, floppy one with roses! MRS. FIELDS wears a summer frock and apron. She removes the apron for Act Two. ESTHER has a maid's uniform.

Props

A good-sized, shabby doll, a funny-looking hat for JUDY; a dustcloth and a candy dish for MRS. FIELDS; a skip rope for CATHY; a magnifying glass for RICKY; many presents, one of which is small and wrapped in red paper and glittering ribbon, popsicles, balloons and streamer decorations, the last spelling out "Happy Birthday."

Freeing Exercises

Most of the situations in this play are part of the "here-and-now" experiences of boys and girls. If your players have not had creative dramatic experience, it is a good idea to precede rehearsals with a general limbering up of the whole group.

To evoke "excitement," you may use either or both of the following situations:

a. You are sitting at your school desk after the last bell has rung. You have to write a sentence one hundred times as punishment for talking in class. As you bend down to the wearisome task, you hear the distant strains of band music. A parade! And it's coming this way!

You sneak a look at Teacher but her stern expression tells you there is no chance of her dismissing you. You try to concentrate on your writing. The parade comes closer—the music excites you—your restlessness increases—your feet and fingers begin to beat the time. You try to write but the drums pound in your head, the trumpets call you, the—

"Put your book away. You can go!" Teacher says suddenly, and—excitement . . . !

b. You look forward to the arrival of Grandpa and especially to the "surprise" he is bringing you. Grandpa comes, he presents you with his gift and you thank him as nicely as you know how. You open the present and find something you have admired a long, long time—a charm bracelet, perhaps, or a baseball mitt.

The best exercises will follow the narration of the true story on which the play is based. Ask your players if they know someone like JUDY. Question them about her appearance, her mannerisms, her actions and motivations. Keep on digging until everyone is not only talking about her but "acting her out." When the players suggest situations, introduce into these scenes many of the characters who surround JUDY in the play.

You will find that young people are surprisingly wise and understanding.

THE EMPEROR'S NEW CLOTHES

AN ADAPTATION OF THE FAIRY TALE* BY HANS CHRISTIAN ANDERSEN IN TWO ACTS

Playing Time   20 minutes approximately

Age   9—14 years

Manner of Presentation   Improvise lines
                                          or
                                          Memorize lines

Staging Suggestions   See end of play

Cast   Two Jesters
            The Emperor
            His Minister
            The Empress

* As translated by Mrs. Edgar Lucas.

Two Guards
Beggars (among them a blind old man, his daughter, his grand-
     child)
Two Tailors
Dancers
Musicians
Street People

Time Long, long ago

Place China

Scenes

ACT ONE The Emperor's Throne Room and the Hall outside
ACT TWO The Tower Room and the Hall outside

ACT ONE

Scene For the Throne Room and the Hall outside, the stage is divided
into two sections. About two-thirds of the area, stage left and center, are occupied by the Throne Room. The space that remains,
stage right, is the Hall. It is separated from the Throne Room by
an arched door frame or Chinese screen. A short flight of steps,
apron right, leads down from the Hall to the audience level. A
Throne, anchored to a dais, is situated at left center. A flowering
tree decorates downstage left, and a Chinese screen stands at the
back of the stage.

Entrances are stage right, stage left, as well as audience level, to the
right of the steps.

When the curtain opens, the EMPEROR *is seated on his throne. He is a good-
natured monarch though he is too fond of fine clothes. His* MINISTER, *a wise,*

old man, and his EMPRESS, *a loving wife, stand on either side of the throne. His two favorite* JESTERS *recline before him. Two brawny* GUARDS *watch at the hall side of the archway.*

The JESTERS *are displaying various jewels and silks to* HIS IMPERIAL MAJESTY, *who is dissatisfied with what he sees. The* MINISTER *is looking through a large appointment book and shaking his head glumly. The* EMPRESS *is watching her husband, a worried frown on her face.*

JESTER ONE:　Look at this blue silk, O Sun of Suns. The coloring is exquisite.

JESTER TWO:　And laced with silver braid, O Moon of Moons, you will have a gorgeous coat for the procession next week.

EMPEROR (*dissatisfied with the display*):　I wore a coat of blue and silver yesterday. I can't wear the same colors twice. Not for the procession. Remember, it celebrates the first anniversary of my reign. All my ten kingdoms will turn out to see me. My robes must be unique.

MINISTER (*he has been trying to gain the* EMPEROR's *attention*):　Sire, may I talk to you, please?

EMPRESS:　Listen to your faithful Councilor, my royal husband. He is wise.

EMPEROR:　Later, my love. Can you not see there are important things on my mind? Jester, show me the red velvet again.

EMPRESS:　But, my husband, you have appointments. There are people here to see you.

MINISTER:　The famine delegation has been waiting for days to speak to you about the lack of food.

EMPEROR:　I said I'd speak to them. Only later. The procession is next week. Do you want my people to see their Emperor in any old thing? I may as well wear the rags I wore as a boy. Now, where was I? Oh, the red velvet. (*He looks at the material then shoves it away.*) No, it's too ordinary. Every little mandarin will be wearing red.

JESTER ONE:　You can line it with satin.

JESTER TWO:　And edge it with pearls.

MINISTER:　Sire, I beg you, the delegation—

EMPEROR (*interrupting*):　My robes come first. I must make a good impression on my subjects. It is my duty as a good ruler.

MINISTER:　But fine clothes do not make the good ruler.

EMPEROR (*getting angry*):　You dare to say I am unfit for my throne? You dare, Old One?

EMPRESS: The Wise One meant kindly, my husband. He loves you.

EMPEROR (*to the* JESTERS):   Take this trash away! And fetch my entertainers instead. Perhaps their music will help me think of a special creation. Fetch them—(*he claps his hands*)—quick! Quick!

(*Bowing and moving backwards as he goes,* JESTER ONE *exits, stage left. In the meantime, cries of "Let us see the Emperor!—The Emperor will help us!—We must see the Emperor!" are heard, off right, audience level. They come from several* BEGGARS *who now appear, audience level, and attempt to surge up the steps into the Hall. The two* GUARDS *jump to the steps and keep the* BEGGARS *from advancing. Among the* BEGGARS *are a blind* OLD MAN, *his* DAUGHTER, *his* GRANDCHILD.)

DAUGHTER: You can't keep us out anymore! We must see the Emperor!

OLD MAN: The Emperor—the Emperor—Take us to the Emperor!

CHILD: I'm hungry! My stomach hurts!

GUARD ONE: Have you an appointment?

DAUGHTER: No, but we must speak to him!

OLD MAN: The Emperor will take pity on a blind old man.

CHILD: I'm hungry! I want a piece of bread!

GUARD TWO: No one may see His Majesty without an appointment.

DAUGHTER: Please, please, let us in! We're desperate! It's a matter of our very lives!

GUARD ONE: His Majesty is occupied just now.

OLD MAN: He wouldn't let a blind old man starve. He's good.

CHILD: I want a piece of bread!

DAUGHTER: If you don't let us in, we'll push our way through!

(*The* BEGGARS *push and the* GUARDS *swing their weapons. In the Throne Room, the* EMPEROR *is too busy thinking about his processional robes to notice the* BEGGARS' *cries. The* MINISTER *and the* EMPRESS *hear them and worry. At a signal from the* EMPRESS, *the* MINISTER *hurries out to the Hall. The* GUARDS *salute him and the* BEGGARS *prostrate themselves before him.*)

MINISTER (*to the* BEGGARS):   My dear people.

BEGGARS: The Minister!—The Wise One!

MINISTER: What is it, my dear people?

DAUGHTER: We're starving, O Wise One. We've eaten little but roots for days!

OLD MAN: Have pity on a blind old man!

CHILD: I'm hungry! My stomach hurts!

MINISTER: The Emperor will help you all he can, dear people. Soon he will fill your bellies with bread. Soon—I promise you.

BEGGARS (*bowing, they move backwards until they are out of sight, audience right*):   Thank you, wisest of men! . . . May your years be many . . . May your years be honored . . . Thank you . . . Thank you . . .

(*As the* BEGGARS *exit, the* EMPRESS *hurries into the Hall.*)

EMPRESS: What was it they wished, Great Sage?

MINISTER: Food, O Pearl among Pearls. Their bellies are empty and all our Emperor can think of is fine clothes.

EMPRESS: You must be patient with him. He had no clothing once. You told me that, O Wise One. Remember?

MINISTER: Yes, yes, I remember. His father's enemies had kidnaped the little prince and left him on the river bank to die. If an old fisherman had not found him, he would have perished. Yes, I remember.

EMPRESS: And do you remember how poor that fisherman was, and how the boy had nothing but rags to cover himself with in the wind? Is it strange that he thinks of little but finery now?

MINISTER: But he neglects his duties. His people starve!

EMPRESS: If only we could find a way to make him see this. To tell him is not enough.

MINISTER: I have a plan—a sort of trap. (*He takes the* EMPRESS *aside so the* GUARDS *will not hear.*) Listen, O Pearl among Pearls. I know two Tailors who, to fill their bellies, will weave him robes of wondrous beauty.

EMPRESS: More finery!

MINISTER: But with this difference. The robes will not exist.

EMPRESS (*puzzled*):   I do not understand.

MINISTER: The Tailors will *pretend* to weave these robes. Special robes with a magic quality. He who cannot see them will know he is unfit for his post.

EMPRESS: Still I do not understand.

MINISTER: The Emperor wishes to dazzle his people at the procession, does he not? For this, he is bound to order the robes. And when he fails to see them, he will know what our words could never make him know, he will know—

EMPRESS (*finishing his sentence*):   —that he is unfit to rule. I understand now. (*Worried.*) Only what if some servant, some courtier reveals that there are no garments, that there is nothing?

MINISTER: They will not dare. Their own posts are at stake. Yet if they do reveal the trick, my head will be the victim.

EMPRESS: Fear not for your head. The Emperor is a thoughtless child but good. He will understand that you tricked him for love of him.

MINISTER: I do not know. But try I must to make him see himself for what he is. He is turning foolish with vanity. And these are not times for a foolish ruler. (*To* GUARD ONE.) Go fetch the two Tailors who wait for me in the courtyard.

(*As the* GUARD *descends the steps to fetch the* TAILORS, *off audience right,* JESTER ONE *returns to the Throne Room, bringing the* EMPEROR's MUSICIANS *and* DANCERS. *The* MUSICIANS *seat themselves on the ground, backstage, and start to play as the* DANCERS *prostrate themselves before the Throne. In the Hall, the* EMPRESS *hears the music and takes leave of the* MINISTER.)

EMPRESS: The entertainers have come. I must return to my royal husband. Good fortune await your plan, O Wise One.

(*The* EMPRESS *rejoins the* EMPEROR *as he signals the* DANCERS *to start their dance. During the dance, the* MINISTER *paces up and down the Hall. The dance comes to an end.*)

EMPEROR (*despairing*): Nothing! I can think of nothing! Take them away, take them away!

(*At his signal,* JESTER ONE *leads the* DANCERS *upstage where they arrange themselves on the floor. As the* EMPEROR *sinks into gloomy thought, the* TWO TAILORS, *honest, humble men, enter, audience right, ascend the steps to the Hall, and bow before the* MINISTER.)

TAILORS: Greetings, O Wise One.

MINISTER: Listen carefully, Tailors. I have decided to go through with the plan we discussed yesterday. You will pretend to weave a magic coat for the Emperor and—

TAILOR ONE (*frightened*): But His Majesty will find we have made no coat—

TAILOR TWO (*frightened*): And he will cut off our heads!

MINISTER: No harm will befall you, I promise you. And you shall be given much bread to take home to your hungry ones today. Now then, I shall bring you before the Emperor at once and you must tell him exactly what I told you to say. Come.

(*The* MINISTER, *followed by the quaking* TAILORS, *enters the Throne Room. The* TAILORS *prostrate themselves at the entrance.*)

EMPEROR (*striking his forehead*): Nothing! Still nothing! I shall be without new robes next week and my people will laugh at me.

MINISTER (*to the* EMPEROR): Sire, I have people who wish to see you.

EMPEROR: Go away!

EMPRESS: Listen to your Councilor, my love.

MINISTER: These are two Tailors.

EMPEROR (*interested*): Tailors you say?

MINISTER: Tailors who weave the most beautiful cloth in all your ten kingdoms.

EMPRESS: Perhaps they can make you a coat for the procession next week.

EMPEROR: A coat! Tailors, approach and show me your wares.

TAILOR ONE: We have nothing with us, O Golden Sun.

TAILOR TWO: We weave only to order, O Pearliest Moon.

EMPEROR: Nothing to show? Minister, what joke is this? Away with the Tailors!

MINISTER (*quickly*): But they make a cloth of wondrous beauty, Sire.

EMPRESS: Of magic quality, love.

EMPEROR: Magic? Did you say magic? This *is* something new. Tailors, what is this magic cloth?

TAILOR ONE: He who cannot see this cloth is unfit for his post, O Sun.

TAILOR TWO: Unfit for his post, O Moon.

MINISTER: With a cloth like this, one can find out who is fit to govern.

EMPEROR: I have nothing to fear, Old One. I am fit. I shall see the cloth. Away with the T—

EMPRESS (*interrupting quickly*): With a cloth like this, you will dazzle all your ten kingdoms.

EMPEROR (*interested*): What is that? I will dazzle all my—? I will, won't I? And my people will be proud of me. (*To the* TAILORS.) Here is what you shall do. All week you shall weave, day and night, until you have made me a coat and trousers and a train. And these I shall wear in the procession next week. If the robes please me, you shall have two purses of gold. If they fail to please me, well . . . Go, Councilor, take them to the Tower Room and see that they have the finest silk and purest gold thread to weave with. (*As the* MINISTER *turns to go.*) One thing more, my sage. You have done me a good turn. I shall remember it. (*To his* JESTERS.) Tell the Dancers to dance again. I am happy.

(*At the* MINISTER's *signal, the* TAILORS *bow themselves out of the* EM-

peror's presence. As the MINISTER follows them, he whispers to the
EMPRESS.)

MINISTER: There will be no robes. And if the Emperor discover this too
soon, there will be no head on me!
   (*The dance begins and continues until*

the curtain closes.)

ACT TWO

Time   One week later

Scene   For the Tower Room and the Hall outside, the stage remains
divided as in Act One. The Throne in the Throne Room, however,
has been replaced by a low table over which sewing tools have been
strewn. A framework suggesting a full-length mirror is downstage
left, angled so that anyone gazing into it also faces the audience.

When the curtain opens, the TWO TAILORS are in the Tower Room bewailing
their fate. TAILOR ONE paces up and down, while TAILOR TWO rocks on his
haunches.

TAILOR ONE: Why did we listen to the Minister? The procession is at hand
and we have no robes. When the Emperor comes—
TAILOR TWO: My children will have a father without any ears!
TAILOR ONE: Without any head, you mean! Oh, why did we ever listen to
the Minister?
TAILOR TWO: Who will help my poor wife when I am gone?
   (*The sound of voices in the Hall alarms the* TAILORS, *and they busy
   themselves with make-believe measuring, cutting and sewing. The
   voices belong to the* MINISTER *and the* EMPRESS *who are ascending the
   steps that lead to the Hall.*)
MINISTER (*to the* GUARDS):   Have the Tailors been working?
GUARD ONE: All night, O Councilor.

EMPRESS: Have you seen the magic garments they are weaving?

GUARD TWO: Not yet, O Majesty. They will let none enter until the Emperor comes.

MINISTER: Well, we shall do so now and examine the robes. The procession will begin shortly. (*He whispers to the* EMPRESS *as they walk into the Tower Room.*) The Emperor has discovered nothing. Our plan is succeeding.

EMPRESS: What if it succeeds too well? What if my husband wants to wear the invisible robes in the procession?

MINISTER: He is not so foolish. He will not wear something he cannot see. Are the real garments prepared for him?

EMPRESS: They are waiting in my chamber.

(*They enter the Tower Room. The* TAILORS *prostrate themselves.*)

MINISTER: Good day, Tailors. Do not tremble. I have told the Empress everything.

EMPRESS: You have done well to listen to the Minister.

MINISTER: Has anyone seen the robes?

TAILOR ONE: No one, O Wise One.

TAILOR TWO (*wailing*):   But when one does . . .

MINISTER: Fear not. Now, when the Emperor comes—it will be any moment now—remember to speak as I have instructed you.

TAILOR ONE: But there are no robes!

MINISTER: The Emperor will see them if you speak correctly.

TAILOR TWO: But his Jesters, his Guards, will they see them too?

MINISTER: They dare not do otherwise.

TAILOR ONE: We beg you, let us return to our families at once!

TAILOR TWO: Our children need their fathers! We beg you!

EMPRESS: The Emperor has a kind heart, good people. When he understands, he will forgive you.

MINISTER: And you shall have much meat for your hungry ones.

EMPRESS (*hearing footsteps*):   Shh. My husband approaches. Let us meet him, O Wise One.

MINISTER (*whispering to* EMPRESS *as they return to the Hall*):   If only fright does not prompt these Tailors to reveal the truth too soon.

(*The* EMPEROR, *followed by the* JESTERS *who hold his train, ascends the steps to the Hall. The* TAILORS *lean against the door and listen.*)

EMPEROR: Well, old Councilor, have you seen my magic robes?

MINISTER: Yes, Sire.

EMPEROR: You have, hmn.

MINISTER: And you will be pleased, Sire. They are as the Tailors promised.

EMPRESS: The most beautiful robes in all your ten kingdoms.

EMPEROR: And magic too, aren't they? He who cannot see the cloth is unfit for his post. Even I—if I were not to see it, which is ridiculous, of course. (*He laughs nervously and everyone echoes his nervous laughter.*)

MINISTER: Sire, it is time to enter the Tower Room and dress. The procession will start shortly.

EMPEROR (*moving toward the Tower Room*):   Yes, yes, I'm going. (*He stops abruptly.*) But the tower stairs have wearied me. I must catch my breath. My good Jesters, you inspect the royal garments and tell us what you think of them.

(*Prodded by the* EMPEROR, *the reluctant* JESTERS *walk into the Tower Room. The* TAILORS *pretend to work feverishly. The* EMPEROR *and his people listen at the door.*)

JESTER ONE: We have come to see the Emperor's robes.

JESTER TWO: And report on their merits to him.

TAILOR ONE (*pretending to sew*):   Wait a minute, Jesters. I must stitch the coat a bit here.

TAILOR TWO (*pretending to cut*):   And snip a few threads off the trousers there.

(*The* TAILORS *hold up imaginary coat and trousers.*)

TAILOR ONE: Here they are, Jesters. The Emperor's robes! (*The* JESTERS *approach to look.*) Watch out, you're stepping on the train!

(*Alarmed, the* JESTERS *jump right.*)

TAILOR TWO: Watch out! You're stepping on the trousers! (*The* JESTERS *jump left.*) Is this not a beautiful pattern?

JESTER ONE (*exclaiming aside*):   My ancestors preserve me, I cannot see a thing! (*To* JESTER TWO.) Beautiful, is it not? The train, I mean.

JESTER TWO: But where is it?

TAILOR ONE (*kneeling*):   Come a little closer. Can you not see it?

JESTER TWO (*correcting himself quickly*):   Yes, yes, I see it. Charming, absolutely charming. I simply meant—where is it—to be worn?

TAILOR TWO: At the procession, of course, in a few minutes.

JESTER ONE: Then we'd better run and tell the Emperor the royal robes are ready.

(*They exit into the Hall. The* TAILORS *listen at the door.*)

EMPEROR: Well, Jesters, have you seen my robes?

JESTERS (*bowing*):   Yes, O Sun.—Yes, O Moon.

EMPEROR: Tell me, how do they look?

(*In their fright, the* JESTERS *talk at the same time and contradict each other.*)

JESTER ONE   ⎰They're yellow.
JESTER TWO   ·· ⎱They're red. I mean, yellow!

JESTER ONE   ⎰They're full.
JESTER TWO   ·· ⎱They're tight. I mean, full.

JESTER ONE   ·· ⎰They're long.
JESTER TWO   ⎱They're short. I mean, long.

EMPEROR (*suspiciously*):   Didn't you see the robes?

MINISTER (*interfering for fear the* JESTERS *will reveal everything in their nervousness*):   Of course they did, Sire. Their beauty stunned them.

JESTERS: Yes, yes. Their beauty stunned us.

EMPRESS: My royal husband, enter and see your robes.

EMPEROR (*hedging*):   Yes, yes, only there's still a little stitch in my side. I shall rest a minute more before I dress. Guards, you inspect this stuff and tell us what you think.

(*The reluctant* GUARDS *enter the Tower Room. The* TAILORS *pretend to work feverishly. The* EMPEROR *and his people listen at the door. The scene with the* JESTERS *is repeated.*)

GUARD ONE: We have come to see the Emperor's robes.

GUARD TWO: And report on their merits to him.

TAILOR ONE (*pretending to sew*):   Wait a minute, Guards. I must stitch the coat a bit here.

TAILOR TWO (*pretending to cut*):   And snip a few threads off the trousers here.

(*The* TAILORS *hold up imaginary coat and trousers.*)

TAILOR ONE: Here they are, Guards. The Emperor's robes! (*The* GUARDS *approach to look.*) Watch out, you're stepping on the train!

(*Alarmed, the* GUARDS *jump right.*)

TAILOR TWO: Watch out! You're stepping on the trousers! (*The* GUARDS *jump left.*) Is this not a beautiful pattern?

GUARD ONE (*exclaiming aside*):   My ancestors preserve me, I cannot see a thing! (*To* GUARD TWO.) Beautiful, is it not? The train, I mean.

GUARD TWO: But where is it?

TAILOR ONE (*kneeling*):   Come a little closer. Can you not see it?

GUARD TWO (*correcting himself quickly*):   Yes, yes, I see it. Charming, absolutely charming. I simply meant—where is it—to be worn?

TAILOR TWO: At the procession, of course, in a few minutes.

GUARD ONE: Then we'd better run and tell the Emperor the royal robes are ready.

(*They exit into the Hall. The* TAILORS *listen at the door.*)

EMPEROR: Well, Guards, have you seen my robes?

GUARDS: Yes, O Sun.—Yes, O Moon.

EMPEROR: Tell me, how do they look?

(*In their fright, the* GUARDS *talk at the same time and contradict each other.*)

GUARD ONE	They're yellow.
GUARD TWO	They're red. I mean, yellow!
GUARD ONE	They're full.
GUARD TWO	They're tight. I mean, full!
GUARD ONE	They're long.
GUARD TWO	They're short. I mean, long.

EMPEROR (*suspiciously*): Didn't you see the robes?

MINISTER (*interfering quickly*): Of course they did, Sire. Their beauty stunned them.

GUARDS: Yes, yes. Their beauty stunned us.

MINISTER: Sire, we cannot delay the procession any longer. Will you enter now? Or do you fear to . . . ?

EMPEROR: Of course I'll enter.

(*The* TAILORS *busy themselves as the* EMPEROR *enters the Tower Room, followed by the* EMPRESS, *the* MINISTER *and the* JESTERS. *The* TAILORS *prostrate themselves.*)

EMPEROR: I have come for the royal robes, Tailors. (*He sneaks a look.*)

TAILOR ONE: Here they are, O Golden Sun. (*Pretending to hold up a garment.*) Here is the coat.

TAILOR TWO: And here are the trousers, O Pearliest Moon.

MINISTER (*touching the "coat"*): Feel how light it is, Sire. (*The* EMPEROR *waves his hand through the empty air.*) Do you not feel it?

EMPEROR: Of course I feel it. As light as a spider's web. (*To the* EMPRESS.) Is it not, my love?

EMPRESS (*touching the "coat"*): Wearing it, one might think one had nothing on.

TAILOR ONE: Will Your Majesty graciously permit us to remove your clothes?

EMPEROR: Yes, yes, help me to disrobe. Councilor, Wife, help me. (*As the* MINISTER *and the* EMPRESS *remove the* EMPEROR'S *clothing, they hand the articles to the* JESTERS *who fold them and put them aside.*) The cloth has pleased me, Tailors. It has my highest approval. So, for reward, the Royal Treasurer will give you each a purse of gold. And henceforth, you shall be known as "The Emperor's Gentlemen Weavers."

TAILORS (*bowing*): A thousand thanks, O Sun of Suns—A thousand thanks, O Moon of Moons.

MINISTER: And now, Tailors, the trousers. (*The* TAILORS *bump into and jostle each other as they "dress" the* EMPEROR.) Will Your Imperial Majesty lift your imperial leg?—And now, the other one?

EMPRESS: Tailors, the coat. Your arm, my love.—Now, look into the great mirror, my husband.

(*The* EMPEROR *peers into the mirror anxiously.*)

MINISTER (*turning the* EMPEROR *around quickly*): Look at the back, Sire. The pattern is magnificent.

EMPRESS (*turning the* EMPEROR *around again*): And see the belt. Its stitching is exquisite.

MINISTER (*turning the* EMPEROR *around*): And wait until we fasten the train. Tailors, the train. (*The* TAILORS *"fasten the train."*) Careful, Tailors, you will step on it. Pull it to the right. Careful! Now, pull it to the left.

EMPRESS: Do the royal garments please my love?

EMPEROR: Oh, perfectly. Only the train, isn't it a little—too short?

MINISTER (*turning the* EMPEROR *around*): No, Sire, long. The longest train in ten kingdoms. Tailors, show His Majesty.

(*The* TAILORS *stagger way back.*)

EMPEROR: Yes, yes, I meant long. But isn't the coat a little—too tight?

EMPRESS (*turning him again*): Full, my love. The belt makes it seem tight.

EMPEROR: The belt makes it seem tight. But the color—a little too red for me?

MINISTER: Gold. It is the royal color.

EMPEROR (*dizzy from the turning*): Gold, yes. The sun was in my eyes.

EMPRESS: The robes will dazzle your people.

MINISTER: The procession, Sire.

EMPEROR: Yes, yes. Only I'm feeling a little dizzy. Perhaps I should lie down and let the Empress go in my stead.

MINISTER (*whispering to the* EMPRESS): My plan has succeeded.

EMPEROR (*overhearing*): Succeeded? What plan?

MINISTER: I meant, my plan to please Your Graciousness with the magic robes.

EMPRESS: But if my husband is not truly pleased, he must not wear these robes today. I have others ready for him. Jesters, go fetch the purple garments from my chamber.

EMPEROR: One moment, my love. Who said I am not pleased? The stitching is exquisite. (*He holds out an invisible "sleeve."*) Do you not see it?

EMPRESS: Yes, I see it, only the purple robes are—

EMPEROR (*showing the* MINISTER *the other "sleeve"*): This pattern is magnificent. Do you not see it?

MINISTER: Yes, yes, I see it, but if only Your Majesty would deign to look at the purple—

EMPEROR (*disregarding the* MINISTER, *he turns back to the* EMPRESS): And the robes will dazzle my people. You said so, did you not?

EMPRESS: Yes, my love, but—

MINISTER: I will fetch the purple garments myself and—

EMPEROR: No! These are the robes I shall wear and none other! (*He summons the* GUARDS.) Guards, beat the drums. Let the procession begin.

GUARD ONE (*calling out to* GUARD TWO): Beat the drums. Let the procession begin.

GUARD TWO (*calling out to* GUARDS *offstage*): Beat the drums. Let the procession begin.

(*Offstage voices take up the call as the* MINISTER *hurries over to the* EMPRESS.)

MINISTER (*whispering anxiously*): He will parade in his underwear. I must tell him all.

EMPRESS (*restraining him*): Tell him nothing. Let him wear the invisible robes. Let him see how his wish to dazzle makes a fool of him. Let him learn how unfit he is for his post. He will learn no other way.

(*They join the procession line that is forming now. The* GUARDS *head the line. They are followed by the* MUSICIANS, *the* EMPEROR *with the* JESTERS *holding up his "train," the* EMPRESS, *the* MINISTER, *the* DANCERS, *etc. As the procession moves down the steps right, the* EMPEROR *fusses with his "clothes." The* TAILORS *remain on stage, prostrated on the ground.*)

EMPEROR: Careful, Jesters, do not step on my train. Move back—(*the* JESTERS *obey*)—further—further—stretch it to its full length. That's better. Now, lift it—high—higher—higher. With both hands! Higher! *Higher!*

(*To musical accompaniment, the procession weaves up and down the streets of the town—in reality, the aisles of the auditorium. People line the streets, among them the blind* OLD MAN, *his* DAUGHTER *and his* GRANDCHILD. *As the people praise and cheer the* EMPEROR, *the* CHILD *runs after the procession, followed by his anxious family.*)

PEOPLE (*ad libbing their praises*): The Emperor is coming . . . The Emperor is coming . . . Aren't his robes beautiful? . . . Look at his train . . . Did you ever see anything like his coat? . . . Isn't he magnificent? . . .

CHILD (*exclaiming*): But the Emperor isn't wearing any clothes!

DAUGHTER (*frightened*): Hush!

CHILD: He isn't wearing any clothes!

DAUGHTER: What are you saying? His clothes fit him to perfection!

OLD MAN: O, he's beautiful—like a sun god!

CHILD: But how can you see him, Grandfather? You're blind.

DAUGHTER: Come home with me! Come away!

CHILD: The Emperor's in his underwear!

OLD MAN: Come away, child! We'll lose our heads!

CHILD: But he's in his underwear! Look. He's in his underwear!

DAUGHTER (*prostrates herself before the passing* EMPEROR): Forgive him, O Sun. He is but a child.

OLD MAN (*prostrating himself too*): He knows not what he sees.

PEOPLE (*ad libbing*): Did you hear what the child said? . . . The Emperor's in his underwear! . . . The child is right! . . . He has no robes . . . He's in his underwear!

> (*The people start to laugh. The laughter grows until even the* EMPEROR *cannot fail to recognize the truth—he is parading in his underwear! The* EMPEROR *finishes the parade with as much dignity as he can muster and returns to the Tower Room. All prostrate themselves before him.*)

EMPEROR (*venting his anger and humiliation on the* TAILORS): What have you done? I have no clothes! You've made a fool of me! Guards, take them away and chop off their heads!

MINISTER: Wait, Sire. They are not to blame. I ordered them to do this mischief. I, alone. My head must be your victim.

EMPEROR: You ordered? You, my Councilor? Why?

MINISTER: Your people are starving, Sire, but you are too busy with your silks and jewels to think of them. I tried to tell you this before but you would not heed me. So I thought of the invisible robes. I hoped that in failing to see them, you would not fail to see yourself for what you are— an unfit ruler.

EMPEROR: But the procession! You allowed me to walk in—(*he points to his underwear*)—this! You made a fool of me!

EMPRESS: *I* allowed you, Sire, not the Wise One. But it was your own vanity that made a fool of you. You would not wear the purple robes we had prepared for you. *My* head must be your victim too.

(*There is a pause. Finally, the* EMPEROR *speaks.*)

EMPEROR (*lifting the* EMPRESS):   You are right. Both of you. I am unfit to rule. (*He raises the* MINISTER.) Thank you, my friend, for a lesson well taught and well deserved.

JESTER ONE: Shall we tumble for Your Majesty and make you laugh?

JESTER TWO: Shall we order the entertainers to dance?

EMPEROR: There is no time for dancing. I must see my poor people at once. They have suffered too long. Take the entertainers away. No, wait! Let them dance. But not for me. For my people. Let them dance while I think of ways to rid my kingdom of its sorrows. (*Taking the* MINISTER's *arm, he moves offstage.*) Come, my friend, you shall tell me whom I must see first.

MINISTER (*as they exit*):   Gladly, Sire. The famine delegation is in the courtyard. Then there are a blind old man and his daughter and his . . .

(*The* EMPRESS, *the* JESTERS *and the* TAILORS *follow the* EMPEROR. *As the* GUARDS *take their positions at the archway, the* DANCERS *dance again. At the end of their movement, the* DANCERS *prostrate themselves before the audience, as they once did before the* EMPEROR, *and*

the curtain closes.)

STAGING SUGGESTIONS

Comments

Although this script has an ancient Chinese background, no attempt was made to "write" it in authentic Chinese dialogue. An oriental flavor was introduced by the players themselves during dramatization and rehearsal, and this was retained in the final, playing version together with more modern turns of speech!

Several phrases and speeches are deliberately used over and over again to simplify memorizing. In fact, two entire scenes were repeated for the same reason. The JESTERS-TAILORS scene of Act Two is identical with the GUARDS-TAILORS scene in the same act. And the subsequent JESTERS-EMPEROR scene is the same as the GUARDS-EMPEROR scene.

Cast

Increase or decrease the number of JESTERS, GUARDS, BEGGARS, MUSICIANS, DANCERS and STREET PEOPLE to fit the needs of your group and stage space. By retaining the number of JESTERS, GUARDS and BEGGARS as given in the play you will safeguard performance in the event of illness among your players. One JESTER, for instance, can carry on for both JESTERS. Keep two TAILORS because audiences are familiar with the original tale and expect to see the pair.

Cast the mature players in the roles of the EMPEROR, the MINISTER and the EMPRESS.

Set

As noted in the stage directions, the background is actually a split set. The right section acts as an outer Hall throughout the play, the left as a Throne Room for Act One, a Tower Room for Act Two.

The archway separating the Hall from the other rooms should have a Chinese motif. The frame may be constructed of wooden uprights and anchored to the floor. A screen painted in Chinese bamboo style may serve in place of the archway. Or—eliminating both archway and screen—two GUARDS, colorfully costumed and standing at the desired spot, will prove equally effective.

The Throne may be a real Chinese chair or any large chair covered with an appropriate cloth. In one production, three gay lanterns were suspended over the Throne. In another, a Chinese umbrella was used.

For the first production, the flowering tree was made out of a large bare branch stuck into a pail of sand. Dozens of tiny, pink, crêpe paper "blossoms" were wired to the branch. This made a charming picture, well worth the effort the children put into making it. A dais or level to elevate the Throne is desirable but not necessary. The Chinese screen upstage is there to decorate the set.

The Throne Room is easily converted into the Tower Room by replacing the Throne with a low table. Weaving and sewing tools cover the table. Conspicuous among them are a pair of scissors, generous in size and made out of wood or cardboard, measuring tape, large spools of thread, etc.

In both of the productions mentioned, no mirror was used. Instead, the EMPEROR pretended there was one located downstage front. Every time he looked into it, he faced the audience.

Costumes

These can be as elaborate or as simple as your group desires. Real Chinese pajamas and kimonos, silk bathrobes or mandarin-neck pajama tops from the family's wardrobes may be transformed into elegant robes for the EMPEROR, the MINISTER and the EMPRESS. Chinese ladies wear trousers with narrow legs. Trousers for the men are wide at the bottom. The EMPEROR may have a fan, a high, Chinese crown (cardboard, glitter and glue), and a train trimmed with jewels, braid, bits of fur. Underneath his fashionable garments, he has on a pair of long, red underwear of course! The EMPRESS wears a smaller crown and carries a fan.

The JESTERS and TAILORS are dressed in short, mandarin jackets and trousers. The jackets may be tunics cut out of lining material and trimmed with real or simulated braid. The GUARDS also wear short tunics decorated with braid. Their legs are bare except for small shields—painted cardboard discs—taped to their knees. They have sandals made out of cardboard or felt and carry cardboard or wooden weapons. Body shields add a nice touch.

The DANCERS, MUSICIANS, BEGGARS and PEOPLE wear trousers and long or short tunics. The DANCERS and MUSICIANS are more richly attired than the rest. All the men have skull caps made out of crêpe paper to which pigtails have been attached.

Music

The simple dances created for the productions mentioned above used the *Sinkiang Drum Dance*, a novel piece of music based on an old, Chinese folk melody. It can be found on the Folkways record, *Folk Songs and Dances of China*.

The *Sinkiang Drum Dance* was also played during the parade and accompanied the children's crosses when they took their curtain calls. Emerging singly from stage right and left, the actors *danced* down to the curtain where they formed a straight line. When the last player to emerge—the EMPEROR—

reached the center of the line, all bowed to the audience, Chinese fashion and in unison, then prostrated themselves, still in unison, their palms and foreheads touching the ground. The effect was fresh, enchanting!

Props

A large, antique-looking appointment book for the MINISTER; silks, velvets, braids and jewels for the JESTERS; instruments for the MUSICIANS; weaving and sewing tools for the TAILORS.

THE BLUE BUSH

A SCIENCE FANTASY FOR BROTHERHOOD WEEK

Playing Time   15 minutes approximately

Age   10—14 years

Manner of Presentation   Improvise lines
or
Memorize lines

Staging Suggestions   See end of play

Cast   Mike (Voice)
Babs (an aggressive teen-ager)
Kate (a superstitious teen-ager)
Pearl (a responsible teen-ager)
Sue (a studious teen-ager)

Debbie (a clothes-conscious teen-ager)
Verium (a commanding creature from another planet)

Time One picnic day

Place Somewhere and nowhere

Scene The stage suggests a wind-swept hill on the edge of a desolate world. A huge rock dominates upstage left, a strange, blue-colored object growing at its center. On closer inspection, this object turns out to be a bush of peculiar composition.

Other smaller rock formations, upstage center and stage right, complete the scene. These serve as sitting and standing areas.

The curtain opens on an empty world. There are a few moments of eerie silence. This is broken suddenly by the sound of an approaching bus, offstage right. The bus sputters to a stop.

VOICES (*offstage right, bantering*): Whoa! . . . Hi ho, Silver! . . . Why are we stopping? . . . Are these the picnic grounds? . . .
MIKE (*bus driver, offstage right*): Engine trouble!
VOICES: Some hot rod! . . . Flat tire? . . . What happened? . . . The other kids will get to the picnic before us. . . . What gives? . . .
MIKE: Tell you as soon as I find out. Joe, get the tool kit out of the trunk. Rest of you—take a ten minute break, will you?
VOICES: Okay, Mike. . . . Pile out, fellow sufferers. . . .
BABS (*offstage*): Let's get out of this mob, Kate.
KATE (*offstage*): No sooner said than—
DEBBIE (*offstage*): Come on, Sue. Let's race Babs and Kate up the hill.
GIRLS (*improvising as they run up the hill*): See that rock? Bet we get there first! . . . Says you! . . . Since when did you get a jet? . . .
(*Amid shouts and laughter, some of the picnickers—BABS, KATE, PEARL, SUE, DEBBIE—run on, stage right. All are racing towards the big rock, teasing and pulling at each other in happy horseplay. It is evident that these girls are warm friends.*)

PEARL (*a sensitive, responsible girl*): Lay off, Babs! You'll break my chain!

BABS (*an aggressive girl*): Oh—oh, Pearl's secret! (*She tickles* PEARL.) Pull the chain out of your blouse and show it to us!

KATE (*a superstitious girl*): Come on, Pearl, let's see the big secret you're always hiding!

PEARL (*laughing*): You'll never get me to show it to you!

BABS: Tell us what it is. We're your friends. What's at the end of your chain? A picture of Eddie? (*She sings.*) "Eddie, my love . . ."

DEBBIE (*a clothes-conscious young miss*): She won't tell us. She never does. (*She combs her hair.* BABS *pulls* PEARL *to the ground and pins down her arms.*)

PEARL: Get off me, Babs Benton!

BABS: Hold her arms, Sue.

SUE (*a studious girl*): You shouldn't force her. It's her privilege to have a secret.

KATE: Maybe it's a witch's charm. I knew an old woman who—

DEBBIE (*interrupting*): Or a diamond ring! Show us, Pearl, show—

BABS (*tickling* PEARL): Show us, show us! Is it really a diamond?

PEARL: No, no—yes, yes. It's a diamond ring. (*She manages to push* BABS *away.* BABS *falls to the ground with a slight thud.*)

BABS: Ouch! (DEBBIE *laughs.*) What are you giggling at, Debbie? The ground's hard as a rock. (*She pulls* DEBBIE *down.*) See what I mean, little one?

DEBBIE: It hurts.

SUE (*examining the rock carefully*): Why shouldn't it? It *is* rock—metamorphic rock!

KATE: Shh—Sue, the scientist, speaks.

SUE: Blue rock.

DEBBIE: Now you're going too far, gal. Whoever heard of blue rock?

SUE: Look at it yourself.

PEARL (*rising*): Sue's right. It *is* blue.

BABS: The whole place is blue rock! (*She rises slowly. The girls are all standing now. Looking around, their sense of uneasiness grows.*)

KATE: Gosh, it's weird. Like something out of the Druids or the Leprechauns. My grandmother used to tell me tales—

BABS: You know, there isn't any grass—not anywhere.

PEARL (*quoting*):   "The world has died and turned to stone."

SUE: Pearl, how romantic can you get! Something *is* growing—there.
     (*She points to the bush left. All look.*)

BABS: What do you know, a bush!

KATE: But it's blue—just like the ground!
     (*She shivers and clings to* BABS *as everyone exclaims.*)

DEBBIE: I'm freezing. The wind's cold.

PEARL: But there isn't any wind. Listen.—

SUE: Oh, drop it, kids. There must be a reasonable explanation for all this. Perhaps the place turned blue from atomic radiation. We can ask Mr. Aldrich when we get back to school Monday.

PEARL: "The world has died . . ." I'm cold.

BABS (*walking to the bush*):   Sue's right. And until Mr. Aldrich tells us different, I'm not going to let a silly little scrub of a bush frighten me.
     (*She is about to touch the bush when a commanding voice, coming from behind the rock and foreign in flavor, calls out.*)

VOICE: Do not touch the bush!
     (*There is a moment's silence which* BABS *breaks.*)

BABS: Who said that? Deb? Kate?

DEBBIE—KATE: No, we didn't say a word. . . .
     (BABS *stretches out her hand to the bush a second time.*)

VOICE: DO NOT TOUCH IT!

BABS (*shakily*):   You're playing a joke, aren't you, Pearl?

PEARL: No.

SUE: The voice came from there—the bush, or behind it.

BABS: Then one of the kids on the bus is having a good time and I'm not going to fall for the gag. (*She walks around the rock trying to catch the owner of the voice.*) Come on out, whoever you are. Stop trying to be funny.

VOICE: You Earthmen will feel fright.
     (*All relax.*)

DEBBIE: Earthmen! Another sputnik gag!

KATE (*in the manner of a news announcer*):   And now, the next voice you will hear is the voice of Mars!

SUE: When did they wire Mars for sound?

VOICE: Not Mars. Verium. I am Verium and I come from a silent star between your earth and the sun.

PEARL: Sputnik again! How corny can you get!

DEBBIE: Sure, sure. And all of you star people speak English as well as Queen Elizabeth.

(She makes a mock curtsy to the rock.)

VOICE: Not all. Only we Examiners. When we saw it was time to contact the Earthmen, we asked our scientists to tune in on your radio waves and teach it to us.

BABS *(reappearing from behind the rock):*   There's no one behind the rock.

SUE: This is childish. I'm going back to the bus.

VOICE: Your bus is not there.

(All are startled.)

DEBBIE: Mike didn't leave us?

BABS: He'd have called us.

VOICE: Your bus is nowhere. You are nowhere. You are anchored to a bit of blue rock that exists only because I willed it to exist for you this day—this moment—now. After the test, it will be no longer.

SUE *(relieved):*   Test! It's Mr. Aldrich playing some sort of science game.

BABS: Where did he learn to throw his voice like that?

PEARL: I don't like games like this.

KATE: You'd think with all the books teachers read on child psychology, they'd know better than to pull a scary stunt like this one.

VOICE: I see there is only one way to make you believe Verium. *(The other-world creature appears suddenly on top of the big rock.)* I am Verium.

(The girls shriek and dash madly toward the marooned bus, right. At the far edge of the stage some invisible barrier stops them. Frightened, they dash to the other side of the stage only to encounter the same invisible barrier.)

GIRLS: I can't see the bus! . . . Where is the path we came up on? . . . I can't get through! . . . There's some kind of a wall! . . . I can't see a wall! . . . The wall's everywhere! . . . Oh Mike, Mike, I'm scared! . . . What is it? . . . I can touch it but I can't see it! . . . The wall's all around us! . . . My father will report this to the . . . WHAT IS IT? . . . Mike, Mike! . . . WHAT IS IT? . . .

VERIUM: It is an invisible barrier. I have willed it to encircle you until the test is over.

GIRLS: Mike! Mike! . . . I've got to get home and study! . . . Where's the bus? . . . My mother will worry if I don't. . . . I'm scared. . . . I'M SCARED. . . .

VERIUM: Do not be alarmed. (*As* VERIUM *talks, the panic subsides gradually.*) The barrier cannot harm you unless you wish it to. Do not be alarmed. Verium is your friend. (*As the girls huddle together*) You cling to one another. That is good. It makes me believe you will surely pass the test.

BABS: What kind of test is it?

VERIUM: Sit calmly while I tell you—please.

>   (*The girls sit down on the ground reluctantly. As* VERIUM *continues to talk, he points at* DEBBIE *who becomes ill. At first no one notices* DEBBIE'*s discomfort.*)

VERIUM: Good. Now, the people on my star are a peaceful species. When first we observed your fathers reaching out toward interstellar travel, we were glad. We desired to meet the clever Earthman and have him for our friend. But there were other things we observed among your fathers—things which disturbed us deeply—wars and destruction, indifference and hate!

>   (SUE *notices* DEBBIE *and whispers to her, alarmed.*)

SUE: Stop it, Debbie. Listen to him.

VERIUM (*continuing*): If we permit these warring Earthmen to reach us, we thought, they would surely harm us. So my people thought and were afraid. And your fathers were not permitted to reach our star. But we are a friendly people too. We desire to be as one with the entire galaxy.

KATE (*as* DEBBIE *doubles up, moaning*): Don't, Debbie! He'll start foaming!

VERIUM (*continuing*): And so we asked ourselves: though the father be bad, need the child be bad too? Does not the future live in the child? And later we agreed to put the child—(*he gestures to them*)—all of you, to the test. If you pass it, one day soon you will be permitted to get through to my star on some nuclear drive. If you fail . . .

>   (*By this time,* DEBBIE *is doubled up with pain.* PEARL, *the only one to feel concerned about her friend, crawls over to her side.*)

PEARL (*whispering*): What is it, Deb? (DEBBIE *can only moan.*) Babs, Debbie's very sick.

BABS (*fiercely*): Don't bother me! He's watching!

SUE: He can kill us with a ray!

PEARL: But Deb's burning up! We *must* help her!

KATE: Don't look at me!

>   (*The girls move away from* PEARL *and* DEBBIE *as* VERIUM *approaches them slowly.*)

VERIUM (*his voice stern*): If—you—fail—

GIRLS (*whispering fiercely to* PEARL): Let us alone! He can kill us! . . . He'll think we're not listening! . . . He'll kill us! . . .

VERIUM (*his voice like thunder*): YOU HAVE FAILED!

BABS—SUE—KATE: Failed? . . . What does he mean? . . . I didn't even see a test!

VERIUM (*pointing again at* DEBBIE *who begins to recover*): *She* was your test, the one you call Debbie. While I spoke, I willed her into illness to see if you would help her at the risk of possible harm to yourselves. You failed!

BABS—SUE—KATE (*frightened*): We were afraid to do anything! . . . We didn't know it was a test! . . . Give us another chance, please!

VERIUM: You are like your fathers—indifferent to the stricken cries of agonized people!

PEARL: That's not true! (*Her audacity frightens her, but she must go on.*) I mean, they are concerned. They have always been. I mean, our own country, America, was founded on their concern.

(PEARL'S courage *infects the other girls.*)

BABS: Pearl's right and the Statue of Liberty proves it.

VERIUM: I have seen your tall lady but—

SUE: Have you heard what she says?

DEBBIE (*quoting*): "Give me your tired, your poor,
Your huddled masses yearning to breathe free . . ."

KATE (*quoting*): "The wretched refuse of your teeming shore,
Send these, the homeless, tempest-tossed to me. . . ."

PEARL (*finishing quote*): "I lift my lamp beside the Golden Door."

VERIUM: Beautiful words. Perhaps your fathers believed them once, but today—

PEARL (*stoutly*): They still believe them. Look at the work of the United Nations. Through its W H O—

BABS: That's short for World Health Organization—

PEARL: They wiped out smallpox in Europe—

SUE: They helped establish Israel for the persecuted Jews—

DEBBIE: They help the persecuted and the sick everywhere, just as Pearl helped me.

VERIUM: Pearl did help you. I had not thought of that. (*Pause.*) You shall have another chance.

BABS (*joyful*): You'll remove the barrier?

VERIUM: One thing alone may cut through the barrier. It is the most valu-able thing you possess. Give it to me and you will rejoin your schoolmates. I leave while you search among you.

>(VERIUM *disappears behind the rock, left. There is a moment's silence while the frightened girls look at one another.*)

KATE: What can he mean—the most valuable thing among us? I've got nothing, only a dollar for candy and cokes.

BABS: What's a dollar to Verium?

PEARL: I have sixty cents. Maybe if we pooled all our spending money . . .

SUE: Our money would be worthless on his star.

KATE (*falling to her knees, crying*):   But we have to give him something or he may kill us.

PEARL (*falling beside* KATE):   I wish I were home doing dishes.

DEBBIE (*falling to her knees*):   Stop bawling, you're not babies!

>(*She cries even harder.*)

SUE: Something valuable, something he won't find on his star.—

>(*Suddenly,* BABS *makes a dash in the direction of the bus. She is brought up short by the barrier which has moved in some yards toward stage center.*)

BABS (*horrified*):   It's creeping in—the barrier—it's creeping in!

>(*The others run to* BABS. *Beating at the invisible wall, they cry.*)

GIRLS: If it keeps moving in any more, it will crush us! . . . (*All but* PEARL.) Let me through! . . . Let me out of here! . . . I don't want to die. . . . Someone—somebody help me!

>(BABS *removes her shoe and tries to beat a hole in the wall. As she runs around the stage, she bumps into the others and screams at them.*)

BABS: Get out of my way, you fool! I'll hit you if you don't!

SUE—KATE—DEBBIE: I hate you, you stuck-up pig! . . . Shut up, you idiot! . . . You're an idiot yourself!

>(*In the struggle,* KATE *is pushed to the ground.*)

DEBBIE (*running wildly*):   It's moving closer!—It's moving closer! (*Wild terror.*)

PEARL (*trying to calm them*):   Deb—Sue—everyone—stop this craziness! Kate—Babs, stop fighting! We're friends!

BABS (*pushing* PEARL *down to the ground*):   Get out of my way! I've got to cut through! I've got to—

>(*She stops suddenly and stares at* PEARL. *The others stop and follow her stare. There is a pause.*)

PEARL (*suddenly afraid*): Why are you all staring at me?

BABS (*menacingly*): Give it to me!

PEARL: Give you what?

BABS: The most valuable thing among us. It can cut glass.

PEARL: What are you talking about?

BABS (*advancing on* PEARL): It can cut through the barrier! Verium said it can cut! Give me the diamond ring at the end of your chain.

PEARL (*clutching her chain*): I have no diamond ring!

GIRLS (*advancing on* PEARL): You said you had a diamond! . . . Give me the diamond! . . . The diamond! . . . That's what Verium must have meant! . . . Give *me* the diamond! . . . No, *me!* . . . *Me!* . . . It's mine, I thought of it first! . . . it's mine! . . . give *me* the diamond!

(*They wrestle with* PEARL *for possession of the chain.*)

PEARL: Leave it alone! Leave it alone! Go away! . . .

(BABS *pulls, the chain breaks,* BABS *grabs it triumphantly as* PEARL *weeps on the ground.*)

BABS: I've got it! I've got it! (*She runs toward the rock, left.*) Verium!

SUE—KATE—DEBBIE (*running after* BABS): Give it to me! . . . It doesn't belong to you! . . . You've no right to take it! . . .

BABS: Who cares about rights? (*Calling*) Verium! Come out! Here is the most valuable—

(*She breaks off and stares at the chain. A soldier's identification tag dangles from it. The others stare and fall silent too.*)

PEARL (*weeping*): I told you there was no diamond ring.

KATE: A dog tag! A soldier's dog tag!

PEARL: My father's dog tag! He was killed in action—in Korea!

VERIUM (*offstage, angry*): Yes, fighting to protect the rights of other people! Fighting aggression and exploitation!

PEARL: It was my special secret. I wanted to keep it all to myself. (*Sobbing*) I told you—there—was—no—diamond.—

SUE—KATE—DEBBIE (*ashamed, each pats* PEARL's *shoulder in turn*): I'm sorry, Pearl . . . Me too . . . I didn't mean it . . .

(BABS *drops the chain into* PEARL's *lap.*)

SUE: We have nothing to give Verium. We've failed again.

DEBBIE: That means the barrier—

(*She is afraid to finish. All the girls, including* PEARL, *inch toward one another.*)

GIRLS (*whispering*): The barrier . . . It's coming closer . . . Closer . . . And we'll be . . . We'll be . .

PEARL (*suddenly*): Let's form a circle—quick!—Not this way, turn around! Face out!—Now, let's lock our arms—like this! (*The girls now form a tight circle facing out.*) When the wall gets near enough, we'll kick at it—all of us—together!

GIRLS: Together . . . Oh! Kate, I'm scared! . . . Here's my hand . . . hold me tighter, Deb! . . . tighter! . . . tighter . . .

PEARL: Together we may be able to break through. I'll give you the signal when to kick—

OTHERS: Together.

(*They stand, tense and still. There is a pause; then* VERIUM *appears on the rock left.*)

VERIUM (*smiling*): You have given me what I desired most—a word—a simple word—"together." It is well. You are free. No longer need your world and mine live isolated one from the other. The future is yours and ours. We shall live together, plan together, work together. *Together!*

BABS: You mean, the barrier is gone?

VERIUM (*disappearing behind the rock*): I mean, the barrier is not here, the test has not been and I, Verium, am no longer.

GIRLS (*breaking the circle, they test the air around them*): We're free? . . . Is that what he said? . . . We're free . . . Where did Verium go? . . . We're free!

(*They hug and tease each other in the happy horseplay of the beginning. They are now the same warm friends whose bus had broken down a minute ago.*)

PEARL: Lay off, Babs, you'll break my chain!

KATE: Come on, Pearl, let's see the big secret you're always hiding!

PEARL: You'll never get me to show it to you!

BABS: Tell us what it is. We're your friends.

PEARL (*suddenly afraid*): We are, aren't we? Friends? All of us?

KATE: Of course we are. Whatever made you ask that?

PEARL (*confused*): I don't know. For a moment, I felt—

MIKE (*offstage*): Hey kids, the bus rides again. Nothing was wrong. Climb on board!

(*Sound of motor starting up, offstage right.*)

BABS (*running off, right*): Coming, Mike. Let's get out of this mob, Kate.—

KATE: No sooner said than—(*She exits right.*)

DEBBIE: Sue, let's race them down the hill—(SUE *and* DEBBIE *run off.*)

PEARL: Wait for me—don't start without me—(*She follows.*)

MIKE (*offstage*): Pile in—pile in—pile in—Ready, kids? And away we go—
(*The bus starts off.*)

PICNICKERS (*offstage*): And away we go! . . .
(*The sound of the bus fades away as*

the curtain closes.)

STAGING SUGGESTIONS

Cast

Increase or decrease the number of PICNICKERS to fit the needs of your group and stage space.

Set

The important feature here is the desolate atmosphere. Create this with the simplest of stage props placed against a cyclorama (some school stages have them) or against the curtains of the stage. In one production, tall, bare branches were anchored in pails of sand to suggest lightning-struck trees. Various-sized levels, painted blue, were placed in different stage areas for the rock formations. Small stools or orange crates may be covered and painted to resemble rocks. See that several of these are sturdy enough to be used for standing and sitting levels. A few leafy branches sprayed with blue paint become the blue bush.

Costumes

The PICNICKERS wear shorts, jeans, blouses and skirts. VERIUM's costume is as weird as the actor playing him wants it to be. In one production, two cartons formed the basis of the outfit—a large one for the body, a smaller one for the head. The large carton hung over the actor's shoulders, the small one had openings for the eyes, mouth and nose. Corkscrew wires and coils extended from the head and the fingers to form antennae. The cartons were painted gray, black and red, then marked with appropriate "space" symbols.

Props

A soldier's identification tag on a chain for PEARL; a comb for DEBBIE.

Sound

A commercial record will give you the approaching and departing bus sound effects. If you can't get a record, replace the motor sound with the sound of boisterous voices. These fade in at the beginning of the play, fade out at the end.

A LINE IN A STORM

A TEEN-AGE FANTASY

Playing Time   12 minutes approximately

Age   10–13 years

Manner of Presentation   Improvise
or
Improvise and memorize

Cast   Liz
Debbie
Mrs. Cooper
Mrs. Blaine
Articles on a Clothesline—among them are: Long Johns—Grandpa;
Girdle—Aunt; Party Dress—Teen-ager; Man's Shirt—Father;
Sweater—Mother; Jeans—Brother
Tony
Bill

Time   The present

Place   The Cooper and the Blaine houses with the back yard that joins them.

Set   The stage is divided into three areas. The center and largest area is devoted to the back yard the Blaines and Coopers share. A clothesline extends across this section upstage. On the line, in this order, hang a pair of long johns, a girdle, a teen party dress, a man's shirt, a woman's sweater, a pair of dungarees.

The area on the right is the Cooper house. This is separated from the back yard by a large bush and is furnished with a sofa, a sofa table, and a telephone.

The area on the left is the Blaine house. It is similarly separated from the yard and contains an armchair, a small table, a lamp, and a telephone.

Entrances are to the right of sofa and to the left of armchair.

The players representing the clothes are behind their respective bits of apparel, blocked from the audience's view by a dark curtain hanging on the line.

The curtain opens on LIZ COOPER, *a languid teen-ager, lolling on the sofa and chatting with her friend,* DEBBIE BLAINE, *over the telephone.* DEBBIE, *a giggling teen-ager, in her house, left, is draped over the armchair. The girls are discussing the school dance they had attended the previous night. A weird moaning of undetermined source can be heard.*

LIZ: I never expected to have such a dreamy time at a school dance, did you, Debbie?

DEBBIE: Me neither. The band was terrific and when they played "You Are My Destiny"—(*They both sigh.*) Where did you and Tony go after the dance?

LIZ: To Sue's. She had a private party. Where did you?

DEBBIE: To the drugstore, for a soda. A bunch of the kids came along. What time did you get home?

LIZ: Almost one o'clock. (*The moaning is somewhat louder.* DEBBIE *looks at her telephone then talks.*)

DEBBIE: I didn't hear you . . . there's a noise on the 'phone.

LIZ: About one o'clock.

DEBBIE: Did your mother say anything?

LIZ: Mommy doesn't give me a curfew—does yours?

DEBBIE: Oh no, she trusts me. She knows I'll come home at a reasonable hour.

MRS. COOPER'S VOICE (*offstage right*): Liz, haven't you talked to Debbie long enough? You promised to take in the laundry. The radio says it may storm and your good dress is out on the line.

LIZ: I'm going, Mom, I was just hanging up. (*Making herself more comfortable, she resumes her 'phone conversation*) Debbie?—Your dress was cute. Where did you buy it?

DEBBIE: At a wholesale place—though Mommy and I saw it at the Teen Shop for a lot more money. Did you like Jane's sheath?

MRS. BLAINE'S VOICE (*offstage left*): Debbie, you've tied up that 'phone for hours. Hang up, dear, and bring in the laundry. It looks like rain.

DEBBIE: Sure, Mom, in just a sec. (*She rolls over in her armchair and continues to talk*) Aren't parents awful? They're always on your neck.

LIZ: Yeh, they never let you alone for even a minute.

DEBBIE: They keep after you to 'do things.'

LIZ: Yes, as though I don't do anything. And look at all the work I do in the house. Slave labor.

DEBBIE: Me too. Work all day at school then work again at home. And if I want to talk to anyone for just a sec, Mommy screams I've been on the 'phone for hours.

LIZ: If we were only sixteen, we could get *paying* jobs. (*Shakes her telephone*) Say, what *is* this noise on the 'phone?

DEBBIE: Must be static, I guess. Or maybe the operator's listening. She likes to snoop. What's Tony like? Are you going to go steady with him?

LIZ: No, just steadily. A girl shouldn't tie herself up to one boy—there are too many cute ones around. Though he can certainly keep the girls' heads spinning.

DEBBIE (*shakes her telephone*): Ouch! The static! (*Resumes conversation*) He *is* dreamy. And so is his friend, Bill. Is Bill smooth when it comes to dancing!

LIZ: Tony said he might call me up today. If he does, we might double-date with him and Bill.

> (MRS. COOPER, *a mother who is always worrying, enters right area. She carries a shopping bag.*)

MRS. COOPER: Still at it, Liz!

LIZ (*puts telephone down but does not hang up*):   I had to say good-bye to Debbie.

MRS. COOPER: I'm going to buy some bread and milk before it storms. Don't forget to bring in the laundry. And put on a sweater when you go out. It's windy.

LIZ: Okay, Mom. I'll get one now. (*She exits right.* MRS. COOPER *looks after her, sighs, then exits left. As* MRS. COOPER *enters the back yard,* MRS. BLAINE *enters left area.* MRS. BLAINE *is a cheerful individual who is always looking at the bright side of things.*)

MRS. BLAINE (*to* DEBBIE):   Still talking!

DEBBIE (*puts telephone down but does not hang up*):   Of course not!

MRS. BLAINE: Get in the laundry, hon. Your good sweater is out on the line. I'm going to fetch Daddy's suit from the tailor's.

DEBBIE: Sure, Mom, right away.

> (As MRS. BLAINE *exits into back yard,* LIZ *returns to right area. The two girls pick up their 'phones and start whispering to each other. At the same time,* MRS. COOPER *and* MRS. BLAINE *greet each other in the back yard.*)

MRS. COOPER: Hello, Mrs. Blaine. Off shopping too?

MRS. BLAINE: No, I'm going to the tailor's. You look worried, Mrs. Cooper.

MRS. COOPER: I guess you can call me that. It's that awful 'phone. Liz is always on it chattering about heaven knows what.

MRS. BLAINE: Oh, the 'phone. I'm used to it. Debbie's older sister put me through the mill.

MRS. COOPER: What do you do about this constant talking?

MRS. BLAINE: Nothing. Let it run its course like a fever.

MRS. COOPER: But all the things Liz neglects—her lessons, the dishes, even making her bed in the morning. How can you sit back and do nothing?

MRS. BLAINE: Because there's nothing else you can do. It's typical teen trouble. Believe me, Mrs. Cooper, if you let it worry you, you'll end up nagging, nagging, nagging, and that's bad.

MRS. COOPER: But just look at this laundry. I've been after Liz for hours to take it in.

MRS. BLAINE: She'll get around to it. Debbie, too.

MRS. COOPER: What if they don't?

MRS. BLAINE: Then we take it in ourselves. Only let's give them a chance to do it first.

MRS COOPER: But the radio says it may storm. The whole wash may get dirty.

MRS. BLAINE: Mrs. Cooper, you're always looking at the gloomy side of things. Liz may take it in sooner than you think—or it may not storm after all.

MRS. COOPER: It will storm. I know it will.

MRS. BLAINE: Then we'll wash the clothes again. That's all. I'll take a chance on it while I go to the tailor's. You take a chance, too, Mrs. Cooper. (MRS. BLAINE *waves good-bye and exits right.*)

MRS. COOPER (*muttering to herself*):   Maybe—I don't know. (*She looks at clothes, starts to remove them, thinks better of it and strides off left*) Let them get dirty. Let the storm come.

(*When the mothers depart,* LIZ *and* DEBBIE *become audible to the audience. As they talk about the boys, the moaning increases.*)

LIZ (*pulling telephone away from her ear*):   Ouch! My ear! The noise is awful!

DEBBIE (*shaking her 'phone*):   There must be something wrong with the connection. Hang up and I'll 'phone you back.

(*The girls hang up. As* DEBBIE *dials* LIZ's *number again, the* ARTICLES *on the clothes line speak among themselves. Only the heads of the players of these garments are visible at any time. Occasionally, the heads pop up and down separately; occasionally, they are all up at the same time and withdraw together. These movements will be indicated.*)

PARTY DRESS (*head up*):   I'm shivering in this wind. My dress is so thin.

SWEATER (*head up*):   I wish I could give you my sweater, darling.

JEANS (*head up*):   Why don't they take us in? Can't they hear us crying?

GIRDLE (*head up*):   How can they? The wind's knocking the telephone wire against our clothesline.

PARTY DRESS: And it's whipping the pleats right out of my dress. I'll be a sight when I go out.

GIRDLE: Why don't they take us in? Don't they ever mind their mothers?

LONG JOHNS (*head up, grumbling*):   Nobody minds their elders nowadays. Nobody minds—nobody minds—

ARTICLES: Can't we do something to make those silly girls take us in?—It may storm.—The wind is blowing up.—I felt a raindrop.—

(LIZ's *telephone rings. All heads duck.* LIZ *picks up her telephone.*)

LIZ: Hi, Deb. What were we talking about?

DEBBIE: Boys. What else?

LIZ: Oh yeh, Tony. He's a doll.

(As the girls speak, the ARTICLES speak, too, their words overlapping those of the girls.)

DEBBIE (to LIZ): You're always falling for a smoothie.

PARTY DRESS (popping her head up, her words overlapping DEBBIE's): You're always gabbing, you dizzy Liz. (head down.)

SWEATER (to PARTY DRESS, her head up and down): Shh! They'll hear you.

LIZ (to DEBBIE): What did you say?

DEBBIE (to LIZ): You're always falling for a smoothie. What did you think I said?

LIZ: You're always ga——

JEANS (popping his head up, words overlapping LIZ's): You're always too lazy to do what you're told. (Head down.)

SWEATER (to JEANS, her head up and down): Shhhhh!

DEBBIE (to LIZ): You're certainly the one to talk, Liz Cooper!

(LIZ and DEBBIE quarrel over the telephone as different heads pop up and down, whispering)

ARTICLES: They heard you!—They're quarreling!—Good thing! Maybe they'll hang up now.—Maybe they'll think of us and take us in.—Shhhhh!

LIZ (to DEBBIE): I'll never speak to you again! (She hangs up telephone.)

DEBBIE (to LIZ): That goes for me too! (Hangs up.) Show-off!

(The girls sit in their spots fuming. The heads in the back yard emerge and stay up.)

LONG JOHNS (head up): Good. Now they'll mind their mothers.

PARTY DRESS (head up): They'd better hurry or the dust will ruin my pleats forever.

GIRDLE (head up): Brrr, the wind is going right through me. I've hardly anything on.

LONG JOHNS: Women! Always talking about clothes!

LIZ AND DEBBIE (jumping up simultaneously): The laundry! (They walk into the back yard.)

SWEATER (excitedly to MAN'S SHIRT): Father, Father! They're coming to take us in!

MAN'S SHIRT (head emerges. 'Father' is the retired, scholarly type): Who? What?

SWEATER: We're going to be in a warm place at last!

MAN'S SHIRT: Everything comes to him who waits. Spinoza said that—or was it Plato? No, not Plato, never! It must have been . . .

ARTICLES (*heads down*):   Shh, Liz is coming!—Shh, Debbie is coming!—Shhhhh!

   (*Walking toward the clothesline, the girls meet at the* MAN'S SHIRT.)

LIZ (*aloof*):   Pardon me, this is the Cooper shirt.

DEBBIE: Pardon me, it is the Blaine shirt.

LIZ: I should be able to recognize our shirt!

DEBBIE: Should you? Well, let me tell you . . .

   (*They are about to quarrel when* TONY *appears left.*)

TONY: Hi, dolls.

   (*Forgetting the articles on the line, the girls rush to greet him.*)

TONY: Tried to get you on the phone but your line was busy.

LIZ AND DEBBIE: Who? Me?

TONY: Both of you dolls. Bill and I thought we might do some bowling this aft—double date. How about it? (*He slaps* MAN'S SHIRT *playfully.*)

LIZ: It may storm, Mother says.

TONY (*putting his arms around both girls*):   There won't be any storm. Not as long as Nature Boy's with you. Well, what say?

LIZ: I'd love to go. Wouldn't you, Deb?

DEBBIE: Sure. I go for the popcorn that bowling alley sells.

TONY: And another thing. Chuck's throwing a coke and pretzel party tonight and asked us to bring dates. Think you gorgeous creatures can make that too?

DEBBIE: Dress or slacks?

TONY: Dress. I want you gals to make an impression.

LIZ: Mom will let me go. How about you, Deb?

DEBBIE: She's always glad to get rid of me. But where's Bill now?

TONY: He'll be here any sec.

LIZ: Come on then, Debbie. Let's go powder our noses.

   (*The girls and* TONY *disappear into* LIZ's *house, the laundry forgotten. The* ARTICLES *begin their moaning again.*)

PARTY DRESS (*head up*):   Oh dear, they're off on a date.

LONG JOHNS (*head up*):   And forgotten all about me! No respect, no respect at all!

GIRDLE (*head up*):   Such inconsiderate girls!

JEANS (*head up*):   What shall we do now? My jeans will get wet.

SWEATER (*head up*):   We must get their attention somehow.

ARTICLES: But how?—How?

SWEATER: Father, Father! (*The* SHIRT's *head emerges.*) Father, you've studied every book, you know all the answers. Advise us.

MAN'S SHIRT (*indignantly*):   Advise you! I can't even speak after the way that idiot, Tony, manhandled me. A man of my dignity!

ARTICLES: You must advise us!—You must find a way!—We need . . .

MAN'S SHIRT: Well . . . I'll consult the philosophers.

ARTICLES: No, no! It'll take until tomorrow!

MAN'S SHIRT: Well then, maybe we ought to . . .

ARTICLES: What?

MAN'S SHIRT: No, that won't work. On the other hand, maybe if we . . .

ARTICLES: What? What?

MAN'S SHIRT: No, not that either. And yet, why not? Hegel would approve. Or wouldn't he?

ARTICLES: What is it?—Tell us.—Tell us—

MAN'S SHIRT: Break up their bowling date. Split them up. Then they'll have nothing on their minds but taking in the laundry.

SWEATER: Shh! Here they come now. (*All heads duck.*)
        (LIZ, DEBBIE, *and* TONY *re-enter back yard right, just as* BILL *approaches from the left.*)

TONY: There's Bill. Let's tell him about tonight.
        (*They greet one another in front of the clothesline.*)

BILL: So you got here before me, boy. There's life in that jalopy of yours after all.

TONY: Look who's talking. All *he* ever rides are bicycles.

BILL: I'll race you anytime, cowboy.

DEBBIE: You haven't told us yet who's dating whom?

BILL: Tony and Liz will pair off, of course, while . . .

SWEATER (*head pops up and down*):   That wack!

TONY (*to* LIZ):   What did you say?

LIZ: I? Nothing.

TONY: That isn't what I thought you said.

BILL: You're hearing things, boy, you're hearing things.

TONY: She said . . .

BILL: Forget it and let's get at it. Debbie's with me. Okay, Deb?

PARTY DRESS (*head pops up and down*):   With you, stupid? Never!

BILL (*to* DEBBIE):   Hey, hold it! Whom are you calling stupid?

DEBBIE: Now you're hearing things.

TONY: Someone called me wack, all right.

LIZ AND DEBBIE: But we didn't call you anything! You're imagining things.

BILL: Imagining! (*To* TONY) That's a new name for it, eh, boy?

LIZ: Listen, if you boys are starting a quarrel just to get out of a date . . .
(*Suddenly* BILL *stumbles. The* JEANS *had pushed him.*)

BILL: Hey, what's the bright idea!

TONY (*stumbles as he is pushed*):   Quit pushing! Cut it out!

LIZ: We're not pushing. You're stumbling over your own feet!

DEBBIE: You're clumsy!

TONY: Oh yeh! And you're two dizzy dames.

BILL: Why we ever wanted to date you I'll never know! Come on, Tony, let's leave them to their remorse.

TONY: And they'll have plenty, believe you me! (BILL *and* TONY *exit left.*)

LIZ (*to* DEBBIE):   See what you've done!

DEBBIE: I? I didn't do a thing!

LIZ (*runs off right*):   Oh, there's no use talking to you!

DEBBIE (*runs off left*):   Who wants you to? I wouldn't answer you!
(*All heads but the* SHIRT'S *emerge quickly.*)

SWEATER (*despairing*):   They've left us again!

PARTY DRESS: We're worse off than ever. They'll never come out now.

GIRDLE: My girdle's killing me. I've got to get into the house and take it off.

LONG JOHNS: This younger generation! No backbone, no backbone at all.

SWEATER: Father, Father! (*The* SHIRT'S *head emerges.*) You have to help us! You must think of something!

MAN'S SHIRT: I'll have to consult the philosophers.

GIRDLE: Never! You did that before and look where it got us.

PARTY DRESS (*wailing*):   If we hadn't insulted the boys, they would be taking the girls to Chuck's party tonight and the girls would have brought in some clothes to wear and . . .

LONG JOHNS: Why don't we reverse our tactics? (*The others question him and he explains*) Pretend to be the girls and apologize to the boys. If the young people make up, they'll go to the party tonight and . . .

GIRDLE: They'll need a girdle . . .

PARTY DRESS: And a dress . . .

SWEATER: And a sweater . . .

LONG JOHNS: But nobody will need pajamas!

SWEATER: Don't worry, Grandpa. If they take some of us, they'll take all of us. Now, Father, you'll telephone Liz and pretend to be Tony and . . .

MAN'S SHIRT: How can I telephone?

SWEATER: Flap your arms around until you touch the telephone wire. You'll get through.

MAN'S SHIRT: A man of my dignity flap?

LONG JOHNS: Don't be an old fogey. Flap!

MAN'S SHIRT: Whom are you calling an old . . . (*In his anger, the* SHIRT *flaps and the telephone rings right.* LIZ *runs in to answer it.*)

ARTICLES: You did it! You did it! (*All heads but the* SHIRT'S *duck down.*)

LIZ (*into 'phone*):   Hello?

SWEATER (*head up and down*):   Speak to her, Father. Pretend you're Tony.

MAN'S SHIRT: Who? I?

LIZ: Hello?

PARTY DRESS: Go on, Father, she's getting angry!

LIZ: HELLO!

GIRDLE: She's hanging up! Hurry!

MAN'S SHIRT (*to* LIZ, *reluctantly*):   Hello . . .

LIZ: Who is this?

MAN'S SHIRT: I . . .

LIZ: I? I who?

SWEATER (*prompting* SHIRT, *head up and down*):   I, Tony.

MAN'S SHIRT (*to* LIZ, *weakly*):   I—Tony.

LIZ: Tony'd never say 'I'. What is this, a gag?

PARTY DRESS (*prompting* SHIRT, *head up and down*):   Hi, doll.

MAN'S SHIRT (*to* LIZ):   Hi, doll.

LIZ: Tony. What do you want?

GIRDLE (*prompting* SHIRT, *head up and down*):   To apologize, beautiful.

MAN'S SHIRT (*to* LIZ):   To apologize (*to* GIRDLE, *grimacing at the word*) beautiful ? ? ?

LIZ: If you're going to be fresh again, I . . .

LONG JOHNS (*prompting, head up and down*):   Never!

MAN'S SHIRT (*shouting at* LIZ):   NEVER! (*Regaining his dignity*) I mean, never. Freshness is a matter of relative age. A vegetable, let us say, is fresh when . . .

LIZ (*puzzled*):   Who *is* this?

MAN'S SHIRT: I—(GIRDLE *prompts him*) beautiful. A word that awakens shudders of . . .

JEANS (*prompting* SHIRT, *head up and down*):   I'm sorry about the fuss.

MAN'S SHIRT (*to* LIZ):   I'm sorry about the fuss. Though, in considering all factors, I . . .

SWEATER (*prompting, head up and down*):   Let's forget it, huh?

MAN'S SHIRT (*to* LIZ):   Let's forget it (*to* SWEATER, *grimacing at the word*) huh?

PARTY DRESS (*prompting, head up and down*):   And go to Chuck's party, tonight.

MAN'S SHIRT (*to* LIZ):   And go to Chuck's party tonight where we shall trip the light . . .

GIRDLE (*interrupting hastily, head up and down*):   What say, dreamboat?

MAN'S SHIRT (*to* GIRDLE, *weakly*):   Not 'dreamboat', please!

LIZ: Well, since you're apologizing, okay. What time will you call?

LONG JOHNS (*prompting, head up and down*):   Tell Debbie we'll call for you at eight.

MAN'S SHIRT (*to* LIZ):   Tell Debbie we'll call for you at eight.

PARTY DRESS (*quickly, head up and down*):   The dress. Tell her to wear her . . .

MAN'S SHIRT (*to* LIZ, *shouting*):   DRESS! I mean, wear your dress.

LIZ: What else? I'll call Debbie now. Bye!

MAN'S SHIRT (*to* LIZ, *almost fainting*):   Bye . . . doll . . .

> (*As* LIZ *dials* DEBBIE, *all the* ARTICLES *poke up their heads in excitement.*)

ARTICLES: You've done it!—At last, we're going into the house!—Just in time, I was freezing!

> (DEBBIE's *telephone rings. She runs in left to answer.*)

LIZ (*to* DEBBIE):   Deb? Now don't hang up. Listen! I've wonderful news. Tony 'phoned!

DEBBIE: Tony?

LIZ: Tony! And he apologized for both of them!

DEBBIE: What did he say?

LIZ: Never mind that now. The thing is our party date is on for tonight! And they'll call for us at eight.

DEBBIE: Oh gosh, I'd better wash my hair right away. What are you wearing?

LIZ: My new dress. I have to get it off the line and iron it.

DEBBIE: Mommy's sweater is out there too. I'll wear it with my good skirt. Gosh, I promised to take the laundry in!

> (*The girls hang up and run out to the back yard. The heads duck down.*)

LIZ (*gathering clothes*): I might as well take in these too. (*She removes* LONG JOHNS, GIRDLE *and* DRESS *from the line.*) See you later, Deb. (*Exits right.*)

DEBBIE (*removing* JEANS *and* SWEATER): Wear your heels and I'll wear mine. (DEBBIE *exits left.*)

MAN'S SHIRT (*head up, calls after the girls*): Wait a minute! You've forgotten me! Girls! You've . . . Oh Plato, what shall I do? Nowhere in my studies of the philosophers have I heard of such a predicament! Hegel, help me! Socrates! Perry Como, help me!

    (*He ducks as* MRS. COOPER *comes in from left, meeting* MRS. BLAINE *who enters right. The ladies are carrying parcels.*)

MRS. BLAINE: We meet again! Did you get all your shopping done?

MRS. COOPER: I had to buy only a few things. (*She notices the clothesline*) Look! The girls took in the laundry after all!

MRS. BLAINE: I told you. Let the fever run its course.

MRS. COOPER: You were right. Though frankly, I didn't expect they would. (*Pleased*) To think that Liz remembered about the laundry and without my nagging, too!

MRS. BLAINE: Children are more responsible than we give them credit for.

MRS. COOPER: It's just amazing! (*She starts to hurry off right*) I must tell Liz how happy she's made me.

MRS. BLAINE: Oh, Mrs. Cooper, is this your shirt?

MRS. COOPER (*disappointed*): Liz forgot to . . .

MRS. BLAINE: You can't expect a teenager to be perfect all the time.

MRS. COOPER (*forgetting her disappointment*): You're right again. (*Takes the* SHIRT) You know, it wouldn't surprise me if I went in and found Liz ironing. To take some of the load off me, you know. It would be just like Liz. She's really so helpful. So responsible, really. Not like other teenagers. I had better run in and give her a hand before she tires herself. Goodbye, Mrs. Blaine, and thank you.

    (MRS. COOPER *starts right again.*)

MRS. BLAINE (*starts walking left*): Good-bye for now. Just look at that sky, will you?

MRS. COOPER: The weatherman fooled us all right. It's going to be a lovely day after all. A lovely day. (*She exits right*) Oh, Liz darling . . . (*Smiling,* MRS. BLAINE *exits left as*

                              the curtain closes.)

STAGING SUGGESTIONS

Comments

Replace the song title, "You Are My Destiny" by the name of a song that is popular at the time of performance. Treat the reference to "Perry Como" in similar fashion.

Cast

Increase or decrease the number of ARTICLES on the clothesline to fit the needs of your group and the stage space.

Character genders may be changed if necessary.

Cast the more mature players in the key roles.

Set

The most important feature here is the clothesline. This may consist of a long, stout rope drawn through a black or dark curtain of non-transparent material. The curtain reaches to the ground and conceals the bodies of the players impersonating the ARTICLES. The actors stand or kneel on ladders, boxes or chairs placed behind the curtain. The articles of clothing hang in full view of the audience.

Painted cutouts, screens, or bushes (tall branches anchored in pails of sand) separate the back yard from the COOPER and BLAINE houses. These home areas contain the pieces of furniture already described or any that are available to your group.

Costumes

Present day attire. LIZ is more "dressed up" than DEBBIE.

Props

Telephones for LIZ and DEBBIE; a shopping bag for MRS. COOPER; a suit box for MRS. BLAINE.

Sound

Sound effects records can give you the ringing of the telephone if you do not have the electrical equipment necessary to produce this sound. Remember the ringing occurs in both the right and left areas of the stage.

IT'S A WISE PARENT

A COMEDY IN TWO ACTS

Playing Time   20 minutes approximately

Age   11–14 years

Manner of Presentation   Memorize with some improvisation

Staging Suggestions   See end of play

Cast   Nancy Royce (a lonely girl of eleven)
Martha (a laundress)
Thelma (Martha's daughter, Nancy's age)
Diana Royce (Nancy's mother)
Steven Royce (Nancy' father)
Edward P. Wolf (an Internal Revenue Agent)

Time   The present

Place   The Royce living room

Scene   This is a pleasant living room. It consists of a fireplace, bookcases and pictures, back wall, a table and occasional chair, stage left, a sofa, stage right, a hassock, downstage left front. A library table backs the sofa. There are magazines and cushions on the sofa, candy and an envelope containing three theater tickets on the library table, more candy at the fireplace, a telephone and lamp on the table left.

Entrances are upstage right corner to the exterior, left wall center to the interior.

ACT ONE

The curtain opens on a living room. The stage is empty. A moment later, NANCY ROYCE *enters, left. She is dressed in jeans. A lonely girl,* NANCY *wanders about the room restlessly—to the table, to the bookcase, to the candy jar, to the library table. She plops down finally on the sofa. As she flips through a magazine without really looking at it, the phone rings. She runs to answer it.*

NANCY (*eagerly*):   Mommy? (*Disappointed.*) Oh, Mrs. Woodley. No, my mother isn't in yet. She's been out all day but she promised to come home early. It's my birthday.—Thank you.—What?—Theater tickets? An envelope was delivered here an hour ago. Wait a minute and I'll see what's inside.— (*She runs to the library table, finds the envelope and examining its contents, returns to the phone.*) Yes, they're here.—Yes, I'll tell Mommy they came. (*She hangs up and looks at the tickets more closely.*) Theater tickets? —One—two—three! (*Her despondency changes to excitement and hope.*) Three theater tickets for Friday night—tonight! Maybe, maybe Mommy's planning to—(*The doorbell rings. She runs to it eagerly.*) Mommy?—Oh, it's you, Martha. Hi. Hi, Thelma.

> (MARTHA, *a buxom, cheerful woman, and* THELMA, *her candy-eating daughter of eleven enter. They are carrying laundry. During the greetings,* THELMA *wanders over to the candy.*)

MARTHA: Your Ma asked me to bring the laundry back Friday, Nancy. There's a lace blouse she wants to wear, she said. Is she in?

NANCY: Not yet but I think she wants it for tonight. She's going out.

MARTHA: Again! Your Ma and Pa are certainly great ones for gadding about.

NANCY: Well, we're new in this town, Mommy says—we've lived here only two months—and Dad, being vice-president of his law firm, has to see a lot of clients.

MARTHA: Tell me, bunny, is Justine here? I'd like to borrow your Ma's big salad bowl. Thelma's having a birthday party tomorrow night with boys and girls and—

THELMA (*interrupting*): We're going to shoot the works—meat balls and spaghetti and garlic bread and—

MARTHA: There she goes—eating again!

> (*Just as* THELMA *is about to pop some candy into her mouth,* MARTHA *takes it away.*)

NANCY: Justine hasn't come back from her day off.

MARTHA: Well, I'll fetch it myself. Your Ma told me okay. Here, Thelma, give me your laundry and I'll put it on Mrs. R's bed. (*She exits, left, with the laundry.*)

> (*As* NANCY *crosses to the hassock and sits,* THELMA *pops another piece of candy into her mouth. One senses the antagonism between the girls.*)

THELMA (*eventually*): I'm having a birthday party tomorrow night. (NANCY *does not comment.*) I'll be eleven. (NANCY *continues to be silent.*) How old are you, ten?

NANCY: Ten! I'm older than you!

THELMA: You're not! When's your birthday?

NANCY: Today. I was eleven today. Which makes me older!

THELMA: Are you having a party too?

NANCY (*hating to admit she is not*): Well—sort of—

THELMA: What kind of an answer is that? Say yes or no. Are you having a party tonight?

NANCY: Not exactly. Parties are for babies really. I'm too big for that.

THELMA: What then?

NANCY: It—I—it's a surprise—for me, I mean. My parents want to surprise me so I can't tell you.

THELMA: But they're going out tonight. That's why your mother wanted the lace blouse. You said so yourself.

NANCY (*making it up in desperation*): I know they're going out. But with me. They're taking me to see a play. (*She runs to the envelope.*) See—here are the tickets—three—count them for yourself.

THELMA: A play, heavens to Betsy! Do you know what? Maybe they'll take you to that comedy about the stolen baby.

NANCY: Maybe. (*She gives in to her curiosity.*) What stolen baby?

THELMA: You know the one I mean—a man pretends his friend's baby is his own so he won't have to pay so much Income Tax. Didn't you see it on television? A part of it anyway? It was super.

NANCY: Oh sure. I remember it now.

(MARTHA *returns with the salad bowl.*)

MARTHA: Thelma, put that candy down! You're getting as fat as a house!

NANCY (*anxious to get away from* THELMA's *questions*): Martha, Mommy left the laundry money in the kitchen bowl. I'll get it for you.

(*She runs out left.*)

THELMA: It's Nancy's birthday today.

MARTHA: And she'll be alone again, poor thing.

THELMA: How do you know?

MARTHA: Justine told me. Nancy's always alone, Justine says.

THELMA: But she's going to see a play with her parents. The one about the baby and the Income Tax. She told me.

MARTHA: Then she told you a story. And who can blame her with a ma and pa running out all the time? It's just as I said. She may get the prettiest dresses but they don't take the place of a parent's love.

THELMA: But Nancy *is* going. (*She picks up the theater tickets.*) Here are the tickets. Three of them.

MARTHA: Well, maybe this time she's not imagining. Maybe she *is* telling the truth. (THELMA *replaces the tickets.*)

THELMA: Why don't you ever take me to a play? A party is so babyish!

MARTHA: You're better off with a party. You like to eat!

(NANCY *enters with the laundry money.*)

NANCY: Here is the laundry money, Martha.

MARTHA: Thanks, bunny, and a happy, happy birthday.

(*The doorbell rings.* NANCY *runs to the door and opens it.*)

NANCY: Mom! (*She hugs* MRS. ROYCE, *a charming, attractive woman who enters with packages.*)

MRS. ROYCE: Hi. (*Everyone returns her greeting.*)

MARTHA: I brought your blouse, Mrs. Royce.

MRS. ROYCE: Oh good. (*To* NANCY.) Is Daddy home?

NANCY: Not yet.

MRS. ROYCE: Did anything come for me, darling?

NANCY: You mean the theater tickets? (*She crosses to sofa.*) Here they are.

MRS. ROYCE: Leave them on the table. Where's Justine?

NANCY: She hasn't come back yet.

MRS. ROYCE: Oh dear, just when we need her. Martha, can you stay with Nancy until Justine shows up? Mr. Royce and I have to visit an important client in Greenwich—for the week end—and we're leaving as soon as he comes in.

NANCY: But my birthday!

MRS. ROYCE: You don't think I've forgotten that, darling? (*She gives* NANCY *a dress box.*) Happy, happy from Daddy and me. (*She hugs* NANCY *who stares at her unhappily.*) Open it. Go on, open it. (NANCY *goes to the hassock and opens the box reluctantly. She pulls out a party dress.* MARTHA *and* THELMA *exchange glances.*) Do you like it, baby? (NANCY *is silent.*) Why don't you go into the bedroom and put it on now? I'd love to see how it fits before we leave. Go on, baby, hurry.

(*Half-crying,* NANCY *runs out, left, with the dress.*)

MRS. ROYCE (*calling after her*): Nan, if Mrs. Woodley calls for the tickets after we've gone, give them to her, will you?

MARTHA (*grimly*): Thelma, fetch me a glass of water in the kitchen. And let the tap run awhile so the water's cold, hear? (*As* THELMA *leaves, left*) And keep your fingers out of the icebox! (MARTHA *now turns to* MRS. ROYCE.) About Nancy, Mrs. Royce.

MRS. ROYCE (*anxiously*): You can baby-sit? We must get to Greenwich in time for dinner. You won't have to stay long. Justine should be back soon.

MARTHA: I'll stay all right only—well, I've no business talking this way but my heart's too big for me so—Mrs. Royce, your girl's lonely. It's her birthday. She hoped you were taking her to a play. Maybe the tickets over there gave her the idea but—

MRS. ROYCE (*distressed*): I know, I know. But I can't do anything about it, Martha. Mr. Royce has to socialize with his clients. It's his job. You don't know how many times I've wanted to be with Nan but he needs me with him.

MARTHA: Maybe if you talked to Mr. Royce?

MRS. ROYCE: His work comes first. Nan and I will have to be patient. When we've lived here longer we'll—

THELMA (*enters with a glass of water. She is eating a banana*):   Here's your water, Mom.

MARTHA: I thought I told you to stay out of the icebox.

THELMA: But this was on the table.

MARTHA: Never mind. You go along home now. I'm sitting here with Nancy until Justine comes.

THELMA (*putting the glass down*):   Good-bye, Mrs. Royce. Have a good time.
       (*She leaves right just as* MR. ROYCE *enters. He is tired. There are general greetings.*)

MRS. ROYCE: Martha, there's a cold supper already fixed in the frij.

MARTHA (*exiting, left*):   Okay. I'll set it out.

MRS. ROYCE (*helping her husband off with his coat*):   How do you feel, Steve?

MR. ROYCE (*lying down on the sofa*):   Too tired to move.

MRS. ROYCE (*hopefully*):   Would you—wouldn't you prefer to stay home this week end?

MR. ROYCE (*sitting up quickly*):   No, I'll be fine once we get going.

MRS. ROYCE (*calling*):   Nan, Daddy's home. Let's see your new dress, darling. (*To her husband.*) It's our birthday present to Nan, dear. She's eleven today.

MR. ROYCE: I haven't forgotten. (NANCY *enters, the dress pulled over her jeans.*) Well, our baby certainly looks grown up. May I have the pleasure of the next cha-cha, Miss Royce? (*He tries to dance with* NANCY *who holds back.*) Well, we'd better get our bags. I told the cab driver to come in ten minutes. Come on, Diana.
       (*He exits, left. His wife follows him, looking back at* NANCY *anxiously. Alone,* NANCY *bursts into tears.*)

NANCY (*pulling off her dress*):   I can't be their child! They wouldn't treat me like this! They wouldn't do this if I were! I won't be their child!
       (*She sits down on the hassock and weeps. The doorbell rings.* NANCY *does not hear it. After a moment, the door opens slowly and* EDWARD P. WOLF *peers in. He wears a derby.*)

MR. WOLF (*noticing* NANCY):   The door pushed open. Is your father home?

NANCY: I have no father.

MR. WOLF (*suspiciously*):   Is this the Royce residence? (NANCY *nods.*) Steven Royce? (*She nods. He consults a form.*) Married to wife, Diana Royce? (*She nods.*) Then you're Nancy Royce?

NANCY: That's what they call me. But they're not my father and my mother! I'm not their child!

MR. WOLF: But you're listed here as such.

NANCY: No—that is—I only live with them.

MR. WOLF: How long?

NANCY: I don't know—since they moved here—that is—OH—

(*She runs out, left, as* MRS. ROYCE *enters with a week-end bag.*)

MRS. ROYCE: Was that for the tickets?—Nancy!

MR. ROYCE (*enters. He carries a bag*):   What's wrong with her?

MR. WOLF: Mr. Royce?

MR. ROYCE: Yes.

MR. WOLF: Mrs. Royce?

MRS. ROYCE: Yes.

MR. WOLF: My card. Wolf—Edward P. Wolf, Internal Revenue Department. You are Steven Royce?

MR. ROYCE (*puzzled*):   Yes, sir. You wrote me several days ago, didn't you? Will you sit down? (MR. WOLF *sits on the sofa, but not before examining it. He puts his hat down beside him.*) Let me take your hat, sir.

MR. WOLF (*putting his hat on his lap*):   I'll keep it, thank you.

MR. ROYCE: Will you tell me, Mr. Wolf, why you've come to see me?

MR. WOLF: Well, as my letter stated, there is some question about a deduction you took on your last Income Tax return. The U.S. Government feels you are not entitled to it.

MR. ROYCE: My accountant plans to send you the information necessary to clear this up. I still don't understand why you're here.

MR. WOLF: My letter was mailed to your old address and a lot of time was lost. The information must be in by tomorrow. So I came to see you. And it's a good thing I did. Since I've arrived here—(*he consults his watch*)—seventy-nine seconds ago exactly—I've learned something that makes your case even more serious.

MR. ROYCE: More serious?

MR. WOLF: I spoke to your daughter, Nancy Royce, who claims she is not your daughter.

MRS. ROYCE (*relieved*):   Oh, Nancy!

MR. WOLF (*continuing*):   Said Nancy Royce further informed me that she has been with you only since you moved to this address—

MR. ROYCE (*apologetically*):   You know children and their imaginations.

MR. WOLF: —which makes the period of her living with you exactly eight and one-third weeks. Why then, Mr. Royce, did you claim her as a dependent on your last Income Tax return?

MR. ROYCE: The whole thing is ridiculous! Nancy is, was, and has always been our daughter since she was a baby—Now *I'm* talking like a child! Look, I'll call her and she'll tell you so herself.

MRS. ROYCE (*calling, left*):   Nan, come here, will you? Daddy wants to talk to you. (*To* MR. WOLF.) May I take your hat now?

MR. WOLF: No, thank you.

(NANCY *enters.*)

NANCY: Yes?

MR. ROYCE: Yes who?

MRS. ROYCE: Daddy means you always answer, "Yes, *Dad.*"

MR. WOLF: No coaching, please. Now, Miss, repeat what you told me in this room—(*he consults his watch*)—one hundred and thirty-nine seconds ago.

NANCY (*embarrassed, she sits on the hassock*):   I don't remember.

MR. WOLF: You said this man wasn't your father, you weren't—

NANCY (*ready to tell the truth*):   That wasn't exactly what I meant. I meant—

(*She is interrupted by the doorbell.*)

MR. ROYCE: That's our cab. Are you ready? (MRS. ROYCE *nods. He opens the door, right, and calls off*) We'll be right out.

NANCY (*hurt again by her parents' neglect*):   I meant, they pretend I'm their child. They—they borrowed me from my real parents just—just so they could save money on their tax. (MRS. ROYCE *exclaims.*) The real Nancy died and they're using me.

(*She dashes out left.*)

MR. WOLF (*accusingly*):   Using her as a dependent to defraud the Government, eh?

THE ROYCES: It's just her imagination—eleven-year-olds are like this—she's disappointed about her birthday and—we can straighten this out easily.

MR. WOLF: With proof?

MR. ROYCE: Certainly with proof. Only you'll have to wait until Monday. Her birth certificate is in my bank vault and the bank is closed now.

MR. WOLF: My boss won't wait.

MRS. ROYCE: But no one in this town has known us long enough to prove anything.

MR. WOLF: If your case is not closed by tomorrow—(*Confessing*) It was my fault your letter went astray and—well, you don't know my boss.

MRS. ROYCE (*concerned about* NAN, *to* MR. ROYCE):   Perhaps if you tried to speak to Nan again—I'm worried about her.

MR. ROYCE: Tell the cab to come back in half an hour. We'll still make Greenwich in time for dinner. I'll get Nancy.

> (MR. ROYCE *exits left and is heard calling to* NANCY.)

MRS. ROYCE (*walking to exit, right, to* MR. WOLF):   My husband will get this all straightened out in a few minutes, Mr. Wolf. In just a few minutes.

> (MR. WOLF *watches her exit; then, in despair, he looks at his hat and claps it on his head*
>
> > *as the curtain closes.*)

ACT TWO

It is twenty minutes later. An exhausted MR. ROYCE *is resting on the sofa. He is in his shirt sleeves.* MR. WOLF *is seated on the hassock, wiping his brow. He, too, is in his shirt sleeves although his hat is still on his head. He rises when* MRS. ROYCE *enters with coffee.*

MRS. ROYCE: Drink this, Steve. You look worn out.

MR. ROYCE: Trying to get your daughter to come out of her room isn't a picnic.

MRS. ROYCE: May I give you some coffee too, Mr. Wolf?

MR. WOLF: Never touch the stuff. It makes me sleepy. (*He laughs at his own joke then becomes depressed again.*) What are you going to do about her?

> (*He gestures in* NANCY'S *direction.*)

MR. ROYCE: She won't unlock her door. I've pleaded for twenty minutes. You'll just have to wait until Monday for her birth certificate.

MR. WOLF: But my boss—

MR. ROYCE: Mr. Wolf, we can't stay here any longer. We'll be late for our appointment.

MR. WOLF (*putting on his jacket*):   But my—

MR. ROYCE (*removing* MR. WOLF's *hat, he thrusts it into* MR. WOLF's *hand*):   Monday.

MR. WOLF (*as* MR. ROYCE *propels him to the exit, right*):   But—

MR. ROYCE (*pushing him out*):   Monday.

(*A moment later,* MR. WOLF *pops his head in. He opens his mouth to speak.* MR. ROYCE *opens his to answer.* MR. WOLF *waves with his hat, puts it on his head and disappears finally.*)

MR. ROYCE: I'll tell Martha we're leaving. Get your coat, Diana.

MRS. ROYCE: No. I can't leave until everything is straightened out.

MR. ROYCE: Wolf can wait.

MRS. ROYCE: That horrid little man doesn't bother me. Nan does. We can't leave her like this.

MR. ROYCE: Don't worry. Soon as your child gets hungry enough, she'll come out of her room.

MRS. ROYCE: I'm not thinking about her stomach but about *her*—inside. She's hurt inside. She's been left alone too much. Don't you think I ought to stay with her? For this week end at least?

MR. ROYCE: You're going to get into that cab when it comes. You need some fun.

MRS. ROYCE: If only she'd let me talk to her—

MR. ROYCE: Nan's at the awkward age, that's all.

MRS. ROYCE: It's not all.

MR. ROYCE: Shhh—I think her door is opening. (*He listens.*) Yes. (*Overjoyed,* MRS. ROYCE *wants to run to* NANCY *but he stops her.*) If Nancy stops fussing, will you come with me to Greenwich?

MRS. ROYCE (*reluctantly*):   If you need me.

MR. ROYCE: Let me talk to her alone. I'll manage everything.

(NANCY *enters, left. She is uncommunicative.*)

MRS. ROYCE: Darling, you must be starved! I'll get you a sandwich. Meat loaf, all right? With ketchup, the way you like it.

(*She hurries out left.*)

MR. ROYCE: Sit down, Nancy. Here. (*He points to the sofa but* NANCY *sits down on the hassock.*) Okay, there. (*He pauses a moment, awkward in the presence of his daughter.*) Coffee, I mean, milk? (NANCY *shakes her head.*) It's been a long time since we were alone together. I mean, together alone. No, I mean together the way we are now, *alone.* I've been wanting to talk to you.

NANCY: If it's about that man and what I said—

MR. ROYCE: No, no, about school and—uh—things. (NANCY *slumps back into silence.*) How's school?

NANCY: Fine.

> (*There is a silence.*)

MR. ROYCE: How's your homework?

NANCY: Fine.

> (*There is a silence.*)

MR. ROYCE: I'm not making a good job of this conversation, I know. The thing is, baby, I want you and me to be friends again. The way we were before we moved here. I love you, Nan. Mom loves you. We want to be with you all the time. (NANCY *turns to him, hopeful.*) I'd like nothing better, honestly. Only it's been hard on Mom, being away from her old friends. She needs to get out.

MRS. ROYCE (*entering, left, with sandwich and milk*):   Here, Nan, eat. And this time, I won't tell you to wash your hands.

> (NANCY *eats.*)

MR. ROYCE: Not so fast, young lady.

MRS. ROYCE: And not so much bread, either. Leave the crusts. You want to have a good figure.

MR. ROYCE: Talking about figures, how about your clothes? Anything special you'd like to buy? (*No answer.*) Shorts or, uh, kilts, or whatever the girls wear today?

> (*No answer.*)

MRS. ROYCE: Daddy wants to do something special for you. For your birthday.

NANCY (*touched*):   If you really want to do something—

MRS. ROYCE: Name it, darling.

NANCY: You're sure?

MR. ROYCE: Anything you like.

NANCY (*bursting out*):   I'd like a party, like Thelma's! Tonight, for my birthday! (*Ashamed of their neglect, her parents turn away from her and from each other.*) It can be for just the three of us. I'd love us so to be together once. (*They do not answer.*) But—if you'd rather not—

MRS. ROYCE: Of course, darling, a party for just the three of us.

NANCY (*beaming*):   You mean it? (*As she runs out, left.*) I'll get the list of stuff and things to eat. I made it up last night when I pretended we might have one.

(*After* NANCY *leaves, there is a moment's silence.* STEVEN *and* DIANA ROYCE *are afraid to look at each other.*)

MRS. ROYCE (*eventually*): She wants a party.

MR. ROYCE (*unhappily*): With us.

MRS. ROYCE (*eagerly*): Perhaps we should, Steve, forget the week end, I mean, and—(*He turns to look at her and she falters.*) I mean, we want to please her to get her to admit she's our child to the investigator.

MR. ROYCE: We're not going to give up the week end!

MARTHA (*entering, smiling*): What's Nancy so happy about? She fairly danced into her bedroom. (MR. *and* MRS. ROYCE *are silent.* MARTHA *looks at them.*) You staying with her tonight? (*They don't answer.*) Oh.

(NANCY *runs in, list in hand.*)

NANCY: Martha! Do you know what? I'm having a party tonight! A birth-day party! There won't be many people, only three, Mommy and Dad and—perhaps you could stay and be in the party too. Okay, Mom? (MRS. ROYCE, *miserable, is silent.*) You're not angry because of what I said to that man, are you? Mom? Dad? I only said it—not because I meant it but be-cause—well—I felt sort of quivery inside, as if my stomach was falling to my toes. I always feel like that when you leave me. You understand? Mom? Dad?

(*They are silent.*)

MARTHA: *I* understand, bunny. And your ma and pa do too. Don't you, Mrs. Royce? And since you'll be with Nancy tonight, I'll just run along home. Thelma needs help for *her* party tomorrow night. (*She is about to exit, right, when the bell rings. She exits, murmurs to someone offstage then calls in to* THE ROYCES.) There's a cab waiting for you.

NANCY (*stunned*): A cab? You're going off to that week end after all?

MRS. ROYCE (*she sits down on sofa. Determinedly*): I'm not going. Do you hear, Steve? I'm not going on that stupid week end. I'm staying home with Nancy. You go.

MR. ROYCE: But Di, you'll have such a good time. You always do.

MRS. ROYCE: I never do! I've hated going away. I just went for your sake, for the sake of your job. I've wanted to be with Nancy.

(*There is a pause.*)

MR. ROYCE (*smiling*): Then what's all the fuss about? Let's all stay home.

MRS. ROYCE (*surprised*): But your work, your clients?

MR. ROYCE: They'll find themselves another canasta partner. I went out so much only because I thought you wanted to go—to make friends.

MRS. ROYCE (*stunned*): Oh no!

NANCY: You mean you both want to stay home with *me?* Oh no!

MR. ROYCE (*twirling* NANCY *until they both tumble down on the sofa beside* MRS. ROYCE): Oh yes!

(*They are all laughing when the bell rings again.*)

MRS. ROYCE: The cab!

(*The parents rise and start to the door. Then, remembering, they sit down again.*)

MRS. ROYCE: Let it ring. We're staying home.

NANCY: We're going to have a party.

(*She hugs them both.*)

MR. ROYCE: We're *having* a party. (*He rises and bows before* NANCY.) May I have the pleasure of this cha-cha, Miss Royce?

NANCY (*rising to the occasion*): You may, Mr. Royce.

MRS. ROYCE (*rising too*): And what about Mrs. Royce?

NANCY: Why don't you join us, Mrs. Royce? We're having a party!

(*The three start to cha-cha while the bell rings and*

the curtain closes.)

STAGING SUGGESTIONS

Comments

This script demonstrates again how a plot may arise out of the group's own knowledge and experience. At the time of dramatization, the father of one boy, a lawyer, was engaged in a tax evasion case. The episode led to the creation of MR. EDWARD P. WOLF, Internal Revenue Department Agent!

Cast

Cast according to talent as well as responsibility.

Set

The living room may be as simple or as elaborate as you wish it. The only things necessary are the sofa, the library table behind it, the hassock, the occasional table and the telephone. Orange crates or chairs, covered with a spread and cushions, may serve for a sofa. Another covered crate may be turned into a hassock.

Costumes

Modern dress, outdoor and indoor: jeans for NANCY; a derby for MR. WOLF.

Sound

Doorbell and phone bell, either real or recorded.

Props

Magazines and cushions for sofa; envelope containing three theater tickets for library table; two candy dishes with candy; phone; laundry parcel and salad bowl for MARTHA; laundry parcel, glass of water and banana for THELMA; stage money and party list for NANCY; packages, a dress box with girl's dress, week-end bag, tray with coffee things, sandwich for MRS. ROYCE; week-end bag for MR. ROYCE; tax form, two business cards and watch for MR. WOLF.

A MIDSUMMER NIGHT'S DREAM

A SHORT ADAPTATION FOR YOUNG PLAYERS OF THE PLAY BY WILLIAM SHAKESPEARE

Playing Time   20 minutes approximately

Age   10–14 years

Manner of Presentation   Memorize lines

Staging Suggestions   See end of play

Cast   Commentator
Puck (a mischievous fairy)
Theseus (Duke of Athens)
The Duke's Retinue
Egeus (father of Hermia)
Hermia
Demetrius (in love with Hermia)
Lysander (in love with Hermia)

Oberon (King of the Fairies)

Titania (Queen of the Fairies)

Fairies (among them Peaseblossom, Cobweb, Moth and Mustard Seed)

Helena (in love with Demetrius)

Bottom (a weaver who fancies himself an actor)

Time   A midsummer night

Place   Athens and a Wood nearby

Scene   Although the play's action takes place in two locales—the Palace of Theseus and a Wood near Athens—it may be performed in a single set. This can consist of a decorative bench, downstage right, a low bank, upstage center, and a high bank, stage left. Flowering shrubs and trees dot the landscape, while puffs of cloud chase each other across a blue sky. Entrances are stage right and stage left.

(The banks may be constructed of different-sized levels and covered with leaves and flowers. Shrubs and trees may be painted cutouts. The clouds, too, are cutouts of various shapes and painted white. These are attached to a sky created out of paper which has been painted blue and stretched across the back wall of the set.)

(Additional set suggestions will be found at the end of the play.)

While the curtain is still closed, the COMMENTATOR *enters, apron right, and introduces the play. His opening comments give information pertaining to the play, its adaptation, the author and the group presenting it. He concludes with—*

COMMENTATOR: Written a short time before 1600, A *Midsummer Night's Dream* is a lyrical comedy of crossed love. The action takes place in that mystical time when sprites and mortals abandoned themselves to dancing and merrymaking. (*The curtain opens slowly.*) Now, in Athens, there lived two pairs of heartsick lovers—Hermia and Lysander, Demetrius and Helena.

Once all had been joyous for these mortals. Hermia loved and was loved by Lysander; Demetrius loved and was loved by Helena. But then, Demetrius cast fond eyes upon the lovely Hermia. And, to bewilder the lovers more, their paths were crossed by Oberon, the King of the Fairies, and Titania the fairy Queen, who with their retinue of sprites and—

    (PUCK, *a mischievous sprite, appears suddenly on top of the bank, left. He holds a scroll in his hand.*)

PUCK (*interrupting the* COMMENATOR): —and Puck!

COMMENTATOR (*confused*): Puck?

PUCK (*jumping to the ground*): Puck! I serve the fairy King.

I jest to Oberon and make him smile
When I a bean-fed horse beguile
Neighing like a filly foal.

    (*He neighs coyly then crosses to the* COMMENTATOR *and crouches.*)

And sometimes lurk I in a gossip's bowl
In very likeness of a roasted crab.

    (*He jumps up quickly, frightening the* COMMENTATOR. *The* COMMENTATOR *screams and hurries offstage, right. Laughing,* PUCK *imitates his nervous steps then crosses down toward the audience whom he now addresses.*)

Gentles, do not reprehend,
If you pardon, Puck will mend,
And a tale he will unfold,
Of Athens and four lovers bold.

    (PUCK *unfurls a white scroll on which is written the legend, "The Palace of Theseus—Duke of Athens." He displays it to the audience just as* THESEUS *himself enters, left.* THESEUS *is followed by his retinue. Two servants quickly place a throne on bank, left, on which* THESEUS *seats himself. During this movement,* PUCK *has hidden himself behind the bench, right, invisible to all but the audience.*)

    (EGEUS *enters hurriedly, right, pulling his daughter,* HERMIA, *along with him. They are followed by two young men,* DEMETRIUS *and* LYSANDER. HERMIA *falls on her knees before* THESEUS, *while the men bow.*)

EGEUS (*saluting* THESEUS): Happy be Theseus, our renowned duke.

THESEUS: Thanks, good Egeus, what's the news with thee?

EGEUS: Full of vexation come I, with complaint
  Against my daughter, Hermia.

    (*kindly*)

Stand forth, Demetrius. (DEMETRIUS *moves toward the* DUKE *and bows.*)
My noble lord,
This man hath my consent to marry her.
    (*angrily*)
Stand forth, Lysander. (LYSANDER *moves toward the* DUKE *and bows.*)
And, my gracious duke,
This man hath bewitched my child,
Turned her obedience, which is due to me,
To stubborn harshness; so, my gracious duke,
I beg the ancient privilege of Athens,
I may dispose of her
Either to this gentleman (*he points to* DEMETRIUS)
Or to her death.
    (*Frightened,* HERMIA *rises and clings to* LYSANDER.)
THESEUS: What say you, Hermia?
Demetrius is a worthy gentleman.
HERMIA: So is Lysander. (*She kneels before* THESEUS.)
I do entreat your Grace to pardon me and say
The worst that may befall me
If I refuse to wed Demetrius.
THESEUS: Either to die the death or to leave
Forever the society of men. (HERMIA *weeps.*)
Take time to think.
    (*He rises.*)
Now, Demetrius, come,
And come, Egeus.
I shall employ you in some business
And confer with you.
Take time, Hermia.
EGEUS: We follow you, my lord.
    (THESEUS, EGEUS *and* DEMETRIUS *leave, stage left, followed by the* DUKE's
    retinue. LYSANDER *kneels beside* HERMIA *to comfort her.*)
LYSANDER: How now, my love! Why is your cheek so pale?
The course of true love never did run smooth.
HERMIA: O, to choose love by another's eyes!
LYSANDER: Hear me, Hermia.
I have an aunt,
From Athens is her house remote;

There the sharp Athenian law
Cannot pursue us. (*He rises and lifts her up.*) If thou lovest me
Steal forth tomorrow night,
And in the wood
Will I wait for thee.

HERMIA: My good Lysander!
I swear to thee, by Cupid's strongest bow,
Tomorrow truly will I meet with thee.

> (*They embrace and depart separately,* HERMIA, *off right,* LYSANDER, *off left.*)

LYSANDER (*making a farewell gesture*):   Tomorrow, then, my love.

> (PUCK *emerges, echoes* LYSANDER's *"Tomorrow, then, my love," and then addresses the audience.*)

PUCK: How now, Gentles, like you this tale?
Yea?
Then to that wood, come, fly away. . . .

> (*He unfurls another scroll on which is written the legend, "A Wood Near Athens." As he continues to speak,* TITANIA's FAIRIES *dance on stage from right and left to musical accompaniment. Among them are* PEASEBLOSSOM, COBWEB, MOTH *and* MUSTARD SEED.)

PUCK (*addressing the audience*):   The King doth keep his revels here tonight.
Take heed the Queen come not within his sight.
For Oberon is wrath
That she withholds the lovely boy
He would have of her.
But here comes Oberon—and here Titania!

> (OBERON *enters from right.* PUCK *jumps to a position behind him. They meet* TITANIA *who enters from left. Her* FAIRIES *group themselves behind her.* OBERON *is in a quarrelsome mood.*)

OBERON: Ill met by moonlight, proud Titania.

TITANIA: Fairies, skip away.
We shall quarrel if I longer stay.

> (TITANIA *and her* FAIRIES *exit right.*)

OBERON (*calling after her*):   I do but beg your little boy
To be my henchman.

> (*She disappears. He is angry.*)

Well, go thy way. I shall torment thee
For this injury.

My gentle Puck, come hither.
Thou rememberest
The magic herb I showed thee once?
Fetch me this herb. And quick!
PUCK (*as he twirls off left*):   I'll put a girdle round about the earth
In forty minutes.
OBERON (*crossing downstage, he addresses audience*):
I'll watch Titania when she is asleep,
And drop the liquor of this herb onto her eyes.
The next thing when she waking looks upon,
Be it lion or bear or wolf or bull,
She shall pursue it with the soul of love.
HELENA (*calling, offstage right*):   Demetrius—Demetrius—
OBERON: But who comes here? I am invisible.
        (*He hides behind the bench.* DEMETRIUS *enters from right.* HELENA
        is pursuing him.)
        (DEMETRIUS *enters from right.* HELENA *is pursuing him.*)
DEMETRIUS (*annoyed with* HELENA):   I love thee not, Helena, pursue me not.
Where is Lysander and fair Hermia?
Thou sayest they meet within this wood.
HELENA (*pleading*):   Demetrius,
Use me but as your spaniel, spurn me, strike me,
Only give me leave to love you.
DEMETRIUS: I am sick when I do look on thee.
HELENA: Fie,
We women cannot fight for love as men may do;
We should be woo'd and were not made to woo.
DEMETRIUS (*running away from her and off, left*):   I'll run from thee and
leave thee
To the mercy of wild beasts.
HELENA (*following him*):   Yet I'll follow thee.
        (*Calling*)
Demetrius—Demetrius—
        (OBERON, *disturbed by the scene he has just witnessed, emerges from
        his hiding place.* PUCK *enters, right, holding a flower in his hand.*)
OBERON (*to* PUCK):   Hast thou the flower here?
PUCK: Aye, there it is.
        (OBERON *retains part of the flower.*)

OBERON: Take thou some of it and seek through this grove
          (*He gestures left where* DEMETRIUS *and* HELENA *have gone.*)
     A sweet Athenian lady who is in love
     With a disdainful youth; Demetrius his name.
     Anoint his eyes:
     But do it when the next thing he espies
     May be this Helena so he shall love her.
     Thou shalt know the man
     By the Athenian garments he hath on.
PUCK: Fear not, my lord, thy servant shall do so.
          (*He twirls off, left. Several of* TITANIA's *fairies trip in from right to musical accompaniment.*)
OBERON: But now Titania comes.
          (OBERON *hides behind left bank as* TITANIA *enters, right, with the rest of her train.* TITANIA *sits down on the bench.*)
TITANIA (*instructing her retinue*):   Come fairies, hence,
     Some to kill cankers in the musk-rose buds;
     Some war with rere-mice for their leathern wings
     To make my small elves coats. And some
     To sing me now asleep.
          (TITANIA *lies down on the bench and the fairies sing.*)
     "You spotted snakes, with double tongue,
     Thorny hedgehogs, be not seen;
     Newts and blind-worms do no wrong;
     Come not near our fairy queen.
     CHORUS:
     Philomel, with melody,
     Sing in our sweet lullaby;
     Lulla, lulla, lullaby; lulla, lulla, lullaby;
     Never harm, nor spell, nor charm,
     Come our lovely lady nigh;
     So, good-night, with lullaby."
          (*When* TITANIA *is asleep, they dance off, right.* OBERON *emerges, crosses quickly to* TITANIA *and rubs her eyelids with juice from the magic flower.*)
OBERON: What thou seest when thou wake,
     Do it for thy true-love take;
     Be it lynx or cat or bear,

Pard or boar with bristled hair. (*He exits, left.*)

(*A moment later,* LYSANDER *and* HERMIA *enter from right. They are weary.*)

LYSANDER: Fair love, you faint with wandering in the wood;
We'll rest us, Hermia, if you think it good.

HERMIA: Be it so, Lysander; find you out a bed;
For I upon this bank will rest my head.

(*She lies down on bank, left.*)

Good night, sweet friend;
Thy love ne'er alter till thy sweet life end!

LYSANDER (*he covers her with his cloak, then crosses to center bank where he lies down*):
Sleep give thee all his rest.

(*They fall asleep.* PUCK *enters, left, still holding his portion of the flower.*)

PUCK (*dejected*):   Through the forest have I gone,
But Athenian found I none.

(*He spies* LYSANDER.)

Who is here?

(*He examines the sleeping man.*)

Weeds of Athens he doth wear,
Demetrius, my master said,
And here his Helena, sleeping sound,
On the dank and dirty ground.
Churl, upon thy eyes I throw
All the power this charm doth owe.

(PUCK *rubs* LYSANDER's *eyelids with the juice of the flower.*)

HELENA (*offstage, left*):   Demetrius—Demetrius—

(PUCK *hides behind* LYSANDER *as* HELENA, *weary, enters left.*)

HELENA (*wailing*):   O, I am out of breath in this fond chase!
The more my prayer, the lesser is my grace!

(*She sees* LYSANDER *and runs to him.*)

Lysander! Dead!—or asleep?
Lysander, if you live, good sir, awake.

(LYSANDER *awakens and under the influence of the magic flower, falls in love with* HELENA.)

LYSANDER: And run through fire will I
For thy sweet sake, lovely Helena.

(*He tries to embrace her. She escapes. He falls to his knees.*)

HELENA: Do not say so, Lysander. 'Tis Hermia you love.

LYSANDER (*following her on his knees*):   Nay!

Who will not change a raven for a dove?

HELENA: O, wherefore was I to this mockery born?

(*She runs out, right.*)

Fare you well. (*Calling again*) Demetrius—

Demetrius—

LYSANDER (*running after her*):   Lovely Helena, stay—Helena—

(HERMIA *awakens. She has had a bad dream.*)

HERMIA: Help me, Lysander, help me! . . .

What a dream was here!

(*She looks around for* LYSANDER.)

Lysander! Lord! where are you?

(PUCK *echoes her cries. She rises in terror.*)

Lysander, speak, if you hear.

Speak, I swoon almost with fear.

(*She runs out left calling*)

Lysander—lord—Lysander—

(PUCK *emerges. Echoing* HELENA's *wails, he pirouettes gleefully. His movements bring him to the sleeping* TITANIA.)

PUCK: Shh—Titania sleeps. Upon her eye the charm doth lie.

Now, who shall be her dear when she will wake?

Surely some vile thing is near.

(*He looks around him mischievously. Suddenly he hears a voice, offstage left. He hides behind the bench.* BOTTOM, *a weaver, enters. He is rehearsing lines from a play. He tries out the lines in several different ways, each time with exaggerated gestures.*)

BOTTOM: "O Thisby, if I were fair, I were only mine—

(*He corrects himself.*)

Thine—thine—

O Thisby, if I were fair, I were only thine . . ."

PUCK (*to the audience*):   An actor he! A clown!

(*He springs in front of* BOTTOM *who recoils.*)

How now, clown! Who and whither wander you?

BOTTOM (*frightened*):   Me, sir? I, sir? Nick Bottom, sir, and I

But rehearse a piece to play before the duke on

His wedding day—at night!

PUCK (*mocking*):   His wedding day—at night!

At night—his wedding day!

What is this piece?

BOTTOM: A very good piece, sir. "The Love and Most

Cruel Death of Pyramus and Thisby," sir.

PUCK (*still dancing around* BOTTOM):   What is Pyramus?

BOTTOM (*his vanity overcoming his fright*):

A lover, sir, who kills himself for love of Lady Thisby, sir.

(PUCK *pretends to be affected.*)

When I do it, let the audience look to their eyes.

I will move storms!

(*He sighs and moans.*)

"O Thisby, if I were fair, I were only thine."

(PUCK *moans in mockery.* BOTTOM *warms up.*)

And if I hide my beard, I can play Thisby too.

I'll speak in a monstrous little voice—

(BOTTOM *assumes a feminine voice which* PUCK *imitates.*)

"Ah Pyramus, my lover dear!

Thy Thisby dear and lady dear."

(*He resumes his normal voice.*)

And then I'll play the lion too; I will roar

Till I make the duke say, "Let him roar again."

PUCK: What if you fright the ladies?

BOTTOM: I will roar you gentle as a sucking dove; I

Will roar as 'twere a nightingale.

PUCK (*addressing the audience*):   This is the ass, is he,

The proud Titania in love will be.

(*He finds a donkey's head behind the bench and claps it on* BOTTOM's
head as BOTTOM *tries out his lines in different voices.*)

BOTTOM: "O Thisby, if I were fair . . . O Thisby, if I were fair . . . O

Thisby, if I were fair, I were only . . ."

(*The donkey's head is on and* BOTTOM's *voice turns to a bray.*)

Hee-haw.

(*Startled, he tries his lines again.*)

(*As* BOTTOM *brays,* PUCK *leads him to* TITANIA. *The last bray awakens
her just as* OBERON *enters from left.*)

OBERON: I wonder if Titania be awakened and whom she'll see.

(OBERON *and* PUCK *hide behind bank, left, to watch.*)

TITANIA (*awakening*): What angel wakes me from my flowery bed?

BOTTOM (*still trying out his voice*): "O Thisby, if I were fair," hee-haw . . . "if I were fair," hee-haw. . . .

TITANIA (*enchanted with* BOTTOM): I pray thee, gentle mortal, sing again.

BOTTOM: Hee-haw, hee-haw, hee-haw. . . .

TITANIA (*falling in love with* BOTTOM *who responds to her attention*): Ah, thou art beautiful . . .
Therefore go with me;
I'll give thee fairies to attend on thee;
And they shall fetch thee jewels from the deep,
And sing, while thou on pressed flowers sleep.
(*She calls her fairies*)
Peaseblossom! Cobweb! Moth! and Mustard Seed!
(*The* FAIRIES *enter from right and group themselves before their queen.*)

PEASEBLOSSOM: Ready—

COBWEB: And I—

MOTH: And I—

MUSTARD SEED: And I.

TITANIA: Feed my love with apricots and dewberries,
With purple grapes, green figs and mulberries,
And pluck the wings from painted butterflies,
To fan the moonbeams from his sleeping eyes.

PEASEBLOSSOM (*saluting* BOTTOM): Hail, mortal!

COBWEB: Hail!

MOTH: Hail!

MUSTARD SEED: Hail!

BOTTOM (*delighted with the attention*): Hee-haw, hee-haw, hee-haw . . .

TITANIA: Come, wait upon him; lead him to my bower.
(TITANIA *and* BOTTOM *exit right, the* FAIRIES *dancing around them.* OBERON *and* PUCK *emerge from their hiding place.*)

PUCK (*mocking* TITANIA): I pray thee, gentle mortal, sing again.

OBERON (*mocking* BOTTOM): Hee-haw, hee-haw, hee-haw. . . .

PUCK: Ah, thou art beautiful.

OBERON: Hee-haw, hee-haw, hee-haw. . . .
(*Laughing, they fall upon the bench.* HERMIA *enters from left, pursued by* DEMETRIUS. OBERON *and* PUCK *hide behind the bench.*)

OBERON (*to* PUCK): Stand close; this is Demetrius whose eyes
I bade you rub with love juice.

PUCK (*dismayed—he had rubbed* LYSANDER'S *eyelids*): Nay—not this the man.

DEMETRIUS (*pleading with* HERMIA): O, why rebuke you him that loves you so?

HERMIA (*weeping*): Where is my Lysander? Where is he?
(DEMETRIUS *tries to embrace her.*)
Out, dog! Thou drivest me past the bounds
Of maiden's patience. (*Calling*) Lysander . . .
Lysander . . .
(*She runs out right.*)

DEMETRIUS (*sighing*): There is no following her in this fierce vein.
Here, therefore, for a while, I will remain and sleep.
(*He lies down on the bank, left, and falls asleep.* OBERON *crosses to look at him.* PUCK, *afraid, remains at a safe distance.*)

OBERON (*to* PUCK. *He is angry*): What hast thou done?
Thou hast mistaken quite
And laid the juice on another's sight
When Demetrius is the man.
Now, Helena look thou find
And bring her here;
I'll charm his sight against she do appear.

PUCK (*running out left*): I go, I go; look how I go.

OBERON (*rubbing* DEMETRIUS' *eyelids with the magic juice*):
Flower of this purple dye,
When his Helen he doth espy,
Let her shine as gloriously
As the Venus of the sky.
(PUCK *re-enters out of breath.*)

PUCK: Captain of our fairy land,
Helena is here at hand.

OBERON: Stand aside.
(*They hide behind bank, left.*)

PUCK (*hiding*): Lord, what fools these mortals be!
(LYSANDER *and* HELENA *enter from left.*)

LYSANDER (*pleading*): Stay, gentle Helena,
Why do you think that I should woo in scorn?

Look when I vow, I weep.

(*He kneels but she turns her back on him.*)

HELENA: Your vows are Hermia's; I love Demetrius.

LYSANDER: Demetrius loves her, not you.

> (DEMETRIUS *awakens and sees* HELENA. *Under the spell of the magic juice, he falls in love with her.*)

DEMETRIUS: O Helen, goddess, nymph, divine!

Let me kiss . . .

> (*He kneels before her.* HELENA *is caught between the two men, each of whom tries to embrace her.*)

HELENA: O, I see you all are bent

To set against me for your merriment.

LYSANDER (*to* DEMETRIUS): You love Hermia!

DEMETRIUS: Keep thy Hermia!

> (HERMIA's *voice is heard, offstage right, calling* "Lysander.")

HERMIA (*running in*): Lysander! Found!

LYSANDER: Why seek'st thou me? I hate thee.

HELENA: False Hermia, have you conspired too

To bait me?

HERMIA: I understand not what you mean.

HELENA: Aye, persevere,

Make mouths upon me when I turn my back;

Wink each at other; (*She moves away.*) Fare ye well.

LYSANDER (*pursuing* HELENA): Stay—my love, my life, my soul!

HELENA (*scornfully*): O excellent!

LYSANDER: Helen, I love thee.

DEMETRIUS: I say I love thee more than he.

LYSANDER (*pulling out his sword*): If you say so,

withdraw, and prove it too.

DEMETRIUS (*pulling out his sword*): Come!

HERMIA: Lysander, why are you grown so rude? Sweet love—

LYSANDER: I hate thee and love Helena.

HERMIA (*turns on* HELENA): Helen! Thou painted maypole!

I am not yet so low

But that my nails can reach unto thine eyes.

> (*She is ready to scratch out* HELENA's *eyes. The men intervene.*)

LYSANDER: She shall not harm thee.

DEMETRIUS: No!

HERMIA (*still battling*):   Let me come to her!

(*Screaming,* HELENA *runs off, right, pursued by an enraged* HERMIA. LYSANDER *now challenges* DEMETRIUS *to a sword fight.*)

LYSANDER: Now follow me if thou darest!

DEMETRIUS: Follow! Nay, I'll go with thee! (*They exit, left.*)

(OBERON *and* PUCK *emerge from their hiding place.*)

OBERON: Quick, Puck,
Lead these rivals so astray
As one come not within another's way.
Then, when they sleep, crush this flower into Lysander's eye
That when he wake, all this derision
Shall seem a dream and silly vision.
I'll to my queen.

(*He exits, right.*)

PUCK (*dancing*):   Up and down, up and down,
I will lead them up and down.
I am fear'd in field and town:
Goblin, lead them up and down.

(*He is standing on top of the center bank when he hears* LYSANDER. *He crouches behind the bank.* LYSANDER, *sword drawn, enters from left looking for* DEMETRIUS.)

LYSANDER: Where art thou, Demetrius?

PUCK (*running to hide behind bench and imitating* DEMETRIUS' *voice*):   Here, villain, drawn and ready. Where art thou?

LYSANDER: I will be with thee straight.

(*He runs around the bench in search of* DEMETRIUS. PUCK *manages to keep out of his sight by running to the bank, left.* DEMETRIUS *runs in from left, searching for* LYSANDER.)

DEMETRIUS: Lysander! Art thou fled?

PUCK (*hidden, imitates* LYSANDER's *voice*):   Come, child, I'll whip thee with a rod—

DEMETRIUS: Thou coward!

PUCK: Follow my voice. . . .

(DEMETRIUS *runs around the bank in search of* LYSANDER. PUCK *evades him by escaping to the center bank where he crouches and laughs at the men—*LYSANDER *who is still running around the bench and* DEMETRIUS *who is running around the left bank.*)

LYSANDER (*running*):   He goes before me and still dares me on.

When I come where he calls, then he is gone.

(He stops wearily.)

Well, here will rest me until the gentle day.

(He lies down at the downstage side of the bench and falls asleep.)

PUCK *(teasing* DEMETRIUS*)*: Ho, ho, ho! Coward!

DEMETRIUS: Where art thou?

PUCK: Come hither. I am here.

DEMETRIUS: Thou mockest me. Thou shalt buy this dear

If ever I thy face by daylight see.

Now go thy way. Faintness constraineth me.

(He lies down on top of the bank, left, and falls asleep. HELENA, *weary, enters, right.)*

HELENA: O weary night, O long and tedious night,

Here sleep me now.

(She lies down at the foot of the bank, left, and falls asleep. PUCK *crosses downstage and counts the sleepers.)*

PUCK: Yet but three? Come one more;

Two of both kinds make up four.

*(*HERMIA, *weary, enters from left.)*

Here she is.

*(*PUCK *hides as* HERMIA *lies down on the bench.)*

HERMIA: I can no further crawl, no further go;

Here will I rest me till the break of day.

(She falls asleep. PUCK *emerges and rubs the magic juice on* LYSANDER'S *eyelids.)*

PUCK: When thou wakest,

Thou takest,

True delight

In the sight

Of thy Hermia's eye.

(He addresses audience.)

Then Jack shall have Jill;

Nought shall go ill;

And all shall be well again.

*(*PUCK *hides when he sees* TITANIA, BOTTOM *and the* FAIRIES *enter from right.* OBERON *follows them in, unnoticed, and hides behind the bench.* TITANIA *leads* BOTTOM *to the center bank and sits with him.)*

TITANIA: Come, sit thee down upon this flowery bed,
While I thy hairy cheeks do coy.

BOTTOM (*scratching himself*):   Hee-haw. Where's Peaseblossom?

PEASEBLOSSOM: Ready.

BOTTOM: Scratch my head, Peaseblossom. (*The* FAIRY *scratches.* BOTTOM *hee-haws at the tickling.*) Where's Cobweb?

COBWEB: Ready.

BOTTOM: Help Peaseblossom to scratch.

        (COBWEB *does so.* BOTTOM *hee-haws his sense of well being.*)

TITANIA: O say, sweet love, what thou desirest to eat.

BOTTOM: Methinks some good, dry oats—and a bottle of hay—a *big* bottle of hay.

TITANIA: Fairies, hear ye? Away!

        (*The* FAIRIES *exit, right.* TITANIA *pulls* BOTTOM's *head down to her lap.*)
Now sleep thou and I will wind thee in my arms.

        (BOTTOM *yawns crudely.*)
O, how I love thee!

        (*They fall asleep. The lights dim. Music plays softly.* OBERON *and* PUCK *emerge. The lights grow brighter.*)

OBERON (*feeling sorry for* TITANIA):   Her dotage now
I do begin to keen,
So, Puck, take this ass's scalp away,
While I release the fairy queen.

        (*He touches* TITANIA's *eyes with the herb.*)
And now, my Titania, awake.

        (TITANIA *awakens.*)

TITANIA: My Oberon! What visions have I seen!
Methought I was enamour'd of an ass!

OBERON: There lies your love.

TITANIA: How came these things to pass?

OBERON: Come, my Queen; and in our flight,
I'll tell you how it came this night.

        (OBERON *and* TITANIA *leave, right, as* PUCK *removes the donkey's head. He hides when* THESEUS *and* EGEUS *enter, left, followed by the* DUKE's *retinue.*)

EGEUS: My lord, this is my daughter here asleep;
And this Lysander; this Demetrius;
And this the day

That Hermia should give answer of her choice.

THESEUS: Go awake them.

> (EGEUS *and several of the* DUKE's *men awaken the lovers. When they see* THESEUS, *they kneel quickly before him.*)

Good morrow, friends.

I pray you all, stand up.

> (*They rise.*)

How comes this gentle concord in the world?

LYSANDER: My lord, truly will I speak. I came with
Hermia hither; our intent was to flee the peril
Of the Athenian law.

> (*He kneels again.*)

EGEUS (*angry*):   I beg the law, the law upon his head!
They would have stolen away!

DEMETRIUS: My lord, I hither followed them, Helena
Following me. But—I wot not by what power—
My love to Hermia is melted as the snow
And now
The pleasure of mine eye is only Helena.
I love her, long for her and will forevermore be
True to her.

> (*He kneels again.*)

THESEUS: Fair lovers, you are fortunately met:
Egeus, I will overbear your will:
And in the temple, by and by,
These couples shall eternally be knit.

THESEUS: So, away with us to Athens! Three and three,
We'll hold a feast in great solemnity.
Come.

> (THESEUS, EGEUS *and the* DUKE's *retinue exit right. The lovers perform a dance to wedding music and exit in turn.* BOTTOM *now awakens.*)

BOTTOM: "O Thisby, if I were fair, I were only . . ."

> (*He stops, puzzled.*)

My life, I have had a rare dream—methought I was—

PUCK (*jumping out of his hiding place*):   Hee-haw—

BOTTOM (*shocked at what he remembers*):   Methought I was—

PUCK (*running to* BOTTOM):   Hee-haw, hee-haw—

BOTTOM: No—No!—NO!—NO, NO, NO.—

(*He runs out, left, pursued by* PUCK's *hee-haws.* PUCK *suddenly remembers the audience and turns back to address it.*)

PUCK: If we shadows have offended,
  Think but this and all is mended,
  That you have but slumbered here,
  And this weak and idle theme,
  Is no more yielding but a dream.
  And so, goodnight unto you all,
  Unto you all, goodnight.
      (*He pirouettes off as*

                                            the curtain closes.)

STAGING SUGGESTIONS

Comments

"Shakespeare" may be acted by children of all ages, even the very young ones, provided appropriate material is chosen. At this writing, a group of seven- and eight-year-old children are having a wonderful time playing the Witches of *Macbeth* with energy and excitement!

Our adaptation of *A Midsummer Night's Dream* has also been presented by children with enchanting results. The best, most spontaneous performance was that given by a group of ten- and eleven-year-old girls!

Most of the lines in the adaptation are Shakespeare's. Some have been shortened through necessity, while some have been invented to clarify the continuity of the story. Many of the poet's lyrical love passages, beautiful though they are, have been omitted and "embraces" kept to a minimum. Romance is generally an embarrassing topic for children.

Cast

Increase or decrease the number of attendants in the DUKE's RETINUE as well as the FAIRIES to fit the needs of your group and stage space. Extra children may be brought on stage to sing TITANIA to sleep.

The COMMENTATOR may be any person, leader or player, who is introducing the play.

Set

The single set used for one production of this script consisted of an old piano bench and different-sized levels grouped to form the banks. These pieces were garlanded with wreaths of leaves and flowers. The DUKE's Throne was a chair, also garlanded.

A battered hat rack and a screen served as Tree and Shrub. The former was disguised with a hood of green material to which flowers and leaves were then attached; the latter with flowers, leaves and multi-colored balloons. Swags of colorful material may replace the flowers, leaves and balloons.

Costumes

For the same production, the players wore attire reminiscent of ancient Greece. Everyone found an old white sheet which he dyed and draped around his body. THESEUS, EGEUS, HERMIA and HELENA wore long garments with appropriate headgear. The DUKE's RETINUE had both long and short garments. DEMETRIUS and LYSANDER were dressed in tunics to give them a military bearing. LYSANDER carried a short cloak. PUCK, OBERON, TITANIA and the FAIRIES were attired in what the children felt was fairy fashion. Wings were made out of aluminum pie plates cut in half. And BOTTOM, in a workman's tunic, rented a donkey's head for the occasion.

Music

The music chosen for the production was—naturally enough—Mendelssohn's *A Midsummer Night's Dream* as recorded by the Vienna Symphony Orchestra. Passages accompanied the COMMENTATOR's introduction, the FAIRY dances, and filled the air with soft magic as all the LOVERS slept. When the four mortals were eventually and happily mated, the *Wedding March* enhanced their dance of jubilation.

There is a recording of the *Fairy Song*.

Props

Two scrolls and a flower—the magic herb—for PUCK; a sword or dagger for LYSANDER; a sword or dagger for DEMETRIUS; garlands for the FAIRIES, which they raise in salute.

BIBLIOGRAPHY

General Reference

Cole, Natalie, *The Arts in the Classroom*. The John Day Co., 1940
Dewey, John, *Art as Experience*. Minton, Balch & Co., 1934
————, *Experience and Education*. The Macmillan Co., 1938
Durland, Frances C., *Creative Dramatics for Children*. The Antioch Press, 1952
Foote, Nelson N. and Cottrell, Jr., Leonard S., *Identity and Interpersonal Competence*. The University of Chicago Press, 1955
Lease, Ruth S. and Siks, Geraldine B., *Creative Dramatics in Home, School and Community*. Harper & Brothers, 1952
Mearns, Hughes, *Creative Youth*. Doubleday, Doran & Co., Inc., 1928
————, *Creative Power*. Doubleday, Doran & Co., Inc., 1929
Simos, Jack, *Social Growth Through Play Production*. Association Press, 1957
Slade, Peter, *Child Drama*. The Philosophical Library, Inc., 1955
Slavson, S. R., *Creative Group Education*. Association Press, 1952
Ward, Winifred, *Playmaking with Children*. Appleton-Century-Crofts, Inc., 1957
Waterman, Emily, *The Rhythm Book*. A. S. Barnes and Co., 1937

Creative Acting

Boleslavsky, Richard, *Acting: The First Six Lessons*. Theatre Arts Books, 1947
Burger, Isabel B., *Creative Play Acting*. The Ronald Press, 1950

276

Chekhov, Michael, *To the Actor*. Harper & Brothers, 1953
Cole, Toby, ed., *Acting: A Handbook of the Stanislavski Method*. Crown Publishers, 1955
McGaw, Charles, *Acting Is Believing*. Rinehart & Company, Inc., 1955
Stanislavski, Constantin, *An Actor Prepares*. Theatre Arts Books, 1955
——, *Building a Character*. Theatre Arts Books, 1949

Writing and Producing the Play

Baker, George Pierce, *Dramatic Technique*. Houghton, Mifflin Co., 1919
Berk, Barbara (Pictures by Jeanne Bendick), *The First Book of Stage Costume and Make-up*. Franklin Watts, Inc., 1954
Davenport, Millia, *The Book of Costume*. Crown Publishers, Inc., 1948
Dean, Alexander, *Fundamentals of Play Directing*. Farrar & Rinehart, Inc., 1941
Dolman, John, Jr., *The Art of Play Production*. Harper & Brothers, 1946
Egri, Lajos, *The Art of Dramatic Writing*. Simon and Schuster, Inc., 1946
Evans, Mary, *Costume Throughout the Ages*. J. B. Lippincott Company, 1950
Gassner, John and Barber, Philip, *Producing the Play and New Scene Technician's Handbook*. The Dryden Press, Inc., 1953
Lawson, John Howard, *Theory and Technique of Playwriting*. G. P. Putnam's Sons, 1949
Leeming, Joseph, *The Costume Book for Parties and Plays*. Frederick A. Stokes Co., 1938
MacGowan, Kenneth, *A Primer of Playwriting*. Random House, Inc., 1951
Rowe, Kenneth T., *Write That Play*. Funk & Wagnalls Co., 1939
Selden, Samuel and Sellman, Hunton, *Stage Scenery and Lighting*. Appleton-Century-Crofts, Inc., 1946
Smith, Milton, *Play Production*. Appleton-Century-Crofts, Inc., 1948
Walkup, Fairfax P., *Dressing the Part*. Appleton-Century-Crofts, Inc., 1950
Wilde, Percival, *The Craftsmanship of the One-Act Play*. Little, Brown & Co., 1932

Material Sources

Chute, Marchette, *Stories from Shakespeare*. World Publishing Company, 1956
Ward, Winifred, *Stories to Dramatize*. Children's Theatre Press, 1952

GLOSSARY

ad lib, to: To improvise lines or stage business for the purpose of filling awkward pauses on stage. From the Latin, "ad libitum" (at pleasure).

apron: The section of the stage between the proscenium opening, with its front curtain, and the audience. The forestage.

arena staging: Staging the play in an area which is entirely or mostly surrounded by the audience.

audience participation: Vocal and/or physical participation, other than emotional reaction, of the spectator at a performance. The Narrator of the play may address the spectator directly and the latter may make certain responses.

backstage: The stage area behind the set; also used to denote the entire space behind the proscenium.

black-out, to: To extinguish all stage lights simultaneously.

block, to: To map out the actors' positions and movements in the play.

clear stage, to: To direct all people on stage to leave the acting area (except, perhaps, for those involved in the scene about to be played).

cross, to: To move from one space on the stage to another.

cue: Signs or words that advise a player when to speak or move.

curtain call: The appearance of the actors in acknowledgment of the applause at the end of a performance.

cyclorama (cyc):   A high, vast expanse of canvas or curtain confining the acting area. It is hung in front of the back wall, sometimes extending beyond the back wall to either side and forming a semicircle.

dimmer: A rheostat or electrical device through which the intensity of the stage lighting may be increased or decreased.

downstage: The area of the stage that is nearest the audience; below center of stage.

dress rehearsal: A rehearsal of the play, generally the final one, at which actors perform in costume and make-up; with sets, furniture, properties, music, sound and lighting, all arranged as for a finished performance.

flats: Frames covered with canvas or muslin and painted to form the walls of a set.

left: Actor's left as he stands on stage facing the audience.

levels: Flat surfaces of different shapes, sizes and heights, generally made of wood and covered with canvas.

lines: The actor's speeches.

off stage: Those areas of the stage an audience cannot see.

on stage: Those areas of the stage an audience sees.

places, take your: Instruction given to everyone on stage and off, to be in his proper position before the act starts.

prompter: An off-stage person who reminds the actor of a speech or movement he has forgotten. The prompter holds a prompt book, a copy of the play complete with final revisions and directions.

properties (props):   Small objects which are placed or carried on stage. These may be hand props carried on the actor's person, such as cigarettes, or handled by him on stage, such as a glass; or they may be stage props, such as lamps, ash trays, which dress the set but are not needed by the actor for personal business.

proscenium: The section of the stage in front of the curtain. The proscenium opening is the arched opening which frames the stage picture as the audience sees it.

red letter days: The holidays frequently printed on the calendar in red ink.

right: Actor's right as he stands facing the audience.

set the stage, to: To put furniture and props in place for a performance.

stage areas: So that an actor may assume the exact positions the director wishes him to, the acting area is divided into fifteen spaces as designated in the following diagram:

UP RIGHT (U.R.)	UP RIGHT CENTER (U.R.C.)	UP CENTER (U.C.)	UP LEFT CENTER (U.L.C.)	UP LEFT (U.L.)
RIGHT (R.)	RIGHT CENTER (R.C.)	CENTER (C.)	LEFT CENTER (L.C.)	LEFT (L.)
DOWN RIGHT (D.R.)	DOWN RIGHT CENTER (D.R.C.)	DOWN CENTER (D.C.)	DOWN LEFT CENTER (D.L.C.)	DOWN LEFT (D.L.)

stage business: The small actions adopted by an actor on stage, such as eating candy, combing his hair, drinking water, etc.

strike, to: To dismantle a stage set.

upstage: The area of the stage that is farthest away from the audience; above center of stage.

walk-on: A small part without speeches.

wings: The areas off stage, right and left.

Index